TO THE MOUNTAINS OF THE STARS

TO THE MOUNTAINS OF THE STARS

by

L. D. BRONGERSMA

and

G. F. VENEMA

Translated from the Dutch
by Alan G. Readett

DOUBLEDAY & COMPANY, INC.,
GARDEN CITY, NEW YORK
1963

Contents

v

Foreword

"TO THE MOUNTAINS OF THE STARS" RECORDS THE EXPERIENCES OF the expedition which in 1959 explored part of the mountainous central regions of Netherlands New Guinea. It will take many years yet to assess the collections of specimens and the data obtained and, in consequence, we can only give here and there a few indications regarding the scientific results; these will be reported in greater detail in the periodical *Nova Guinea*.

Many people, in the Netherlands and in Netherlands New Guinea, contributed to making the expedition a reality. It is not possible to list them all here, but we particularly wish to mention certain names. Prof. Dr. Ir. F. A. Vening Meinesz, who first took the initiative, the Councils of the Association for Scientific Research in the Tropics (Maatschappij voor Wetenschappelijk Onderzoek in de Tropen) and of the Royal Netherlands Geographical Society (Koninklijk Nederlandsch Aardrijkskundig Genootschap), together with the Foundation of the Expedition to Netherlands New Guinea (Stichting Expeditie Nederlands Nieuw-Guinea) deserve our hearty thanks; we are very happy to single out the members of the Council of this Foundation: Prof. Dr. H. J. Lam (Chairman), Prof. Dr. Ir. F. A. Van Baren (Vice-chairman), Mr. Hendrik Muller (Treasurer) and Mr. C. A. J. von Frijtag Drabbe (one-time Director of the Topographical Service) who undoubtedly contributed in a very large measure to the success of the expedition.

There is hardly a Government Department in Netherlands New Guinea which did not devote some effort to the expedition in one way or another. Of the many people there who assisted the expedition or helped to make preparations for it, we would particularly name His Excellency Dr. P. J. Platteel, the Governor of Netherlands New Guinea, Mr. A. Boendermaker (at that time Resident of Southern New Guinea), Mr. Th. C. Van den Broek, LL.D., Dr. J. W. Schoorl and Mr. A. A. M. Hermans.

The members of the expedition greatly facilitated the writing of this book by the reports which they handed in and by the verbal accounts which they gave us each time on their return to the base camp. There is no need to enlarge on their achievements in the field, since these are described fully in this book, the story of the expedition.

Leiden, June 1960.   L. D. Brongersma.
                                                G. F. Venema.

List of Plates

xi

The photographs were taken by;

Dr. L. D. Brongersma, 4; 7 (2); 8 (1); 10 (2); 11 (1); 13; 17 (2); 23; 30 (2); 35 (1, 2); 41; 43 (1, 2).

C. Van Heijningen, 30 (1).

J. Klaarenbeek, LL.D., 8 (2); 12 (2); 21; 24; 26; 28; 33; 34; 36.

P. Ter Laag (Kantoor Voorlichting en Radio Hollandia), 2 (1, 2); 3; 7 (1); 9 (2); 22; 25 (2); 27 (1, 2); 40 (1, 2); 44 (1, 2); 45; 46 (2); 47 (1); 48 (1, 2).

Marine-Lieut. C. B. Nicolas, 19 (1, 2).

J. J. Staats, 31 (1); 39.

Surg. Lt. M. O. Tissing, 31 (2); 42.

Cdr. Air G. F. Venema, 25 (1).

Dr. H. Th. Verstappen, 14; 47 (2).

Dr. W. Vervoort, 5; 6; 10 (1); 11 (2); 15; 16; 17 (1); 32; 37; 46 (1).

Dr. A. G. de Wilde, 1; 9 (1); 12 (1); 18; 29; 38.

U.S. Air Force; Netherlands Topographical Survey Archives.

The line drawings are by H. Heijn and W. C. G. Gertenaar; Fig. 13 was prepared by Ir. J. J. Reynders and fig. 23 by A. Spark.

List of Line Drawings

The Prelude

NEW GUINEA HAS HAD AN IRRESISTIBLE ATTRACTION FOR MANY EXPLORERS.
It is rare to find south of the Equator such great differences in climate
and terrain so close together. Coral reefs with a wide variety of animals,
beaches of brilliant white sand backed by waving coconut-palms,
extensive swamps and jungles, large rivers and lakes, a high mountainous
region broken up by many valleys and with permanent snow and ice on
the highest peaks. Places with an annual rainfall of 240 to 280 inches,
where there is no distinction between the seasons, and others with no
more than 60 inches of rain a year, where a very wet season alternates
with a dry one. All these factors have had their effect on the plants of
the region and on the distribution of the animal species, and have
also undoubtedly influenced the men and women who live there.

A hundred years ago, explorers had to restrict themselves principally
to the examination of the littoral regions, so that at the beginning of this
century the map of Netherlands New Guinea was marked by a large
white patch in the centre; this was the region where no white man had
then penetrated and of which little more was known than the situation
of the high mountain peaks visible from the coast. Various expeditions
set out from the northern and southern coasts towards the interior, a
team of army explorers ranged to and fro across the country (1907-
1915), local government officers journeyed outwards from the posts
they established and the white areas on the map grew smaller and less
numerous.

In spite of this, a large "white" patch remained in the heart of the
island, although you could not have told this from the map. Aerial
photographs made it possible to plot the position of the mountains
and the course of the rivers and the blank regions of the map were
thus filled in. Yet this region was to remain "white" and unknown,

until the features drawn in on the map had been checked by observations on the spot, and until accurate information had been collected about the population and the flora and fauna of the region, about the structure of the mountain ranges, and so on.

In May 1953, the Netherlands Association for Research in the Natural Sciences in the East and West Indies (Nederlandse Maatschappij voor Natuurwetenschappelijk Onderzoek in Oost- en West-Indië) and the Royal Netherlands Geographical Society (Nederlandsch Aardrijkskundig Genootschap), decided—on the initiative of Prof. Dr. Ir. F. A. Vening Meinesz—to send out a joint expedition to explore the eastern part of the central mountain region and thus eliminate the last white patch on the map. It was to differ from the earlier expeditions to the interior in having a larger number of scientific members and large-scale use would be made of aircraft.

A major enterprise of this kind calls for a great deal of preparation, and so it was almost six years before the expedition reached the mountains. All eventualities were exhaustively discussed, consultations held with the Government and with the Governor, and expert opinions sought on all sides. The Foundation of the Expedition to Netherlands New Guinea was set up to plan the expedition, and by 1955 its work had progressed sufficiently far for the leaders to be chosen: Dr. L. D. Brongersma as the general and scientific leader, and Cmdr. G. F. Venema (Royal Netherlands Navy Air Service) as the technical leader. Both of them knew the country and had already worked there together.

*   *   *

The expedition was to make use of air support, and the first thing to be done was to prepare an air-strip in or near the mountainous region to be explored. That there might be a possibility of this had been indicated in a report made by the Netherlands New Guinea Mining Company (Mijnbouwmaatschappij Nederlandsch Nieuw-Guinea), which had surveyed the edge of the Star Mountains in 1938/39; ground which appeared suitable for the building of a landing-strip had been seen in the valley of the Ok Sibil. The aerial photographs of the region were scanned again carefully and three outwardly suitable spots picked out for closer examination. Then District Officer J. W. Schoorl, Head of the government post at Mindiptana, was charged by the Resident of Southern New Guinea to make a journey into the Sibil Valley; he left on 14th November 1955, accompanied by Mr. Hermans, an administrative official, eight Papuan policemen, two interpreters and a number of bearers.

About a month later Schoorl returned home with an encouraging report. The plain through which the Ok Sibil flows certainly offered possibilities; it was covered with a kind of tall alang-alang grass and wild sugar-cane, but there were no woods there, so that the preparation of the air-strip would be a much easier matter. To get some idea of the conformation of the terrain a strip 800 yards long was cleared parallel to the river. The ground consisted of black soil, and presumably native gardens had previously been there; it would be possible to make a good job, provided that proper drainage was arranged.

Schoorl's report had a decisive influence on further plans. Everything now seemed to be cut and dried, although in the summer of 1956 little headway was made in the preparations in New Guinea. There was a busy correspondence, but the great distance was making its influence felt, and much precious time was lost. In consequence the two leaders undertook the journey to New Guinea, to talk things over; this made it easier to solve many of the problems.

Brongersma and Venema therefore left Holland on the 25th July 1956, travelling to Biak as passengers in a Mariner amphibian flying-boat of the Royal Netherlands Navy Air Service. The journey took 12 days, and it was a golden opportunity for Brongersma, since wherever they landed en route there was something for him to collect: insects, lizards or frogs. The men in the R.A.F. camps or the staff of the hotels where they stayed watched his activites with astonishment, finding it rather amusing that all kinds of "vermin" should be caught on their ground or that a small snake should be captured in their dining-room.

In Hollandia and Merauke discussions were held with a number of people in authority, on many of the problems connected with the expedition. The Resident of South New Guinea, Mr. A. Boendermaker, was clearly an enthusiastic supporter of the expedition and we were to find later how important this was for the execution of the expedition's plans. A technical official from Hollandia was instructed to examine more closely the terrain selected by Schoorl along the Ok Sibil. The leaders returned to the Netherlands in September, fully satisfied. In a final discussion with the Governor, Dr. J. van Baal, it was decided that the expedition could begin in January 1958: there were thus just a good twelve months in which to finish the preparations.

At this point, when everybody thought that the whole affair was settled, it was reported from New Guinea that the technical official sent out had completely rejected the ground chosen for the landing-strip. "Quite impossible," ran the report, "it's a marshy piece of land where you can poke a stick a yard into the soil without any difficulty." Once again, the aerial photographs and Schoorl's report were examined and experts in the construction of landing-strips consulted, with the result that the Council of the Foundation was unable to avoid the impression that there was a mistake somewhere. Everything indicated that the ground examined by Schoorl could be made to serve the purpose. Without a landing-strip there was no question of sending the expedition to the mountains.

Long and intensive discussions were held. Venema was asked for his opinion; he could only see one solution—the Foundation must undertake its own investigation; for it was quite out of the question that there should be no suitable plot of ground for a landing-strip anywhere in the area examined. If he were sent to the Sibil Valley with an engineer, then an appropriate site would no doubt be found. This new reconnaissance would not be cheap, since it would need the services of two helicopters. But it was soon learned that they could be obtained from Port Moresby (Papua) from the middle of June to the middle of July. After a certain amount of indecision, it was settled that Venema was to examine the situation in the Sibil Valley together with an engineer, T. K. Huizinga. The Ministry of Overseas Affairs fully supported this proposal; the feeling in New Guinea was rather one of "wait and see", for they could not believe that an engineer from Holland would know better than the expert on the spot.

Thus the reconnaissance expedition began.

The starting point for the reconnaissance was Mindiptana on the river Kaoh; the supplies could be shipped as far as this, and the two helicopters would provide transport from here to the Sibil Valley. On the 3rd June 1957 Boendermaker (the Resident) and Venema set off in a single-engined Beaver seaplane, to see the lie of the land there. The landing on the river was easy, but when, two hours later, they wanted to take off again, the situation had completely altered. A bandyir (a sudden flood or spate) had raised the level of the river by several yards and huge tree-trunks were floating on the surface. There was no choice. To stay where they were meant the complete destruction of the aircraft, which was tugging at its buoy; the only hope was to take off through the fast-moving logs which covered the wildly eddying river.

Venema, himself a flier, at one time the commanding officer of Gottschalk, the pilot of the Beaver, who was now flying for Netherlands New Guinea Airline (known as De Kroonduif), knew from his own experience how unpleasant it is in that sort of situation to have someone looking over your shoulder; he therefore climbed in behind, while Boendermaker went in the front seat next to the pilot. Gottschalk climbed on to the small float and quickly cast the aircraft loose, so that it immediately started driving with the current. As nimbly as a monkey he slipped into the cockpit and started the motor, which fortunately fired first time. Zigzagging between the drifting logs, now and then narrowly scraping past a trunk, the plane began to move at increasing speed over the water. Venema possessed his soul in patience, since he could after all do nothing to change the situation. Through the small side window he stared at the racing white water which hissed away under the float. The trees lining the bank melted into a green wall. Thirty-five seconds passed before the aeroplane left the water and began to climb over the jungle. Boendermaker turned round with a grin and gave the "thumbs-up" sign.

When they landed at Merauke that afternoon, they looked in vain for the mooring buoy, and eventually decided to tie up the Beaver to a raft normally used to store the petrol barrels. These had been carried away by the foaming water. It was a good hour before they were able to land; the small boat which should have fetched them off was drifting somewhere out to sea with a faulty motor and had to be picked up again. When they eventually reached the quay, the harbour-master was waiting for them with the news that the Mimika, the small ship that was to bring the supplies from Merauke to Mindiptana, had capsized in the Marianne Straights in a heavy ground swell. The ship and the supplies had been lost, but the crew had been able to escape by wading through the thick clayey mud, reaching Kimaän on Frederik Hendrik Island, exhausted by their efforts.

The Resident felt that it was time to calm everybody's nerves with a glass of cool beer. They had hardly sat down to partake of this when the harbour-master arrived again, perspiring freely in the midday heat. "I'm sure he's thirsty too," said Boendermaker. "Resident, the Beroaer's on fire in the engine-room." The Beroaer was a motor-ship, which was towing a lighter containing the petrol for the helicopters. "Good job the beer's still good," remarked Boendermaker laconically.

Those are just a few of the events which repeatedly occurred in New

Guinea, and were also in store for the main expedition. It was not
without cause that one could hear from time to time the remark:
"The situation is hopeless, but not alarming." It often looked as though
things had reached a deadlock, but a solution was found every time.
That is New Guinea.

Thanks to the co-operation of the Royal Netherlands Navy, the expedition had at its disposal a Catalina amphibian aircraft, P-217,
commanded by Lieutenant G. Smelik (Senior grade). Reconnaissance
flights along the route to the mountains were carried out with this aircraft; supplies and fuel for the helicopters were brought up from
Merauke to the airfield at Tanah Merah on the Digul River, and thence
carried by boat up the Digul and the Kaoh to Mindiptana. Catalina
P-217 was the last flying-boat of this type in use with the Naval Air
Transport Service in New Guinea, and this operation was the last carried
out by the plane itself. It is tragic to record that Lieutenant Smelik lost
his life in August of the same year in an accident to another naval aircraft which was to drop supplies to the government post in the Sibil
Valley.

*   *   *

The helicopters which were to fly from Mindiptana to the Sibil
Valley—a distance of 80 miles over thick jungle—would need emergency-landing sites along their route, in case they met bad weather or
had engine trouble. Clearings would have to be made in the forest at
intervals along the route; on occasion, native gardens could be used
as an emergency-landing strip, but a firm horizontal platform would
have to be made in every clearing for the helicopter to land on. A
detachment of the General Police under the command of Police-
Sergeant Raaff was responsible for making the clearings.

This group left Mindiptana on 9th June 1957, along the route
previously used by Schoorl, and on 22nd June the last landing-ground
was finished near Katem, at the confluence of the Ok Iwur and the East
Digul; this was a fine achievement, for they had prepared 22 clearings
in a fortnight. From Katem to the Sibil Valley itself the country is completely open and it was unnecessary to prepare special landing-grounds.
Raaff returned to Mindiptana with part of his detachment while some of
the police pushed on to the Sibil Valley with Dragt, a civil servant.

A. Hermans flew by helicopter to the Sibil Valley, and when Huizinga
and Venema arrived there on 29th June, a modest camp had already
been set up; a radio receiving and transmitting set had been installed

to ensure communication with the outside world. Reconnaissance of the area began immediately. Soil samples were taken and measurements made. It was clear that a landing-strip could really be prepared on the site indicated by Schoorl, and that the judgment of the expert who had examined the ground had certainly been too pessimistic.

Hermans knew how to get the local inhabitants to work, and he encouraged them like a cheer-leader. The policemen and the Muyu bearers, who had come with the patrol, were equally affected by enthusiasm. On 1st July a group of about 100 men began to clear the selected area and by evening an area of 3,000 sq. yd. had been cleared of all undergrowth. Next day there were even more men on the job. Despite the rain, which soaked everything, the Sibillers (people of the Sibil Valley) managed to burn the masses of cleared reeds.

Huizinga and Venema could now return home. The government officials were to remain in the valley to ensure that the landing-strip was completed. The enthusiastic Sibillers and Muyus worked hard. The high reeds had to be shifted, together with the tough root mass; over an area of 600 by 30 yards the surface layer of peat was dug out. Boulders were brought up out of the river to provide a firm base for the strip and when they had been covered with a layer of clay, this was settled by means of a "roller" consisting of large, heavy tree-trunks, which were rolled over the entire strip by the Sibillers and the Muyus to make the whole area compact.

A strong and low-growing species of grass was then sowed, to bind the top layer of soil firmly. Around the landing-strip deep ditches were dug to provide drainage. In this way, a landing-zone was prepared entirely by hand, suitable for use by light aircraft, such as the Twin Pioneer used by De Kroonduif or the Cessna used by the Zendings Luchtvaart Vereniging. The inhabitants of the Sibil Valley had worked hard on the job, but they were only really to understand what an airstrip is when the first aircraft landed months later.

Before the expedition had got out into the field, the landing-strip was twice threatened with catastrophe. On the first occasion it was infested with caterpillars, thousands of which were found blissfully feeding on the grass, so that it seemed that the landing "carpet" would soon disappear. The Sibillers were mobilised to deal with this threat; they walked across the strip in rows, picking the voracious caterpillars off the grass stems and . . . eating them with gusto; clearly they thought them a delicacy. An entomologist hastily brought from Hollandia to investigate the plague was almost too late. It was with difficulty that two caterpillars were found for him to examine.

When the strip was being prepared the Sibil people objected to the use of stones from the river to make the strip firm, saying that no good could come of it. "In the river the water flows over the stones, it always has done and therefore water must always flow over the stones; if the stones are now moved, then the river will of necessity follow," reasoned the Sibillers, and in March 1959 it almost looked as if they would be right. In twenty-four hours, just over 4 inches of rain fell; the Ok Sibil burst its banks and water actually did flow over the landing-strip, but happily without causing serious damage.

Thanks to the collaboration of government officials, naval personnel and police, and also to the pioneer work of the two helicopter pilots— Jean Cecille, a Frenchman and Jones, an Australian—the reconnaissance expedition was a success and the scientific expedition proper was made possible. Jean Cecille is another who is no longer alive; during helicopter operations in British North Borneo in June 1959, he was killed in an accident.

*   *   *

The successful reconnaissance was a considerable stimulus to the organisers of the scientific expedition. This had brought them out of the impasse which they had entered as a result of the government report that it was impossible to prepare a landing-strip. More detailed plans could now be made. Of course, it was not true that all the difficulties were over. It was repeatedly necessary to make modifications in the plans, to bring them as far as possible within the limits of the still very restricted funds available.

Having at one stage suggested the use of helicopters of the Alouette II type, because they are more suitable for operations at great heights, the planners discovered at the last minute that they are so expensive that they would have to be satisfied with Bell helicopters, which cannot operate so high in the mountains and can only carry lighter loads. The starting date was advanced several times, but at the end of 1958 the decision was taken: the expedition would be in the field by April 1959. A very busy period then followed, since the equipment and supplies had to be delivered and shipped; the time had come for the members of the expedition to be definitely chosen.

The Press now began to give more and more attention to the expedition; the leaders had repeatedly to hold press conferences, and the publication of articles describing the expedition's plans gave rise to a stream of letters from people who wanted to go with the party or who even thought that without their participation the enterprise would irrevocably fail. When the leaders asked the papers to publish an announcement that nobody could be accepted and there was therefore really no need for people to write in, many more letters were received the next day. It was pretty obvious that adventure still attracted many people. The age of the applicants ranged from 15 to over 60; most of the candidates were prepared to do any kind of work. The professions represented varied very widely, from a butcher who could cook a meal for twelve people and was also skilled in slaughtering and a hotel waiter to an employee of a gentlemen's tailor, a beach-tent attendant (with a vast experience in the erection of tents) and a house-painter etc. etc.

Even the gentler sex showed considerable interest: a young lady who spoke French and Dutch and was learning Spanish; three girls aged 18 and 19, who were willing to keep house for us and mend our clothes, and who thought cannibals less dangerous than buses in a modern city. The letters came not only from Holland, but also from Hong Kong, Pakistan etc. It was a great pity that we had to disappoint all these people. The expense of transporting the participants out to New Guinea was so great that we could only send a few specialists from the Netherlands; the other members of the party were selected on the spot.

Industry contributed a good deal to the expedition, both through the provision of funds and the presentation of supplies, but even here there were some strange proposals; there was an offer of lorries, very suitable for use in the mountains (and this in a country where every yard of the track had first of all to be felled and cleared), boats for the rivers (which are completely unnavigable in the mountainous regions) and many more articles besides. All the letters were carefully read, and anything that seemed useful was examined more closely.

* * *

On 15th January 1959, a wintry day with a light fall of snow and icy roads, the members of the expedition came together from many places in Holland to hear about the plans. There were a striking mixture of scientists and technicians; there were geologists, an anthropologist, fliers and mechanics. Names were exchanged and hands shaken and each member of the party tried to size up the others as companions in the jungle. The Chairman of the Foundation Council, Professor Dr. H. J. Lam, said a few words of introduction and the Press took photographs.

The two expedition leaders described the plans and emphasised that, once the expedition was in the field, a great many details of these plans would have to be changed, according to how the situation developed. New Guinea was an unpredictable country and things would often turn out very differently from what had been set down on paper. Questions were asked and answered about dates, routes and equipment. The meeting broke up late that afternoon, in an enthusiastic state of mind which promised well for the future. This enthusiasm was also due to the fact that at last something was going to happen; the expedition was to be carried through and in three months would be in the field.

It took a good twelve months to get all the supplies and equipment together. There was a busy correspondence with experienced men; there was Resident Boendermaker, and Police-Superintendent Oosterman—who had joined the group responsible for the expedition and had done a deal of important preparatory work in New Guinea. The supply branches of ministries and large firms gave advice. Information about the Star Mountains was gathered from government and police reports written by their officials working along the edges of the range. Of course, preparations like this could have gone on endlessly, but there came a moment when a line had to be drawn under the whole account, since otherwise one would have spent ten years busily preparing without a single scientist ever having been near Antares.

Will the material selected prove satisfactory in practice? Are the quantities right? These and similar questions exercised the leaders' minds as they looked at the piles of equipment and supplies, several yards high, in a large warehouse on the Borneo Quay in Amsterdam. The future would show, but one thing was certain: postponement or withdrawal were no longer possible. As they stood in the glare of the lamps set up for a television broadcast, they answered the questions of journalists, officials and packers as to the objects of the expedition, provided information for formalities and answered queries about the distribution of goods in the packing-cases and so on.

"Mind your backs!" A packing-case was rolled past them, dragged by two packers. Above the central gangway an overhead crane was lowered, and chains were thrown around the case. An electric winch began to hum and with a creaking of wood the huge package rose inch by inch from the ground. "Thirty-one and a half hundredweight; that's a bit overweight, but I can take something out otherwise they won't be able to unload it in New Guinea."

Someone tugged at Venema's sleeve. He broke off his discussion with Brongersma as to whether Velpon could be put in the hold, or whether this bird-lime would have to travel as deck cargo. As he looked round, he saw one of the packers standing behind him, accompanied by someone who bore every mark of being an official busy in the discharge of his duties; he had a threatening, somewhat aggrieved look in his eyes, and wore a dark raincoat—police pattern—while a silent colleague stood in the background, ready to spring to his side if required.

"It's a puzzle to me," began the man immediately. "There's a heap of meat here so big that I'm bowled over, and we don't know anything about this job. The whole lot's for export and not a bit's been inspected."

"What do you mean?" began Venema quietly. Brongersma made a tactical withdrawal. This was not a scientific matter and it was therefore no concern of his.

"Well, sir, I'm from the Food Inspection Department and my boss says that I must take samples of this consignment of meat," and then, clearly with the idea of excluding any argument, added, "otherwise it doesn't leave the country." His silent shadow nodded in agreement; he seemed to be approving the attitude of his superior.

"I don't get it," repeated the latter. He seemed to be very much struck by the ignorance shown by those around him with regard to the regulations for the export of meat. Venema started to explain hesitatingly that these were the supplies for a scientific expedition to the Star Mountains and that all this meat had been tinned specially for the purpose.

"I've got to take samples," said the official stubbornly. "I've got my orders."

The shipping agent, a man of professorial appearance, complete with pointed beard and spectacles, offered to help.

"I've got a list here for the gentleman. Perhaps it will be of some use; the suppliers' names are there as well." The meat inspection official glanced down the list. The customs official who was also present looked on from his strategic position, standing in a current of warm air fed into the warehouse through two large pipes, without showing any interest. As long as the Customs and Excise regulations were not transgressed, he would not bother very much. He fumbled in his pocket for a packet of cigarettes, took one out, remembered that he was standing right in front of a large notice bearing the words "No Smoking", and resignedly continued on his way, his unlit cigarette in his mouth.

"Oh, the deuce," exclaimed the meat inspector, reading his list; there was horror in his voice. "Thirteen hundred tins of corned beef. That's an endless job. I've got to take ten per cent of that as a sample, that makes a hundred and thirty tins. Now how do I go about that?" For the first time his satellite had something to say: "They'll all have to go in the incubator." His voice betrayed enthusiasm without any obvious reason. Venema was not at his ease. To have to break open cases which had to be shipped now! Ten per cent of the meat supplies gone for a burton in the Meat Inspectorate's incubators. The man himself obviously felt the unfortunate nature of the difficulty. "This stuff comes from Rotterdam. They ought to have inspected it at the factory. Now they shove it off on to us here, in Amsterdam. I think the best thing is for you to give my chief a ring," he said to Venema.

The telephone call did little to help. The chief also thought that samples would have to be taken of the consignment. At that moment the packers decided that it was time to knock off for lunch, whereupon the official from the Meat Inspectorate said that he would come back later in the afternoon to fetch the samples. How the whole affair was finally solved was never quite clear; the samples were not taken and the necessary papers arrived from Rotterdam.

That was just one of the accidents, large and small, which generally blew over like thunder showers, but did every now and then break in all earnest on the preparations for the expedition.

On the 23rd January 1959 the M.S. Musilloyd left Rotterdam with a good 30 tons of equipment and stores; a week later the two Bell helicopters were taken on board at Genoa. But that was not the end of the busy period for the leaders. There were press conferences, a television interview, short articles had to be written about the expedition's objectives, and meetings held with the Council of the Foundation, all of which took a great deal of time. Items of equipment which had arrived late were made ready for shipment in February, and then, on 4th March, Brongersma and Venema left by plane, flying over the Pole to Netherlands New Guinea. They went a month earlier than the other members as there would be a good deal remaining to be settled in Hollandia and Merauke. They also had to make contact with the expedition members employed in government service in New Guinea. It was a complete rest for them once they were able to sit down in the aircraft.

In the early hours of the 7th March, Brongersma and Venema arrived in Biak. Marine-Lieutenant C. B. Nicolas was there to welcome them; he was to accompany the expedition as commandant of the detachment and had a great many questions to put. Brongersma registered at the K.L.M. Hotel "Het Rif", while Venema went out to the new naval barracks which had replaced the primitive but extremely friendly camp known as the "Base".

After they had more or less slept for a few hours, (the rhythm of day and night being completely upset by the rapid journey over the Pole) Brongersma was woken up by a loud banging on the door. It was Venema, accompanied by Captain Beudeker of the Navy, who bore a telegram from His Royal Highness Prince Bernhard; "To Messrs. Brongersma and Venema. Wish you and other members of expedition successful and prosperous journey to the Star Mountains. Shall follow your operations with interest."

2

Tanah Merah

THE ROAR OF THE DAKOTA'S ENGINES BEGAN TO DIE DOWN AND THE nerve-racking din in the aircraft's bare interior gave way to a low-toned hum, as the plane slowly sank between the high-piled clouds, preparatory to landing at the airfield of Tanah Merah.

Nineteen of the twenty-two seats were occupied by members of the expedition: Brongersma, Venema, Marine-Lieutenant Nicolas, Police-Sergeant Kroon and, finally, fifteen constables of the Mobile Police, who were draped in the most picturesque attitudes in their seats, their carbines and other equipment dangling on the seat-backs or in the luggage racks, swinging to and fro with every movement of the aircraft. You could have cut the air in the plane with a knife. The reek of strong tobacco mingled with the musty smell of clothes still only half-dried. The last shower of rain on the airfield at Merauke had ensured that no one was dry on entering the aircraft.

The illuminated panel over the communicating door to the cockpit flicked on, with the warning: "Fasten seat belts—No smoking", a form of words clearly based on the expectation that even less-experienced travellers would understand such plain English. Kroon turned half-way round in his seat and, glancing critically at the policemen under his charge, said "We're there!" He gave the thumbs-up sign and looked at Brongersma as though he wanted to add: "Well, we've got him so far."

Brongersma grinned back in friendly fashion, and reached for his camera, which threatened to fall off the arm of the seat in front of him as the plane went into a sudden pretty steep turn. The pilot had evidently found a gap in the cloud cover through which he could circle down to land.

Venema pulled his legs back out of the gangway and stared out through the window. Being a pilot, he followed the course of each landing closely; it was second nature for him to do so. Beneath him he could see the river, every now and then hidden from view by wisps of cloud. There was the khaki ribbon of the Digul River, dappled with cloud shadows, winding through the jungle, a patchwork of many shades of green. From the air the landscape looked virtually lifeless. The ground-glass surface of the river radiated heat. The aircraft was moving as though it were sliding downwards over a badly-made switchback.

The heat as the aircraft descended lower and lower did not improve the atmosphere inside it. One of the policemen was overcome and just before the landing grabbed one of the waterproof bags freely provided by every airline. Immediately after this, the plane skimmed low over the houses. The red roofs slid away below and a few seconds later the wheels bounced over the red surface of the air-strip.

Fanoy, the senior local official at Tanah Merah, who was also harbour-master and agent for the Netherlands New Guinea Airline "De Kroonduif", was waiting for the leaders with a lively smile. As they walked towards the "station building", they were just able to escape with their lives by jumping aside with great presence of mind as the expedition jeep and trailer bored their way through the crowd at great speed. "We had hoped that you would have come yesterday," said Fanoy, "but with so much rain the ground was too soft for a Dakota to land." Here the group had to move out of the way again, as a long row of blue-clad bearers came towards them from the aircraft. They put their loads down on flat rubber-tyred trucks, drawn by two sapis (tame oxen), on which the supplies were to be carried on the next stage.

One thick-set figure separated itself leisurely from the crowd of interested whites and Papuans; it was Oosterman, the Police Superintendent, who had done such valuable work during previous months in preparing the Digul route and in storing supplies in Tanah Merah. He immediately began to report on the situation: "Things are beginning to look right now. The *Cycloop* came in yesterday with the last eight marines from the detachment and with a terrific quantity of barang (gear). Then the *Hans Führi* is lying in mid-stream; she's unloaded everything and can sail at any moment." He shook his head gravely: "It's for all the world like an avalanche suddenly dropping on our roof. Good thing the marines are here and that the police detachment is up to strength, otherwise we certainly shouldn't get everything straightened out." The very thought that there might have been no marines or police clearly filled him, however unnecessarily, with concern. The accommodation of the group of forty-odd men who had arrived at Tanah Merah in such a short space of time had been very neatly arranged by Oosterman. The marines were lodged in the police-barracks canteen; the police who were to accompany the expedition were to sleep in New Guinea's only skittle-alley.

The jeep was roaring impatiently, but the marines had to be patient for a little longer. The newcomers had a good many hands to shake, and this was followed by the departure of the air passengers going to Merauke. The expedition leaders climbed on to the jeep with those who were able to find a place and were not going to let slip the opportunity of saving themselves ten minutes' walk in the midday heat. The first motor-car in Tanah Merah started to move, with a great deal of hooting, and to shouting and cheering from the crowd, while to left and right dark figures who still found this means of transport somewhat frightening ducked off the narrow red-clay track into the high grass at the sides. From the air-strip came the roar of the aeroplane engines which had just been started up.

*   *   *

Tanah Merah, a very quiet spot, situated three days' sail from the mouth of the Digul, was originally an internment camp, built about thirty years ago on the red clay which gave it its name. At that time it had no airfield. Once every three months a tiny steamboat arrived with the necessary supplies for the internees and their guards, and for the small garrison which, ravaged by malaria and blackwater fever, led a monotonous existence in the stifling atmosphere of the steaming hot jungle. It was an ideal place for this large prison, for, even if a prisoner managed to elude the eyes of the guards, the likelihood of his reaching the coast safely was very small. At that time the population in these areas was not yet particularly friendly towards strangers, and there was a considerable risk that an escaped prisoner would be murdered and eaten on his journey to the coast.

Since the improvement of communications and the penetration of these regions by government officials, life is a little more eventful although there are still very few people living there. In fact there are probably less, since the garrison, together with its following of soldiers' families and Chinese merchants, has disappeared. The police detachment and the prison personnel have also been considerably re-

1.   Tree-house in Lumabib (Wambon district)

duced, since the prison had begun to lose importance after the war. Now, scarcely a hundred cannibals and murderers lead a quiet and secure life there. They work in the prison garden and fish in the river to their own benefit, since this gives them a more varied diet; in addition, they do paid work loading and unloading aircraft and ships.

After finishing their sentence, some of them stay on to work in Tanah Merah, either because they are not anxious to meet the family of the tribesman they murdered (because the latter often take little notice of the fact that the government has already exercised justice), or else because they have no more liking for the primitive kampong (village) life.

Thus, the first-rate house-servant employed by our host Fanoy was an ex-murderer; one former cannibal—who can still boast of having helped to consume a European years ago—is now a reliable government employee in a trim uniform. The style of the houses still recalls the pre-war period, for they are large, stone buildings containing spacious rooms with high ceilings; houses like this are, moreover, now only to be found in the older settlements such as Fakfak and Manokwari. The new things are the airfield and the electric-lighting plant.

When the leaders arrived in Tanah Merah on 26th March, the place had a most unusual air of busyness. The coaster *Cycloop* of the K.P.M. lay alongside the jetty unloading expedition supplies from Merauke. In mid-stream the government coaster *Hans Führi* lay at anchor. She had brought up from Sorong part of the equipment sent out from Holland; unloading had been finished, but she was waiting for a spare part for her engine which had been brought out in our plane. News had been received from Sorong that the *Orion* was also under way.

The consignment from Holland had been too big for the *Hans Führi*, and Bär, our geologist, who was keeping an eye on the passage of supplies through Sorong, had had the coaster *Orion* placed at his disposal by the Netherlands New Guinea Petroleum Company. Thus three boats tied up at the quay at Tanah Merah in the space of one week.

The unloading of the *Cycloop* aroused great interest among the population. The large packing-cases were hoisted out of the hold and deposited on the quay; here they were unpacked, while the jeep and trailer carried the equipment and supplies to a shed in the grounds of the police barracks. The empty cases were dragged away by the marines and the police, and lined up along the track; there they could still be used for temporary storage. During a sudden shower of rain, they were

2. (1) Aerial photograph of the Sibil Valley; left, the Ok Sibil, centre, the air-strip, right, Mabilabol base camp.
(2) The helicopter takes off from Juliana Camp.

also very much valued as shelters; at least ten Papuans could stand inside one.

It had clearly rained hard in the mountains, for the level of the river was high; the water almost reached to the surface of the quay and everything had to be got away as speedily as possible. A little more rain would have increased greatly the risk of having everything washed off the quay, and work therefore went on feverishly. The jeep and its trailer were not still for a moment; they were driven right up to the end of the quay . . . trailer uncoupled . . . turned round . . . coupled up again . . . loaded and driven off, all in a very few minutes. Roaring in first gear, the combination crept up the steep slope to the track which led to the police barracks. Here the goods were sorted and stored in groups according to kind.

Superintendent Oosterman exercised his dominion from the large shed of the police barracks. He sat on a folding chair behind a packing-case which served him as a desk. Next to a pile of sheets of paper, half-used notepads, a lot of bent nails and a pair of pincers stood a half-glass of cold coffee; the ground around him was strewn with cigarette ends and ash. Imperturbably he sat noting the various supplies as they arrived, instructing Marine-Sergeant De Wijn where to put them: "What's that? . . . in the case there? . . . Camp-beds? . . . fetch eight of them out. They're meant for Katem. And get eight blankets off that pile in the corner. They're for Katem too."

Police-Sergeant Kroon had taken on the responsibility of weighing the various articles. Under his guidance one of the policemen was writing, with an unsteady hand, the weight on each packet in black figures. Another team—under Oosterman's silent, pantomimed instructions—rapidly sorted out ten-cwt. lots, which were then driven to the airfield. Here stood a line of eight packing-cases, and one such lot was stowed in each case; they represented so many loads for the Twin Pioneer which was available for the expedition's use from the second to the sixth of April, although this period had to be shared with the government, who had to supply the civil servants and police in the Sibil Valley. Oosterman looked sombrely at the unending flow of goods. He knew well enough that a great deal was necessary, but it was a bit too much that there had to be such a lot of it. Above all, the great piles of scientific equipment surprised him. He shook his head at the sight of 7 cwt. of old newspapers being carried in. "What the dickens are they going to do with all that rubbish?" he sighed. "The godown is much too small to take all that lot. Old newspapers . . ." His voice betrayed his horror. Standing next to him, the scientific leader was quite unmoved by this remark; without newspapers, the botanists would be unable to dry their plants. The same considerations applied to so many items of scientific equipment which seemed superfluous to the layman. But it all had to go to the Sibil Valley.

This business of managing the supplies and assembling the loads to be transported was not easy for Oosterman. There he sat in the middle of an avalanche of stores and tried to comply as far as possible with everyone's wishes for transport. The technical leader and the scientific leader each had their own requirements for the carrying of bedding, clothes, glass jars of alcohol, the zoologists' case No. 23, at least 10 packets of newspapers, 10 sacks of flour, etc. etc.

Oosterman listened to everything with unfailing patience: "Certainly, Mr. Brongersma, that must take priority. Of course, Mr. Venema, I'll have it set aside. What were the other cases you said you wanted unpacked? I haven't seen any guy ropes, and there aren't any on the consignment list . . ." He stood up with a sigh, took a handkerchief out of his pocket and began to wipe the sweat from his face and neck. "Oh, my gosh!" he sighed. He didn't seem to have a minute to breathe. A new consignment was carried in and a crowd of amateur packers fell upon it. Somebody sat on a freshly-painted mark and started swearing.

So, day by day, everyone worked hard in the stores, with new supplies constantly reaching Tanah Merah, while some of the goods were sent up the Digul to the camp at Kawakit. Two Mappi boats (motor-boats of the Holland launch type) travelled up the river to supply this camp, which the geological group was to pass shortly on its trek to the Sibil Valley. On Easter Saturday, the 30th March, the deep penetrating note of a ship's siren sounded over the kota (town), echoing from one wood to another. The coaster Orion came into sight round the bend on the river, her silhouette gliding along against the wall of trees forming the edge of the forest. Her heavy engines throbbed dully in the oppressive midday heat, disturbing the farthest corners of the spot with their deep note. The silence which followed once the ship lay alongside the quay and the engines were stopped seemed like something suddenly felt, until broken by the cries of the crew and the rattle of the chains.

With the Orion there arrived the first scientific member, Cortel, the mining engineer. He brought with him a team of twenty-five bearers from the region around the village of Sansapor, which lies on the northern coast of the Vogelkop Peninsula. The people of that district have always been employed on the Oil Company's explorations, because they are generally men with the necessary endurance and, in addition, accustomed to rough ground. To have a margin in the erection of the camp by the Sansapor bearers, it was decided, in consultation with the Orion's captain, that they would sleep another night on board the ship.

A day later, a Catalina of the Netherlands New Guinea Oil Company arrived, bringing Bär and Escher. The geological group was now complete, and the plans for their journey could therefore be discussed again in detail. On 2nd April they set off up river with the two Mappi boats.

The twin Pioneer began its transport flights from Tanah Merah to Sibil on 2nd April. Van Hulten, the Kroonduif pilot, got things going quickly. On the day of his arrival he managed to make a return trip to the valley: three-quarters of an hour flying, a quarter of an hour unloading and another three-quarters for the return flight to Tanah Merah. He then reloaded for the next flight which, however, only took place the next day, the clouds above the valley having thickened too much to allow of flying safely over the ridges of the Ariem and Digul ranges. The first time the loading took forty-five minutes, but on the following days this was reduced to twenty or twenty-five minutes by the indefatigable loading team of marines and police.

While the Twin Pioneer was en route to the Sibil Valley, everything was being prepared for the next flight at Tanah Merah. The loads were brought out of the packing-cases and laid out precisely as they would be distributed over the floor of the aircraft. A group of prisoners rolled two drums of petrol from the store out on to the airfield. Once the plane had landed, the load was carried in and lashed down; the prisoners, supervised by the second pilot, fed the fuel into the aircraft's tanks with a hand-pump; the first pilot filled in the landing papers. In the heavily-rusted sheet-iron "station building", the pilots gulped down coffee or swallowed a stand-up lunch; meanwhile two marines were already turning the propellers over a few times by hand. After a rapid check, the fliers stepped in and the Twin Pioneer set off again for the Sibil Valley. In this way, three to four flights could be made every day in good weather, carrying almost a ton of freight and passengers each time.

Brongersma, Oosterman, Kroon and some of the marines and police soon went to the Sibil Valley. About the 7th April, the expedition members from Hollandia and from the Netherlands were expected to arrive and there were still a few things to be made ready for their reception. Venema remained in Tanah Merah to wait for the helicopters, since he was to show their pilots the way to the Sibil Valley.

*   *   *

The crates containing the helicopters and the cases of parts had been transhipped in Sarong to the *Kasimbar*, belonging to the K.P.M., and were to arrive in Merauke on this boat. The pilots and mechanics had already arrived there on 21st March, and had made all the preparations for assembling the craft rapidly. It had been expected that the helicopters would be able to fly to Tanah Merah on 7th April but things turned out differently in the event. The *Kasimbar* was delayed for a few days and did not reach Merauke until the 6th April. Under the leadership of Nieraeth the work was pushed forward energetically, sometimes till late at night. Because of the long rotor-blades, the helicopters had to be assembled out in the open and heavy showers of rain delayed operations.

Every day Venema enquired by radio-telephone how work was getting on in Merauke and every day Brongersma asked from the Sibil Valley what had become of everything. Bär was expecting to receive new supplies at the East Digul on 10th April. True, he had a few days' food in reserve, but the supply operation could not be too long delayed, as he had to return with his group to Kawakit. On the day when Bär, on the East Digul, was looking out for the helicopters, the work in Merauke had progressed far enough for the first helicopter to make a trial flight, and the second was ready on 13th April. Chief-Pilot Zijlstra sent a report to Tanah Merah that both helicopters would arrive on 14th April.

In Merauke the flyers had had ample opportunity to get information about the region they would be flying to. Government officials who had travelled in the marshy regions of Southern New Guinea, police officials, pilots of De Kroonduif had all recounted the difficulties. On the map everything still looked pretty simple, but the tall stories (with a basis of truth, although somewhat overdrawn) convinced them it could well turn out to be a difficult job of work. There was no possibility of dropping down on to another airfield, and if you had to make an emergency landing it might easily last a couple of weeks before a rescue team could reach you, even supposing you were found in time.

The route was selected in consultation with Venema; it was to run from Merauke over the extensive marshland of the upper Bian River to the Digul, followed by a stretch 25 miles upstream along this latter river to Tanah Merah. Petrol reserves were carried in jerrycans, for they might well be needed on a journey lasting some two hours. A Netherlands Naval Transport Service aircraft, a Martin Mariner, was to patrol along the route to keep a sharp look-out. The helicopters were to be linked by radio to the aircraft, which was in turn to pass on to Merauke news of any special incidents.

*   *   *

Thus on the 14th April half Tanah Merah stood on the airfield waiting for the helicopters, which were to arrive at twelve-thirty. These craft fly at 50—60 miles per hour, and if they have to face a head-wind, their ground-speed may well drop to something like 30 miles an hour. The journey was thus likely to last a good two hours. High above Tanah Merah, the Mariner, a giant amphibian aircraft, flew over with a deep drone of engines. The sight of such an aircraft keeping you company was good for the morale of the helicopter pilots, for you can feel pretty lonely in a glass bubble like that flying over 150 miles of jungle. But the time was passing; one o'clock came and there were still no helicopters.

Lieutenant Nicolas went off to the radio station to ask Merauke if they knew of any reason for a delay. He had hardly gone when an uproar began in the rows of interested Papuan spectators; they had already heard the note of the motors a long way off, and it was still a good ten minutes before the helicopters came into sight, flying low over the tree-tops. With a great deal of noise and roaring, the "choppers" sank slowly to the platform. Zijlstra climbed painfully from his seat and walked over to the anxious reception committee. He looked tired and sweaty and was somewhat dishevelled.

"Whatever happened to make you so late?"

"About half an hour from here my oil pressure failed and I had to make an emergency landing. By a stroke of luck we were pretty high, and I saw under me a fine, level green bit of land by the river. I decided to drop in there quickly, so I started going down. When I eventually got down that far, it was a real sell, for the fine, green, flat strip was a marsh, overgrown with a thicket of reeds four or five yards high. I disappeared in that lot, helicopter and all. Just as though I was sitting in a basket. There were reeds all over the shop," recounted Zijlstra.

"I landed near him," grinned Van den Bos, "and then we lost each other completely. The only way I could find him was to ask him to make a noise."

Zijlstra sighed once, deeply: "I lost a whole lot of oil out of the tank. We couldn't find out precisely why, but there wasn't more than a couple of pints left. Fortunately we had a jerrycan of oil with us and once Menge had got hold of it and filled the tank, we started off again. The helicopter almost looked like a mowing machine: the rotor cut all the reed plumes off and the bus is still full of them. What a country, what a country!" Menge nodded cheerfully. "I was knee-deep in the water; once you've run back and forwards over the reed bed once or twice it sinks down into the marsh. It's a nice place for our scientists to go collecting round there; the place is alive with lovely butterflies and any amount of mosquitoes!"

Venema climbed into the jeep with the pilots to go and have a spot of lunch with them in the government rest-house. Over the meal, the next plans were discussed. The supplies for Bär's group had to be set up urgently. Meanwhile Sergeant De Wijn loaded Venema's personal luggage into P H-H E O, while P H-H E N had a 380-lb. load of freight lashed down on board. About 2 o'clock the two aircraft took off on the way to Kawakit.

3

The Digul Route

THE PRELIMINARY SURVEY MADE BY SCHOORL IN 1955 AND THE RECON-
naissance expedition in 1957 had, as recorded above, chosen Mindiptana on the Kaoh river as the starting-point for the trek to the Sibil
Valley. The route had the advantage that it was well known and that the
emergency landing-places for helicopters, which had been cleared in
1957 by the police patrol under Sergeant Raaff, were capable of being
put in order with remarkably little trouble. But there were also difficulties about the use of Mindiptana. Coasters like the *Cycloop* cannot
reach the spot and there is no airfield. These objections did not apply
to Tanah Merah, on the Digul, since tons of equipment could be brought
here by ship ready to be flown to the Sibil Valley in the Twin Pioneer of
the Kroonduif Company.

The shortage of funds which beset the expedition from the beginning
led to the use of the helicopters for the transport operation as well.
A whole new route, complete with emergency-landing facilities, had to
be made, with Tanah Merah as the starting-point. Bär, our geologist,
was to take on this task. He had previously carried out geological investigations in the region and now wished to supplement his information with data collected along the East Digul as far as Katem. The Digul
route was therefore selected for the helicopters; this was also the shortest
return route, should the expedition be forced to come back on foot.

The Digul River winds through the lowlands in great twists and
meanders, forming huge, wide loops. The distance from Tanah Merah to
Kawakit is about 33 miles as the crow flies, but about three times as
much by river. Thus you can travel for hours on end without making
much progress in the right direction; some of the loops are so marked
that they almost bring you back to where you started from. On the
outer side of the bends, where the current is strongest, the river has

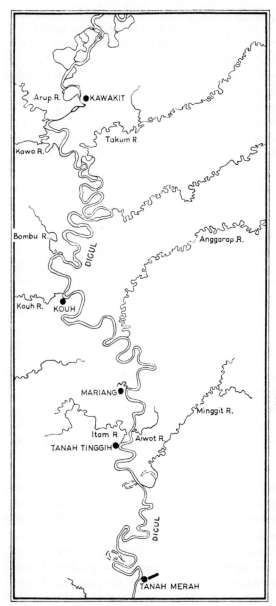

Fig. 1. The Digul River, from Tanah Merah to Kawakit.

undermined its bank, cutting out great masses of earth which fall into the river carrying trees and all with them, and sweeping everything away in the current; on the inside of the curves sandbanks are deposited and the river-bed fills up again.

Thus the river changes its bed over the years. Finally, the small strip of land which separates the beginning of one of these great loops from the end is so eaten away that it breaks through, causing a "short-circuit", and the river then flows straight through again, leaving the loop behind as an ox-bow lake, which slowly becomes overgrown with water-plants and finally silts up. Flying over the plain, one can see, to right and left of the river, many of these cut-off loops; it almost seems as though a gigantic horse has galloped through the region, leaving his footprints behind.

*   *   *

Work began very early on the days when the "Mappi 26" and the "Mappi 27"—the two motor-boats which were to carry men, equipment and supplies to Kawakit—were to leave. At the break of day, the whole of Tanah Merah was scared awake by the roar of the expedition's jeep, carrying loads to the harbour. The freight was quickly loaded on board and the boats were already leaving while the inhabitants of Tanah Merah were still sitting at breakfast. Because of the strong current the journey lasted two days, but travelling was restricted to the daytime.

Navigating the river calls for considerable alertness. If the water is low, the sand and gravel banks have to be avoided with care. If the river is in spate, trees, masses of cane and slices out of the islands are swept along by it, and water-logged tree-trunks float hidden below the surface. To run into them would have bent propeller shafts and buckled the blades, and the boat, rattling and squeaking, would then have had to return to Tanah Merah for repairs. Our Papuan helmsmen had to be on the look-out the whole time and they needed to be able to manoeuvre quickly to avoid the obstacles. As we stood on the forecastle we could, from favourable spots which gave a clear view across the river to the north, see in this direction the blue peaks of the Ariem Range—the outliers of the central mountainous region. Of course, the weather had to be clear for us to see so far; more often rain or patches of mist hanging low over the water hid the view, or the mountains were wrapped in thick masses of cloud, which warned the motor-boat crews of the approach of a bandyir which, after the lapse of some twenty-four or thirty-six hours, could swell the river very rapidly by the addition of great masses of dirty water. At such times only the higher settlements are safe, everything along the low river-banks being inescapably swept away.

Each evening, as the sun went down, the boat was moored to the bank; the crew prepared their meal and crept forward under the klambu (mosquito-net). The swarms of insects which then arrived could make life outside the mosquito-netting most unpleasant. The songs of the birds ceased, and only an odd night-bird could be heard. But it did not become quiet, for there now began a tremendous chorus of crickets, cicadas and frogs.

The following morning, when the heavy banks of fog began to lift, slowly revealing the jungle in the first light of day, while the mosquito-nets and tarpaulins were still heavy with dew, the motors were started and warmed up. The smell of fresh coffee would mingle with the diesel fumes. Carefully balancing on the small iron platform above the rudder, passengers and crew washed away the last traces of sleep with a few buckets of the muddy, yellow river-water. As a wisp of fumes rising from the throbbing exhaust threatened to choke them, they jumped back into the boat to the accompaniment of a few very pointed remarks.

The boats had already got under way while breakfast—consisting of a few water biscuits with jam, cheese or corned beef and a cup of coffee—was eaten. Although it was still pretty cold on the river of a morning, it was enjoyable to feel the gentle breeze produced by the movement. By now the heavily-loaded boats were slogging away on the last stretch of the journey, from the mission-post at Kouh up to Kawakit. The outward trip lasted two days, but with the current behind them, the boats were back in Tanah Merah within a day. For weeks on end the Mappi boats did this journey to bring supplies to Kawakit and to carry loads which would later be transported further by helicopter.

For many people, however, travelling up the river was a monotonous business; there was nothing to see beyond the water, frequently very muddy, and the green wall of bushes and trees along the banks. However, anyone with an eye for landscape and for plants and animals would have no reason to be bored for a single moment; for him there was a continually-changing picture. He could feast his eyes on the various kinds of trees, of creepers—sometimes adorned with vivid-coloured clusters of flowers—and of ferns.

Now and then the green wall lining the bank was broken where a village, surrounded by gardens, had been built. Here we saw the inhabitants in their little slender proas, in which they closely hugged the banks. In this area too one would come across an odd rumah tinggi, or "high house"—dwellings raised high above the ground on piles or in trees, to give their occupants greater safety. As the country is brought progressively under the closer control of the government, so safety is increased, and these raised houses tend to disappear; instead, the natives settle in neat villages.

It was most impressive to see how great stretches of the bank had caved in, causing huge trees to be swept along in the fast-flowing muddy river when swollen by a bandyir. Once we saw a freshwater turtle (*Carettochelys insculpta*), comfortably sunning on the surface, only to sink noiselessly into the water as one of the approaching motor-boats frightened it. Along the banks stood great white herons (*Egretta alba*), which can easily gorge themselves in a river so rich in fish as this; on a dead branch of a fallen tree lying in the water sat an Indian sea-eagle (*Haliastur indus*), with red-brown back and wings, set off by a white head and breast. Between the bushes kingfishers flitted like living blue streaks. The woods on the bank were loud with the hoarse cries of groups of lories—small brightly-coloured parrots which make a noise suggesting that they ought to be lubricated for once in a while! Hornbills (*Rhyticeros plicatus*), generally in pairs, flew across the river with heavy, noisy wing-beats.

There is always something to see on the river. The Papuans are very observant and anything moving along the river bank attracts their attention, because it means food. A tremendous commotion was produced on board when somebody signalled the presence of a crocodile on a mudbank. "Buya" shouted everybody, and the cry was immediately followed by an absolute fusillade; the boat was rapidly steered towards the bank and the crew of Papuans hastily jumped overboard to grab the wounded reptile, before its last convulsions could carry it into the water. Our zoological collection was the richer by the reptile's skin and skull, while the connoisseurs of crocodile meat were sure of a good meal. The freshwater crocodile (*Crocodylus novae-guineae*) is the only species met so far up-river; its skin is of very little value in the leather trade.

Upstream of the point where the Arup (or Casuaris) River flows into the Digul, the police had built Kawakit Camp for us. It was situated on a hill that rose like an island in a sea of trees and was completely safe from any bandyir. It had not been a simple job to build this camp, for enormous trees had to be felled to make room for the living-hut, as well as storage places and helicopter platforms. Only material from the surrounding forest was used in its construction: timber, rattan and palm-leaves; there was not a single nail in the building. The floors and walls were made of small tree-trunks split lengthways and firmly fastened to each other with strips of rattan; the roofs were of palm-leaves. The sleeping-places had been arranged on a para-para—a raised floor of thin canes, on which one could either lay mattresses or set up a camp-bed. Over this were stretched long rattan stringers to carry the klambus, since without the protection of mosquito-nets there was no hope of a normal night's sleep.

The living-hut stood at the top of the hill with a helicopter platform near-by; the stores and the petrol supplies were a little lower down and a second platform had been erected still nearer the river. Cooking was done over wood fires under lean-tos outside the hut. A band of little Papuan boys washed the utensils in the river, an undertaking which was not always completely successful, hygiene being a completely new idea to them. A clean frying-pan was paid for at a higher rate than a less carefully washed one, so that the camp officer, Corporal Van Ingen, slowly became satisfied with his young helpers. The payment always consisted of a handful of water biscuits, perhaps supplemented by the remains of a meal. Although the inhabitants had never tasted cooked food before, they were well able to appreciate the dishes which we prepared.

The near-by Papuan village lay by the Arup, where there were sago swamps from which the natives obtain their staple food. Now that the camp was inhabited, a number of Papuans had settled at Kawakit and so a small kampong had sprung up. By working here (principally at cutting wood) they were able to earn all kinds of things which they valued, such as matches and knives. They now seemed quite willing to have to make a couple of days journey to get new supplies of sago.

On 3rd April the Mappi boats brought Bär, Cortel and Escher to Kawakit, from where they would start the trek to Katem. Escher was to stay in Kawakit for the moment to supervise the supplying of Bär's group; this would also give him the opportunity of seeing what possibilities would be offered by using the helicopters for the field work. The equipment (e.g. tent-cloths for camps set up en route, clothing, food, machetes) was divided as far as possible into similar lots, to ensure that each bearer carried an equal load and thus, early on the morning of 5th April, the party was ready to start. As Escher and the marine party at Kawakit gazed after them, the group, thirty-two men strong, disappeared into the jungle: Bär, Cortel, Constables Swabra, Yani and B. Kamagaimu of the mobile police, the survey headman J. Wattimena, Leo Sumambai the cook, and the twenty-five Sansapor bearers. They followed the course of the Digul as far as possible, since the helicopter pilots would be able to orientate themselves by the river as they brought up further supplies for the group.

The procession was led by the clearing party, who had to cut a path for the others; they were followed by Wattimena, who measured the ground covered with a fifty-metre cord. At regular intervals he set a stick or cut in a tree his symbol—the W of his name—and a number. He also carefully read off and recorded each change of direction.

Behind him came Bär and Cortel making their geological investigations along the route; the markers placed by Wattimena enabled them to plot their observation points on the map with great accuracy. Since the clearing party progressed only slowly, and the bearers, bringing up the rear, still more slowly, there was no risk of Bär and Cortel being left behind.

If their studies required them to stop for a while at one point, they were easily able to overtake the main group. The track was not easy, being muddy and full of tree roots sticking out of the ground. Sometimes the path ran up-hill, only to drop down again, and there were innumerable little brooks to be crossed; in the marshy spots, the walkers sank deep into the mud. What with showers and perspiration, there was soon not a dry stitch of clothing among them.

In this way the thirty-two men wound through the jungle in a long file, like a snake wriggling over the ground. At intervals of roughly three miles, open spaces were cleared to serve as landing-places for the helicopters; platforms to support the aircraft were built out of branches collected together.

Camp was set up in the afternoon—an operation which took very little time with these experienced men; the tent covers were stretched, a para-para built and the klambus hung up. The cook put the rice on the stove with some meat or fish and sayur (vegetables) and the meal was ready. It was still possible to try to dry one's rain-soaked clothing by the fire, but it was a fairly hopeless job. Everybody crept under the

mosquito-net early because outside it the mosquitoes made life very disagreeable, and the camp was soon quiet. Next morning, after swallowing
a cup of coffee, everybody put on his clothes and shoes, still wet from
the day before. Breakfast was eaten rapidly and the party then trekked
another two or three miles to make the next helicopter clearing.

Thus the days passed, and each day the party looked with increasing
excitement for the arrival of the helicopters. It had been promised that
new supplies of food would be brought up by 10th April at the very
latest, but what the men in Bär's group did not know was that there
had been still further delays, that the boat had reached Merauke several
days late, that bad weather had again hindered the work of assembling
the helicopters, and that they were not even in Tanah Merah by the
10th April.

With the limited number of bearers in the party, it had only been
possible to take some five days' food, and to avoid any unnecessary
risk, Bär sent Constable Swabra back to Kawakit with thirteen Sansapor
bearers to fetch fresh supplies. Now that the path had been cleared, this
group made good progress and four days later, reinforced by the
addition of marines Hendriks and Straathof, they had caught up with the
main column. Bär and Cortel had not advanced very far in the meantime,
as the remaining twelve bearers had to do the trip to the next camp
twice to bring up all the gear. They did not take to this shuttle traffic
very kindly; bringing a load to the new camp site and then going back
to the old one for another load struck them as much worse than
doing a journey of twice the normal length.

At all events Bär was now in a position to proceed further with his
men. Fortunately the ground became somewhat drier; they were
beginning to climb and did not have to wade so often through little
streams and tributaries or through marshes. The river was also becoming
noisier; the current ran more rapidly and where the party broke through
the woods, they could see that the banks were closer together and
steeper. By now the group was at the point where the river became completely unnavigable. A little beyond this was the first side valley and
here they began looking for a spot to set up a big camp which could
serve as a permanent stopping-point on the helicopter route.

The site selected by Bär was of overwhelming natural beauty. The
East Digul, barely one hundred and twenty feet across, ran past it in a
roaring sheet of foam. A terrace some fifteen yards above the water
seemed very suitable for building a camp; the woodland was not

particularly heavy, apart from some three or four 150-foot giants. The first axe blows fell as the last of the group straggled into camp. On 15th April a beginning was made with the construction of the "Kloof Camp", Camp 9 on the route to Katem.

*   *   *

On 14th April the helicopters had arrived in Tanah Merah, and they made one flight to Kawakit the same day. Venema acted as navigator, sitting next to Zijlstra, map in hand. The only features which could be used for orientation were the mouths of the tributaries, and the villages along the Digul. The twists in the river were too numerous to be much use for navigation; moreover, the map was pretty old and some of the bends, here and there, had changed in the meantime, so that they could no longer serve as reliable fixes. The villages had been sketched in on the map only a few months before and they still seemed to be situated where the map showed them. In New Guinea villages tend to change position every now and then. The inhabitants are not so particular about their domicile; if a certain place no longer suits them for one reason or another, they shift away with the entire village to another spot.

At a height of 1,500 feet the helicopters set course towards the north. The river twisted like a khaki-coloured bandage between the dark green woods. Little white dots moved here and there just above the tree-tops; these were great white herons (Egretta alba) and sulphur-crested cockatoos (Cacatua galerita), the latter in pairs or small groups. Near the Arup, some eight minutes' flying time short of Kawakit, things became more complicated. The river here was split up into a maze of different channels. The landscape looked like a stretch of dark-green parkland, broken up by grassy meadows of lighter green and the wide sweeps of the various winding channels, flowing past pleasant islands. The fliers christened this region "The Great Park". Incidentally, this was a very deceptive impression, for these marshy, reed-grown areas all have the appearance of smooth meadows when seen from above, as Zijlstra had found during his flight from Merauke to Tanah Merah.

They recognised Kawakit while still some way off. It was not because there was a space cleared for landing, since that could not be seen from a distance, but because the vivid red, white and blue of the Netherlands flag stood out sharply against the monotonous surroundings. A few minutes later the first landing at Kawakit had been completed, to the tremendous excitement of the inhabitants and to the enthusiastic

3.   A Sibiller with his stone axe.

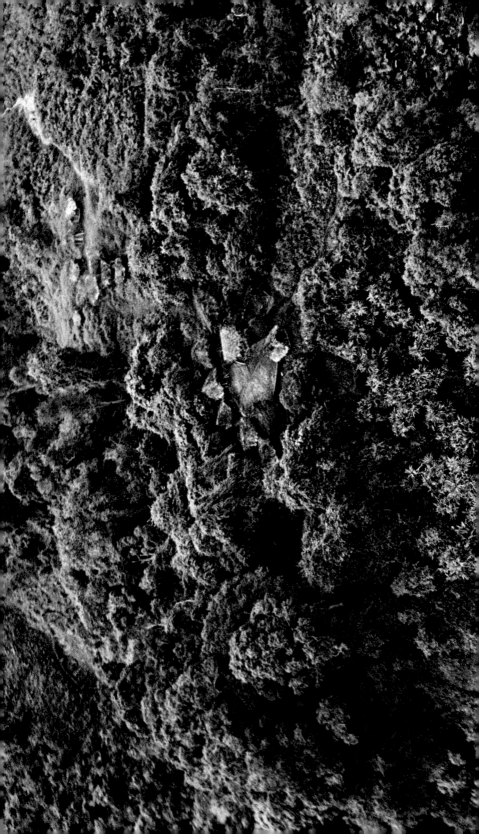

satisfaction of the expedition members there, led by Escher, who was busy recording the whole event very fully on film.

A further interested person was the Rev. Klamer, who was about to begin his missionary work in the region. The large clearing made for the camp gave him plenty of room to build a house; until this was finished, he was living in his Mappi boat, together with his Papuan helmsman. In fact the building work was not progressing very fast, as most of the Papuans were working for the expedition. The fact that a large part of the population had gone off to fetch new supplies of sago, leaving only the old people, the children and the invalids in the new settlement, made it specially difficult to reach a satisfactory distribution of the labour force.

One of the helicopters was still losing oil; Venema and Zijlstra ducked under the aircraft's tail and examined the oily marks. There was a filthy mess, and it was clearly impossible to find out where the leak was. There was nothing for it but to have the engine thoroughly examined by the mechanics back at Tanah Merah. Venema pressed for the repair to be finished quickly, as the helicopters could now not be spared for a single day. After a stop of about ten minutes, the two helicopters set off again for Tanah Merah, the fliers having promised that at least one could return next day, whatever happened.

Venema stayed in Kawakit to supervise the transport of supplies. That evening he discussed the situation with Escher. First of all, Bär must be supplied, since without this he would have had to return to Kawakit with his job unfinished. It was not that he required a great quantity of supplies; for the time being about 180 lb. of rice, meat and fish would be sufficient. To keep up their spirits, a parcel of cigarettes was added, together with a bottle of whisky to keep out the wet.

It was oppressively warm in the camp and everybody joined in hoping that the first helicopter landing in Kawakit would be celebrated with a can of beer. Corporal Van Ingen had clearly made arrangements for this, having hung the cans in a jute bag in the river to cool them. This method was quite effective, except if a bandyir occurred, because then the entire ration was swept off downstream. Sure enough, on 15th April Van den Bos arrived with one helicopter; the supplies for Bär were loaded into the racks above the floats, and Escher climbed up next to the pilot. He was to make this flight in order to find where Bär had got to, since no one knew how far he had been able to advance; in addition, Escher could go further with the helicopter, to decide where

4. Aerial view of Betabib; centre, the village with the iwool; top right, a "suburb" on the track to Mabilabol; top left, a hedged garden.

the next clearings could best be made. It had been arranged that the ground party was to light a big smoke fire, to indicate their position to the helicopter pilots.

*   *   *

The steeply-sloping terrain necessitated the construction of rather heavy platforms for the helicopters; the necessary rigidity could be obtained only by using stout tree-trunks and this tended to slow things down. In addition, the marines had remained behind with nine bearers to enlarge the previous clearing. Consequently the work at Kloof Camp progressed slowly; the landing-strip was still being cleared. Suddenly, about a quarter past eleven, the noise of the axes ceased, and there was a call of " 'copter . . . 'copter!" The bearers had heard the approaching aircraft, long before its sudden appearance in the narrow river valley, as it flew towards the smoke fire which had been lit in one corner of the clearing.

"For heaven's sake, let's hope he doesn't try to land! The platform is not done yet. . . . Keep off, keep off!" shouted Bär, waving his arms like a madman to tell the pilot that they were not ready for him. Even the tall figure of Cortel seemed to be imitating an old-fashioned Dutch windmill.

Above them Van den Bos and Escher sat in the helicopter grinning. They passed over the half-finished camp very slowly indeed. "All right, we'll have another shot tomorrow," called Escher to Van den Bos, "but let's see if we can drop the mail and some of the rice." The pilot nodded and manoeuvred the chopper into a good position over the clearing, while Escher leaned out and cut the packages loose. "Bundles away!" The letters and the food tins tumbled to earth and Escher quickly drew back from his difficult position. The last things they both saw were the wildly-waving figures below. The first contact had been successful and next day the news was radioed from Tanah Merah to the base camp in the Sibil Valley, and here too everybody's spirits began to rise; at last the helicopters were on the move.

On the next day, 16th April, the pilot made the first landing and was warmly received by Bär's group. A few Wambons, the tribesmen of the region, had come to take a look. They had heard the noise and, standing at a safe distance, observed the strange proceedings with great interest. The arrival of the helicopter considerably enhanced the prestige of the group; men who could work magic like this must indeed be very powerful. Escher stepped out and shook hands. "Have you had a chance to look at the ground farther ahead?" asked Bär. "Yes, and it doesn't look too difficult. It remains to be seen whether you'll be able to keep to the river, because farther on the ground rises very steeply. It's very rough and hilly and heavily indented."

"How did the clearing strike you?" Bär asked the pilots.

"They're good enough, but in the wild stretch of ground ahead they ought to be a bit closer. And now that we're working at a higher altitude, they ought to be somewhat bigger as well; I should say about thirty yards longer—and if the idea is to make a permanent camp here, then you'll need to clear a larger area," said Van den Bos.

Bär turned to Escher, "If we stop here any longer, we shan't get on at all. The heavy going and the shortage of clearers has delayed us too much already."

"Will you tell the Commander what the situation is? I suggest we leave the marines here with two bearers. They can form the first team and look after the supplies. The Commander was going to send Corporal Bril up here as well. Ask him to do that quickly and he can take charge here. And tell him that we're going to cut down the distance between the clearings. That'll mean a few extra days' work." Escher nodded and agreed to take the message. It was also arranged that the next supply drop would take place about five days later.

The helicopter returned to Kawakit, and Bär advanced carefully with his group. True, contact had been made with the inhabitants previously, but the expedition had to wait and see how they would react to this penetration of their territory. Two white men had lost their lives here ten years earlier, and in 1939 a mining expedition had been delayed for about six months in this region by hostile tribes. In the event, everything turned out very well. The Wambons were shy and suspicious, but bush-knives (machetes), axes and matches exercised a great power of attraction for them. To avoid any possible cause of friction, the group marched round the villages, rather than pass through them.

Now the going became very difficult. The limestone slopes, rough and thickly wooded, rose so steeply in many places that a great deal of time was lost in finding an easier path which after all could not be too far from the route mapped out in advance. But when the deepest and steepest part of the narrow valley had been reached, it was clear that no further progress was possible without a great loss of time. Number 15 became the last camp on the river and it was here that a disappointment occurred: the fliers could not land at this camp.

The deep kloof, almost two hundred yards deep, through which the Digul rushes with much noise and force on its way to the plain, was only about one hundred feet wide. A small plateau was found on the edge of this chine, by a river which plunged into the depths in an awe-

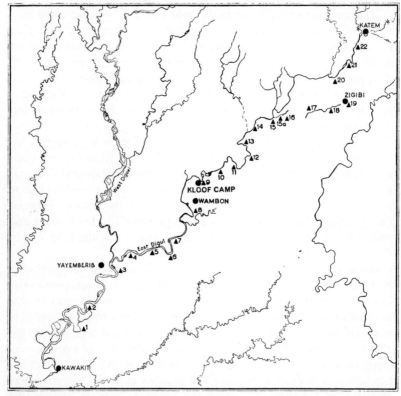

Fig. 2. The Digul Route from Kawakit to Katem; ▲ landing-places for helicopters.
● Permanent camps (Kawakit, Valley Camp, Katem) and villages.

inspiring waterfall. The trees in the dense forest were felled; straight into the river they dropped with a thundering crash, to be swept away at a frightening pace by the water and hurled into the Digul below.

A flat area thirty yards broad and about eighty yards long was cleared in this fashion. But this was still not sufficient for the helicopters. The high trees surrounding the area would not have constituted an obstacle

5.   Our landlord, Bomdogi, from Betabib; the man in
the background is wearing a cowrie-shell necklace.

to landing, but it would have made it almost impossible to get into the air again. The normal take-off procedure was to fly the aircraft over the river as it left the platform, but the valley was so narrow at this point that even small helicopters had no room to manoeuvre. The wild surroundings—with this tremendous steep-sided valley and the foaming river far below—did not form a very attractive picture to the airmen, who had no desire to risk their little craft over the seething rapids.

After circling for some time, Van den Bos, who was flying this supply sortie, clearly indicated to the party on the ground that he could not land. Bär decided to trek farther into the forest, in an attempt to find a suitable spot. Supplies were running low, and it was a matter of urgency to do something if the party were not to be left completely without food. If they were not revictualled quickly, the whole group would have to return to Kloof Camp, but for the time being they decided, somewhat disappointed, to continue until 25th April. They followed the bed of the stream, wading through fast-running but shallow water which flowed down the slope over a series of giant steps which it had carved out of the rocky bottom. These steps were fifty or a hundred yards long, but fortunately, since they were not high, progress was still quite easy.

However, it was not possible to keep to this natural route for long. The path the group had to follow led eastwards, at right angles to the course of the Digul, and as the bed of the stream suddenly swung round in a southerly direction, they had to drive straight into the jungle, clearing their path as they went. It was a stiff climb, over the rough limestone slopes to the top, which rose a good hundred yards above the surrounding ground. It was clear that the rock at the summit was flat and that there was ample room for a helicopter to land, but it was really not adequate for anything more than that, because the flat top was barely fourteen feet square.

At Camp 16 the group sat tensely watching for the helicopter. The fire was carefully kept smoking, so that it gave out a horrible reek which must have been visible a long way off. Towards ten o'clock the bearers began to stir with interest. They had heard a helicopter approaching and a few minutes later they spied it approaching; this time they could see it from a long way off, because of the way in which the summit stood out above the surrounding terrain. The aircraft could be seen as a small black speck just under the clouds, which lay pretty low, and was coming from the direction of the Digul. Rapidly the spot grew and grew, and soon the helicopter was circling the landing platform.

6. Wasonim, the iwool-keeper of Betabib, with his necklace of pigs' teeth.

Once the landing was over, the pilot looked around him with considerable surprise; getting out looked like being quite an experiment, as the ground dropped away steeply right alongside and in front of the helicopter floats. Carefully holding on, he worked his way back to the tail, where there seemed to be somewhat more room, though even here care was necessary. He had not brought a great deal with him, since this was a trial landing to test the new landing-place. Next time the two helicopters returned with full loads, but just as the first was about to land it began to rain heavily. They were just able to circle briefly and then disappeared, leaving a disillusioned group behind them. There was nothing left but to wait till another day; Bär went off with a dozen bearers to select the place for the next clearing. They were slowly climbing into higher ground and there would probably be more flat stretches than in the region they had traversed up till then.

Cortel stayed behind with the rest of the bearers to receive any supplies that might arrive. The bearers huddled themselves together over a damp and smoking fire, trying to shorten the waiting time by sleeping. They did not feel quite at ease in this unknown area, far from their villages in the Vogelkop Peninsula. They did not trust the Wambons a yard, but they could not make a bolt for it, as locally-recruited bearers would have done. In the past, numbers of patrols had to break off their journeys prematurely because the bearers hired locally had run off with their cooks. About 9 o'clock the clouds began to break up, and little patches of blue sky began to show here and there. The appearance of the sun soon dispersed the wisps of fog and the drizzle stopped. Everyone began to look up at the sky hopefully.

Just about an hour later, Zijlstra landed with supplies for several days. The loads were quickly distributed and Cortel set out to fetch Bär.

Two days later they were on the limestone ridge near Zigibi. From this height they had a marvellous view northwards over the East Digul, which at this point ran in a broad valley, where woods and grassy meadows alternated with steep rock formations. On the horizon they could see the mountains, blue with haze. To the north the massif of Antares stood out behind the lower chains of hills; to the north-west, the Orion Mountains were visible between the thin cloud-banks. On clear days, which were unhappily all too rare, it was even possible to see from Zigibi the distant snow-and-ice-clad Juliana Summit.

Bär and his group still had some four days' journey ahead of them before reaching Katem, but everybody's spirits had been raised by the view of the valley.

At the end of this stretch they would be able to get a short breathing-space in the camp at the confluence of the Ok Iwur and the East Digul. They now had a landing-place, which was undoubtedly the finest anywhere along the route. Once again they were waiting for the helicopters; the weather seemed good and there was not the slightest reason why the pilots should not come. The morning passed; the afternoon came and with it rain, but no helicopters. The men in the camp made harsh remarks about the unreliability of helicopters. Next day however, they really boiled with indignation when, around noon, they saw a few miles off a helicopter flying in the direction of Katem. The stupid pilot seemed to have missed the great fire which they had made to attract his attention, and he was flying in a straight line towards the north, without even deviating once in a way that might suggest that he was on the look-out. It was a rotten business!

"They must be round here somewhere," said Zijlstra. Their camp ought to be somewhere to starboard, on top of the ridge, if everything's all right. There's Zigibi,˙ over there." He pointed eastwards, where the ridge of hills stood out, clear down to the smallest details. They were flying somewhat below this level, following the East Digul through the valley. The weather was magnificent. "That's them," he shouted, indicating a column of smoke rising near an obviously inhabited spot. "The smoke is much too thick for an ordinary village fire; on the way back we must land for a minute to see how things are getting on," replied Venema. Calmly they flew on, and an hour later, to their satisfaction, made the first helicopter landing of the expedition in the Sibil Valley.

Next day the weather was again bad and in consequence two days elapsed before Bär's group received fresh supplies. The same helicopter brought Corporal Bril up from Kloof Camp; he had been instructed to follow the route taken by Bär's group in the opposite direction— that is from Zigibi to Kloof Camp—with two constables from Bär's party and four bearers. His task was to establish a new landing-strip between the high-lying Camp 16 and the discredited camp on the river, which the helicopters had found unusable; if possible he was also to clear another landing-place between Camps 15 and 14, because the difficult terrain along that stretch offered little opportunity for the helicopters to land if bad weather were to cut them off from both starting-point and landing area at once.

This was a job after Bril's own heart; there was nothing he liked better than trekking through difficult country looking for edible plants —of which he had a considerable knowledge—and making contact with the population, while photographing everything of the slightest possible interest. Originally a baker by trade, he far preferred rambling through the jungle, and when his colleagues returned to Holland without regrets after six months in New Guinea, Bril applied for a six month's extension. His whole approach and manner were such that it seemed to be of particular assistance to him in making the acquaintance of new groups of the population. He had no need at all of specialist assistance to set up his camps or to carry his barang (gear). In less than no time he always managed to have a party of Wambons busily clearing and building, without offering any prospect of great rewards. Chattering merrily, he would walk round among the men, his bushy beard giving him the appearance of a patriarch, and armed with a long staff, which he used as a pointer. The fact that there was no common language in which he could make his wishes known seemed to present no obstacle at all to satisfactory understanding.

After the first greetings, Bril quickly turned his gaze to the surrounding countryside. "Nice spot here," he said with satisfaction. "Good place to take some colour photos." "It does you good to look at it," replied Bär, "but you'd better get a move on, you'll have to move south as soon as possible. D'you know what you've got to do?" "I've heard some of it. The Commander said that the clearing work would have to be done quickly. It's a nice job," he said, looking round with a satisfied air. Bril was never one to allow his surroundings to get him down. He was a marine of special qualities and a great asset to the expedition.

The pilot asked for further instructions. "The day after tomorrow, 2nd May, we shall be in Camp 20 on the East Digul. We shall need four days' food there. And for the love of Mike, get there on time," said Bär. The helicopter pilot shrugged his shoulders: "The bad weather can hold us up at any time. We can never be sure of getting through. Above all, up here on the ridge the clouds tend to lie pretty close, even though it's fine all round. It really isn't our fault if we can't come. If the weather's reasonable you can count on us."

On the 1st May Bär and his group debouched from the jungle into the broad valley of the East Digul, just after noon. The man from Zigibi who had served as their guide along the path, so difficult to find, pointed to the opposite side, where a tributary noisily flowed into the East Digul. He had completed his task; the East Digul had been reached at a point directly opposite the Ok Ke (Ok Kair). Close by the river they selected a dry, level spot where a good landing-strip could be laid out with little trouble and where there was ample room for a camp. The bearers put down their loads and stretched themselves. They had a good stint of scrambling behind them, weighed down as they had been with their load of 44 lb. of heavy tins and bundles of tent-cloths. From Zigibi they had dropped down the 1600-ft. limestone cliff along a barely-recognisable path, wading through streams and floundering in a mixture of mud and humus which covered the ground in most places. While Leo, the cook, was lighting his fire in a surprisingly short time and preparing a meal for the party of twenty-five—the menu comprising rice, dried fish and katyang idyu (green peas)—axe-blows signalled the end of the day's journey, as they had now done for more than three weeks.

The helicopter pilot was as good as his word and landed on 2nd May with good supplies of food, so that Bär did not have to hang about, but with a brief "so long!" set off, followed by Wattimena and several bearers. His route ran along the East Digul in a westerly direction, to the point where the deep cleft begins; along this path he collected geological data. His route then took him in an easterly direction over the Ariem Range.

Meanwhile, Cortel and the main party had got under way again; having made two clearings en route, they arrived on 5th May at Katem, followed a few hours later by Bär.

The trip from Kawakit to Katem had been completed in just one month. This had been somewhat longer than had previously been estimated, but the helicopter pilots' request to have more and larger landing-strips had necessitated longer stops en route; the failure of the helicopters on occasion to get through with the necessary supplies had also caused some delay.

A distance of $71\frac{1}{2}$ miles had been covered, not on existing tracks, but frequently through areas of thick forest where every yard had to be cleared laboriously, with the men splashing in swamps, slithering and slipping in greasy mud or wading through water, sometimes in fine weather, sometimes in pouring rain, as is quite normal on a journey in this island.

The party had traversed the Wambon region without difficulty, although this tribe had previously been known as troublesome and hostile. The helicopter route to Katem was completed and it was now possible to bring up equipment and supplies to Katem and the Sibil Valley. While Bär was still on the move, supplies had been ferried to Kloof Camp; large quantities of food had been deposited there, ready to be transferred to Katem when the weather allowed. Corporal Bril worked hard on improving Kloof Camp with his marines; he built a fine house and laid out a garden, so that the expedition members could live there for the duration of operations, sometimes without contact with the outside world for weeks on end, but in a comfortable style and well provided for.

4

Mabilabol

ON 5TH APRIL BRONGERSMA SAW HIS OPPORTUNITY AND STEPPED INTO the Twin Pioneer, which carried him in three-quarters of an hour from Tanah Merah to the Sibil Valley, to the most colourfully-decorated airfield in New Guinea, entirely surrounded by yellow African marigolds in full bloom. There was the usual interest as the aircraft landed; all the occupants of the camp and a large number of interested Sibillers anxious to see who and what had arrived this time. The cargo was quickly unloaded and the aircraft flew back to Tanah Merah to fetch further supplies (Plate 2, (1)).

Over towards the flank of the Orion Range, which forms the northern boundary of the Sibil Valley, runs a series of low hills, the remains of an old river terrace. It is obvious that the Ok Sibil was formerly a much larger river, which carved itself out a very broad valley, and this terrace is a part of the old valley floor; later the smaller Sibil cut more deeply into this floor forming the present, narrower valley. One of the hills is called Mabilabol by the local inhabitants, and it was here that we set up the expedition's base camp. Our friend Bomdogi, an important man from the kampong (settlement) of Betabib, was untiring in telling us how he had given permission to Tuan Herremans (Hermans) and Tuan Senepki (Sneep), two government officials, to settle at Mabilabol; during the recital he waved his arms very widely to show that this was all his territory, after which we were treated to a demonstration of how he blew to the four cardinal points to clear the region of spirits (See Plate 5).

Hermans and Sneep had built here the government post known as "Sibil"; this comprised a primitive house, a barrack for the police and a storage place for supplies. Next to it the expedition camp was under construction and since the 19th March, when Brongersma and Venema had paid a short visit, building had progressed satisfactorily. The first structure was the "silver house", with walls and roof of corrugated aluminium sheeting. This was to accommodate our H.Q., and after the expedition was to be used by the Government officials. There were four small rooms in the silver house for the leaders, for the doctors and the lieutenant of marines, together with a large room used as a dining-hall, a sick-bay, and sleeping quarters for the helicopter crews. The hut for the scientific workers was provided with an aluminium roof, but this building could not be completed until the arrival of the tenting for the walls. Of two other buildings—the marines' hut and the biologists' laboratory—only the wooden frameworks were erected; here again the builders were waiting for the canvas panels to be delivered. One electrician and two marines were busy laying lighting cables; a diesel generator-set was to provide the current. The Sibil folk were struck dumb with amazement as we gave the generator a test run, and put the lights on and off by turning the switch. Policemen were splitting and cutting tree-trunks into planks to make tables for all the huts, and benches were being constructed from thin branches. Behind the silver house stood a mandi-shed (bath-hut) and the toilets.

Brongersma installed himself in the silver house, choosing the best room—the one with two windows (but no glass). In this way he could look out on the Tamal, the mountain ridge which bounds the Sibil Valley to the south, while through the other window he could survey the Sibil Valley as far as the Digul Mountains in the south-west.

It was a fine, sunny day and the view was magnificent; a really fine spot to settle in for six months. Along the wall of his room was a rack, which very quickly became filled with a whole quantity of clothes and scientific apparatus. His satisfaction grew visibly as his room steadily took on the appearance of a second-hand shop with a bed in the corner. While he was contemplating with pleasure the outcome of his work, Oosterman appeared in the doorway. His anxiety showed on his face, for the expedition members were expected in two days' time and the huts were not finished. Search had been made in vain in Tanah Merah for the tent-cloths which had been bought in Holland, and without these it would not be possible to complete the camp. As usual when such problems arose, Brongersma fetched a packet of strong shag out of his pocket and rolled a cigarette: "I'll ask about it again tomorrow, but for the moment the chaps will have to live in the silver house; we shall need to use the sick-bay for a dormitory." Oosterman thought this an

7. (1) Sibiller in full paint: the upper part of his face stained red, a bunch of cassowary feathers on his forehead, a piece of shell in his nose, and a pigs'-tooth necklace with a pig's tail attached. (2) Sibil valley man with a necklace of two boars' tusks and cowrie shells.

indifferent solution, but there was not much else to be done. Brongersma changed the subject; "What's it like for animals round here? Are they easy to come by?" Oosterman shook his head: "Nothing to be seen; no birds, no lizards, nothing. There must have been rats here, but they've gone since the government post brought cats in. No, if you're after animals you'd better go to Tanah Merah or Merauke." This reply did not disturb Brongersma unduly, for it would be most unusual if in a tropical region such as this, with lush vegetation, there were absolutely no animals to be found. When Oosterman had left to keep an eye on the building operations, Brongersma set off to reconnoitre the surroundings.

The camp site was dominated by *Araucaria* trees, which rose far above the huts; their slender stems were sixty feet and more in height, and the short side branches only strengthened the impression of slenderness. The branches of these "fir" trees are covered with short, stout, prickly needles; the cones on the trees, as big as hens' eggs, bear short curved spines. The Araucarias had been left standing in the vicinity of the camp, so as to avoid destroying the characteristic picture which they presented. A little farther away many of them had been cut down for use as building material; not only do they provide good timber, but the bark—which can be peeled away from the trunks in great strips—can be used as a roof covering. A couple of hundred yards from the camp and a little below it stood a kind of log-cabin known to us as "Hansel and Gretel's house" because it looked much more like a house out of a fairy-tale than a real dwelling. It was built of *Araucaria* trunks, and was roofed with sheets of bark. This cabin was inhabited by two missionaries, John Greenfield from America and Menno Heyblom, a Dutchman from New Zealand, who were living there for a time to learn the language before starting their missionary work. But it seemed a poor sort of house to live in and did not strike us as particularly water-tight.

The Sibil Valley lies in a limestone region and there are also karstic phenomena; thus we found here and there water-filled sink-holes forming deep indentations in the ground. One such sink pool was situated directly behind the camp; on the surface of the water small grebes (*Podiceps ruficollis novae-hollandiae*) swam in circles—small birds with a chestnut-brown neck and a bright yellow patch by the beak. Every now and then they dived out of sight, looking for food. The bushes were full of bird songs and a lizard was slipping away into the grass. "There y'are, there's nothing wrong with the animal world," thought

8. Men wearing the kamil or hair extension; (left) from
Kigonmedip, (right) from Tomkadin (Bonsigi).

Brongersma to himself, as he walked back to the camp, a satisfied man.

Kalkman, the botanist, the only scientific member of the expedition at Mabilabol at that moment (he had come on foot from Mindiptana), came strolling up. "Are you coming in for a bite? While we're still so few, we're eating at the government post. Oosterman's looking after the kitchen, so there'll be a good dish of rice served up." The word rice was sufficient to clear Brongersma's mind completely of all cares with regard to the future and to set him following Kalkman with long strides. While they were sitting at their meal, a little brown figure came trotting in and squatted by the table; this was "Mina", a little Sibil girl of about seven, who was allowed to eat up the left-overs. Sometimes of course there were things that she did not find very tasty, but it was not good manners to leave the not-so-tasty things to waste; so Mina would eat the whole lot up nicely, although she did find an opportunity of slipping something that she really found disagreeable to Flap, Sneep's dog, who stood watching with interest. With a feeble smile as a sign of thanks, Mina would then disappear again. This ceremony was repeated every day, until one day Mina stayed away. It seemed that she had taken some katyang tanah (peanuts) from the missionaries' garden; she had been scolded for this and now did not dare to show her face again. This was a big gap in our daily ritual and we offered a bar of chocolate if Mina would come back, but she was so scared that it was months before she returned.

That evening the last worries about the supposed absence of animals disappeared; hundreds of insects descended upon us, attracted by the light, and the sink-hole was full of the noise of frogs.

Next day everybody began work with new courage. At half past six Sneep went down to the rain-gauge to record the amount of precipitation in the previous twenty-four hours. This would decide whether an aircraft could land or not. As is the case with all grass-surfaced airfields, there is a limiting rainfall figure; if there is more than $\frac{3}{4}''$ in twenty-four hours, the airfield must be closed for the day. At ten minutes to seven the radio link-up began. There were two receiving and transmitting sets in the government station, one being used for the airline services and the other for telephone conversations via the Post Office network. Sneep would stand in front of his house surveying the weather, while one of the Muyus would switch the set on, and the weather report could then be sent out. "Sibil to Sentani," Sneep would say into the microphone of the airways transmitter, to be answered from the loudspeaker with the words: "Sentani to Sibil." Then would come the report: "The weather is calm, C. Charlie—A. Able—L. Love—M. Mike—; cloud cover five-eighths stratus at 1,000 feet and four-eighths alto-stratus/alto-cumulus at 6,000 feet; visibility more than fourteen miles and rainfall point six of an inch; got it?" "Received and understood," Sentani would reply. "Call up again at 7.30, we haven't spoken to the Twin Pioneer at Tanah Merah yet." "Will do," would be the answer from Sneep, who now had to wait and see what would happen. Our weather might be very reasonable, but this would not mean that the same was true at Tanah Merah, south of the mountains. Throughout the whole expedition period, this was one of the most important moments in the day; would our aircraft be able to land or would we draw another blank? As long as there was a possibility of a Twin Pioneer getting through to Sibil, a weather report would be sent out every hour, and everyone would look anxiously at the sky as the mist began to rise from the woods and mountain slopes under the heat of the sun, or as patches of cloud came driving down the valley. Everything we needed in the way of equipment and food had to be brought in by air, and a remote post of this kind is just the place for you to learn the perils of air traffic.

The other receiving/transmitting set would then be switched on and at seven o'clock Merauke would come on the air; "This is Merauke calling all stations; Sibil, weather report, please." If required, a telephone conversation would be arranged with the Resident's Office or with the bank, but before this could take place Merauke had to speak to all other stations in the south—Okaba, Kepi, Bade and Agats. We had to queue for our turn on the telephone, and so had to "hang on". This was true of each of the radio stations, but many of the people in their homes would tune their wireless sets to this wavelength and listen in to the conversations. Confidential messages were only transmitted if it could not be avoided, since in this way they would become common know-ledge over the whole of South New Guinea; it was rather comic to receive a message in these conditions with the added words: "That's between ourselves, of course."

Just as everybody else was able to participate in the expedition's experiences by this means, so we shared all sorts of events which were taking place in the south; for instance, how Okaba had its transmitter out of action for weeks, and could thus only receive "one-sided" messages, how a policeman had had twins born to him or how the different posts made various requisitions. Then Merauke would end its transmission; "Good-bye and good luck; over and out with Sibil." "Thanks very much; same to you—over and out," Sneep would reply, switching over to Hollandia, where the communications were in the hands of Mr. Valenbreder, who came on the air every day with a friendly word. He would say, for instance, "Delighted to hear your musical voice on the ether," or would reply to our question "How are you receiving me?" with the words "With open arms". At 8 o'clock Tanah Merah would come on the air and, if necessary, Hollandia would do so again at 8.30 a.m. and Merauke at 3.30 p.m. Originally, Tanah Merah came on at half past four in the afternoon, but there was so much interference that the conversation was postponed till 8 o'clock each morning. From seven to nine, Brongersma sat at the radio every morning transmitting requisitions, asking for information and answering requests for conversations with the Sibil base. The discussions regarding the aircraft and whether they were coming or not were an object of general interest, and of a morning it was quite usual to find a number of expedition members in the government post, listening to the radio conversations.

On 7th April, the members of the expedition coming from Holland landed on Biak Island at the Mokmer airfield; here they were met and brought to the naval air station at Buruku, where they boarded a Martin Mariner amphibian flying-boat which brought them to Sentani, the airfield at Hollandia. The intention was that they should then transfer to a Twin Pioneer which would bring them to the Sibil Valley. On paper this transport operation was very well organised, but there was one circumstance which made all the arrangements completely null and void; this was the fact that we happened to be in New Guinea. On 7th April it became clear that over two inches of rain had fallen in the preceding twenty-four hours and that the Sibil Valley airstrip was thus too soft to allow of a landing. The newly-arrived members from Holland were accommodated in the government hotel; they did not consider it a very serious matter to spend a short while there, as it was pleasant to rest and recover somewhat from the tiring journey. As soon as there was another opportunity, the people waiting in Hollandia would be flown in first; there was a linguistic expert, Dr. J. C. Anceaux, together with Dr. J. Pouwer, the ethnologist, Ir. J. J. Reynders, the soil expert, and Surgeon-Lieutenant (Senior grade) M. O. Tissing.

The official beginning of the expedition was on 10th April, but it was

only a small group that were able to celebrate it in the field; the members
who had come from Holland had to do this in Hollandia. The Governor
and the Resident sent telegrams and the government officials issued a
ration of spirits.

Although there was still not a great deal of genuine expedition
activity to be seen at Mabilabol by reason of these difficulties, there was
one operation of considerable interest to philatelists. The Post Office
had issued a special postage stamp to mark the expedition, on which
there was a picture of a Papuan staring at a helicopter flying over the
mountains; the man was carrying a stone axe on his shoulder, although
the design of axe was not that of those used in the Sibil, but one resembling the axe found in the Baliem Valley. The philatelic association had
distributed first-day covers, but it looked as though the envelopes and
stamps would be post-marked on 10th April everywhere but on the
expedition ground, because the cancellation stamp for the Sibil station
had not yet arrived. There was a great deal of telephoning to and fro
and finally the postal authorities gave permission for an emergency
stamp to be used. Hand printing sets had been taken along to print
labels, and an emergency stamp was made up from them. The number
of first-day covers was not sufficient to meet the demand and about
eighty ordinary envelopes were overprinted as emergency first-day
covers. It turned out later that the philatelists considered this a great
joke, because in addition to the genuine envelopes with a cancellation
stamp from one of the large post offices and a first-day postage stamp,
there were now about a couple of hundred even more genuine covers
in circulation, bearing the most unusual emergency cancellation stamp
for Sibil and the special postage stamp that was used on all letters sent
by the expedition. The expedition members read the excited comments
in the newspapers with considerable pleasure.

The next group of participants from Holland only arrived on 14th
April; they were: Dr. W. Vervoort, the zoologist, with the two assistants,
C. Van Heijningen and J. J. Staats. Dr. Th. Verstappen, the geomorpho-
logist, Dr. A. G. de Wilde, the anthropologist, and Dr. B. O. Van
Zanten, the botanist. They were accompanied by Dr. J. Romeijn,
a government doctor from Hollandia. They had already been out to
the airfield at Sentani in vain on two occasions, arriving there early in
the morning only to be told that the weather was bad while on another
occasion they were informed that the weather in the Sibil region was
glorious but that heavy rain near Hollandia had brought about a land-

slide which had blocked the road to the airfield. These were the things that one had to get used to soon after arriving from Holland, where travelling can be kept to a fixed time-table.

The expedition members at the base camp were not disturbed by this delay, since it gave them time to bring the camp into an even greater state of readiness. The tent-cloths bought in Holland were finally considered lost and heavy tarpaulins had therefore been sent for. This made it possible for at least one half of the research workers' building to be provided with walls. A low balustrade was built along its open front, and jute awnings stretched over it to protect the scientists who had to live there from the wind, but the building remained rather an airy one. In the middle of the shed, benches and tables were set up; a stove was made out of an empty oil drum. This gave out a comfortable warmth in the evening, and on a shelf about it, plants and insects could be set to dry. At the beginning this was not an unqualified success; every now and then a sheet of flame would shoot up and another store of herbarium material would be lost.

Everyone was now waiting for the helicopters and the complete equipment. The expedition members made short trips in the vicinity; they were now in a position to accustom themselves to the climate and to the terrain—a very necessary thing for those who were in New Guinea for the first time. They returned very tired from their first outings, and one of their number found the forest exceedingly untidy; it was not a very agreeable pastime to go walking over slippery mud tracks full of tree-roots. There was also a considerable shortage of good shoes, the first pairs having been completely worn out by the heavy going.

Meanwhile, everybody in the base camp was wondering what Venema and Bär were up to in the south. There was still no news about the arrival of the helicopters. Communications were not yet as good as they might be, but the radio-links were not only bothered by technical faults. Two of the stations in the south did not adhere to the agreed transmission times, and as we were trying one afternoon to get in touch with Tanah Merah, we found these two stations still in the process of holding a pleasant conversation, and it even seemed to us that we could hear one of the users amusing the other by singing songs into the microphone. Sneep's attempts to break through this conversation or to bring it to an end were without success. Next morning Sneep informed Merauke in quite unmistakable terms what he thought of this state of things. That helped; his powerful language was heard and understood over half New Guinea, and Merauke probably added a little spice of its own. As we set our radio in operation that afternoon, we heard two men talking at express-train speed, repeating every now and then the warning: "We haven't got much time left, Sibil will be on the air in a minute." At precisely half past four we began to call Tanah Merah; "Calling Tanah Merah, Tanah Merah, this is Sibil calling Tanah Merah," and then suddenly there was silence on the air—complete silence; Tanah Merah was not answering us. We called for ten minutes, but it was pretty clear there was a fault, as the only thing that issued from the loudspeaker was a nerve-racking howl.

Later we learned that Venema had left for Kawakit, intending to try to reach the Sibil Valley as quickly as possible by helicopter; we also heard that Bär and Cortel were progressing slowly because there were now more clearings to be made. There was also news of the leaking oil-lead which was keeping one helicopter grounded. To speed things up we set Operation "Burung Kunde" ("Crowned Pigeon") under way; this name was used because Police-Sergeant Kroon (Crown) was in charge of the operation. He was to ensure that the clearings were completed between Katem and Sibil, so that once the helicopters could reach Katem, they would be able to continue direct to the Sibil Valley. The Sibillers were not particularly enthusiastic about acting as bearers as far as Katem. It took a great deal of trouble to get fifteen of them to take on the task, although each of them could earn a large knife for this short journey. "There is only one pleasure and that is pleasure in the misfortunes of others." And this seemed to be true here. Each time one of the fellows allowed himself to be won over his friends were highly delighted, until their turn came along. On 19th April, Kroon left with Marine Boon, four policemen, six Muyus, and sixteen Sibillers.

On 23rd April, the Twin Pioneer arrived again from Tanah Merah, but unfortunately it turned out that the cargo on this occasion consisted entirely of axes for the survey group, which was still to arrive. The second flight brought some equipment for us, and three bags of mail. As the Twin Pioneer taxied gently over the landing-strip, the left-hand wheel suddenly sank into a weak patch in the ground. Fortunately, the plane was not travelling very fast, but it was still quite a good time before it stood on the air-strip ready to take off again. It was understandable that the airmen were not particularly keen on coming back again that day.

Regular work was now carried out on the air-strip to strengthen a number of weak spots; in addition, the camp was also improved. Some of the Sibil Valley people, grown men and boys, fetched gravel from the river to be used on the paths. There were a few important men who found that it was too far for them to go down to the river. They sat down at the edge of the airfield and were given a stone or two by the less important people, as they came up with their load. Once these men had gathered a moderate load themselves they carried it up to the camp. When it came on to rain, work did not progress very quickly. The Sibillers would then stay at home or hang about all day in the camp huts, a habit for which we could not blame them. The research workers' hut generally accommodated these customers, and at such times there would be a good fifteen Sibillers sitting comfortably warming themselves at our stove.

At last, on 29th April the first helicopter was flown in by Chief-Pilot Zijlstra; Venema came with him as a passenger. About noon we heard a faint message over the radio from Katem that the helicopter was on the way, and everybody went down to the airfield to be sure not to miss this event. One or two pessimists went away again about a quarter past twelve; we had heard so many times that the helicopters would arrive soon, without anything coming of it. We sat in a row on a thick tree-trunk (which did service as a roller for the airfield) staring towards the pass in the south-east, as that was the direction from which the helicopter must come. It looked rather as though the clouds over the pass would shut down completely, and by half past twelve hardly anyone believed that the helicopter would arrive, apart from the general leader of the expedition, who had to have confidence officially and who had no wish to show that he also was capable of being assailed by doubts. We rolled and smoked cigarette after cigarette. And then . . . there was a wild cry from the Sibillers: "'copter, 'copter"; they knew the sound of the chopper from the reconnaissance expedition of 1957. And there it was—the first expedition helicopter—coming in not from the south-east but from the north-west, high over the Orion Mountains. After a wide sweep over the camp, Zijlstra set his aircraft down on the landing-strip. All the amateur photographers—still and ciné—moved into action to record the arrival of the technical leader. Zijlstra still seemed a bit worried. "Is this the usual route from Katem?" he asked Venema; "Not really," was the answer, "we should've turned off to the left a bit earlier, but I didn't see the valley quickly enough. However we've got

9. (1) Herberts paying out wages (matches) in Mabilabol.
    (2) Romeijn taking blood samples.

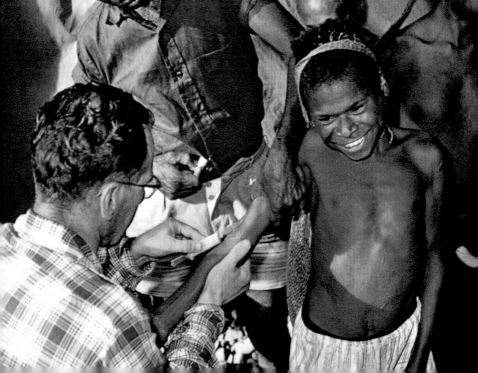

here all right." Zijlstra was not entirely satisfied; the cleft valley of the Digul to the north of the Orion Mountains, without a single landing-strip, was not such a pleasant area to fly over in a helicopter. A meal was quickly eaten and then Zijlstra looked up into the sky; he reckoned he could get over the pass once again. Our anthropologist de Wilde was to go with him to Kawakit and Tanah Merah, to see why his gear had not arrived. They took a bag of mail with them, every letter being rapidly overprinted: "First helicopter flight, Sibil to Tanah Merah, 29th April 1959."

Everybody's spirits were running exceptionally high now that the link had been made; many new plans were formed and lists drawn up to fix priorities for the inward transport of the equipment. Fortunately nobody imagined that weeks would elapse before the helicopters were stationed at our camp. The birthday of H.M. the Queen of the Nether-lands was celebrated by a police colour parade. The national flag was hoisted together with the Orange pennant, the policemen presented arms, and the ceremony was over. We were not in a position to issue a ration of spirits, as we had none. As a special treat, all the members of the expedition, the marines, the police and the Muyu bearers were given a bar of chocolate, and we took the afternoon off.

Now and then we had visitors. Every day Sibillers were arriving to work at the camp. But there were also Papuans from the Kiwirok Valley (some 15 miles north-east of Sibil) and from Ariemkop (about 3 miles south-east of Sibil) who came to look around. They were given a complete conducted tour. Bomdogi or one of the other Sibillers took charge of them. Everything was carefully inspected, the party wandering quite boldly through our living-huts; if somebody happened to be taking an afternoon nap, that didn't matter at all. A long-drawn "Ieee" expressed their wonder at many of the strange objects we possessed. They greatly enjoyed looking through prismatic binoculars; with one hand they would hold the glasses, reaching out meanwhile with the other in an attempt to grasp what seemed to be so near them. But the great hit was always Anceaux's set of false teeth. At first the beholders were frightened but later filled with awe, as he removed the upper denture, and then the lower, subsequently replacing them both. Many a Papuan tried to do the same with his own teeth, and was really only too glad to find that they were not as loose as that. This demonstration had to be repeated every time for new visitors, and their cry of "Ieee" was quite genuine. Many of the Sibillers came at meal times to help eat

10. (1) Species of orchid (*Dendrobium* sp.) from the Sibil Valley.
(2) Blooms of *Rhododendron konori*.

up our left-overs, but one day when we found ourselves obliged to prepare a European meal, we attempted to introduce them to sauerkraut; for four days the Sibillers kept away from our house, anything as horrible as sauerkraut being too much even for them.

On 3rd May the Twin Pioneer set up a record by flying from Tanah Merah to the Sibil Valley five times. On the last flight it touched down at half past five and stayed the night in the valley. That evening we had a big feast with our three airmen guests. But this was the last flight that we were to have for the time being. It began to pour with rain that night and 1.3 inches fell in the space of a couple of hours. The Twin Pioneer was able to take off, but further landings were out of the question for the time being, and the plane therefore set off for Hollandia. The air-transport situation had worsened considerably since the other Twin Pioneer had damaged its tail while landing at Arso. New Guinea had to make do with a single Twin Pioneer for more than five months, but this aircraft had many other stations to supply in addition to Sibil.

The helicopter came occasionally. It arrived at Sibil on 5th May with Alfred van Sprang, the radio correspondent, and on 6th May Bär arrived to discuss plans for the future. He wanted to set out with his group from Katem direct to the Antares Mountains. The trek from Kawakit to Katem had been such a long business that he now did not want to lose any more time. But everything depended on the supply operation, which was not yet running as smoothly as we would have wished. Only partly satisfied, Bär boarded the helicopter again to fly back to Katem. From this point he was to prepare the route along the Ok Iwur. Information came from Tanah Merah that two of the helicopter pilots, Zijlstra and Van den Bos, had gone down with Biak 'flu, a virulent form of influenza which is accompanied by a high fever. Although Menge, the third pilot, was very active, transporting supplies to Katem with only one helicopter was a slow affair; what was more, the aircraft could not carry more than 400 lb. on each trip. The inward transport to the Sibil Valley with the Twin Pioneer could have been better too; to speed up the collection of supplies at the base camp, we tried to charter an aircraft from Australian New Guinea, but without success. Fortunately, the reserves of food in the Sibil Valley were not unsatisfactory, and there was enough for a large party to eat its fill. Katem had ample stocks to maintain a small group for weeks. It was nevertheless advisable to bring up to the Sibil Valley everybody whose presence was not essential in Katem, for so long as the helicopters were unable to bring in supplies.

Cortel and Kroon arrived with their Sansapor bearers at Mabilabol on
10th and 11th May, followed by Bär and Lt. Nicolas on 19th and on the
22nd by Reynders (who had gone by helicopter to Katem on 8th May
to carry out soil investigations) with de Wilde (who had come from
Mindiptana on foot). On the other hand, on 20th May, Verstappen set
off for Katem to explore the vicinity. The government ciné cameraman,
P. Ter Laag, stayed for about ten days filming the expedition activities.
The team at the base camp was further strengthened by a group of
Survey Department Officials fifteen strong, led by Van der Weiden; they
were to carry out astronomical fixes and map a part of the mountains.
Groups of research workers would go off on trips of varying length,
so that the actual population of the camp was constantly changing. On
the rare days when they were nearly all present in camp, we organised
evening talks in which one of the investigators would explain the scope
of his work. This was necessary if each one was to understand the
others' objectives. Some of the expedition members, and especially Van
Sprang, the radio correspondent, achieved self-expression in "the
Sibillertje", our news-sheet, which had a daily edition of one; it rarely
published much news (and when there was any everybody knew it
beforehand anyway), but usually contained humorous-cum-critical
remarks about the supply problem and about events in the camp.

The fact that not all the scientific equipment had been brought up did
indeed tend to restrict research work, but fortunately there were a
number of studies which could be made with a small amount of gear.
Pouwer had ample work with his ethnological studies, and so had
Anceaux with his linguistic investigations. There were quite enough
Sibillers who could give them information about their customs and
language. These two research workers were but little troubled by the
deficiencies of the transport of equipment; as long as they had paper
and a pencil, they were satisfied. Our botanist, Kalkman, went out every
day with what the non-botanists called his "reading case", two sheets of
cardboard with a number of newspapers between them used to dry the
plants he had collected. Reynders quartered the region with his earth
drill and shovel, to study ground sections and take soil samples.

The local inhabitants slowly came to realise that the zoologists were
willing purchasers of animals of all kinds. Each day they would bring
frogs and lizards, receiving a bead or a button in payment. If they
brought four frogs or three lizards at a time, they would be paid with
an okatu (small mirror). Papuans are good business men and it

frequently happened that they would try to obtain their okatu for three frogs or two lizards. Hardened by practice, the zoologists did not give way; experience had taught them that if they paid out a mirror for three frogs, a fourth would be held in reserve in the carrying-net and then be offered in return for a button. If the supplier really had not the requisite number of creatures to entitle him to a mirror, he could either make up the count later (and be paid then) or borrow one from a neighbour. It was in fact some time before this commerce got well under way; after all, these animals are used as food by the inhabitants. On one occasion a little boy stood gazing with wonderment at a jar of lizards preserved in alcohol, and said, with a delighted expression; "Nam-nam", which means "eat". We sometimes wondered what the Sibillers thought of this strange trade; did they perhaps think that this was our way of foraging? Pouwer questioned one of his friends from the kampong at Betabib on this point. The answer was surprising. "I think that this man when he goes home to his family wishes to show what sort of animals live in the Sibil"—a reply which was not so very far from the truth. In regions where the inhabitants treat all sorts of animals as food, they are good at distinguishing the different species. We began working with drawings, to show the kinds of animals we wanted, and so learned some of the general names; all kinds of frogs are known as "kol", with a special name added for each different species, e.g. "kol wopwor" for a brown species of tree-frog; snakes and lizards are grouped together under the name "awot". To distinguish snakes from lizards and e.g. obtain a snake, one asks for an "awot semitki" (a long lizard). In addition to this, there are yet again special names for all the kinds of snake and lizard; e.g. "awot mapom" is the name for a brown snake (Boiga irregularis), which is found in the bushes.

Each evening a great deal of work was done on catching insects attracted by the light. Their numbers varied according to circumstances. The catch was largest at the new moon, and on occasions when it began to pour with rain at about 6 o'clock. Hundreds of insects would then come flying in: large cicadas, which make a rasping noise, would fly through the house on powerful wings, always ending up by banging into the aluminium walls with a great clatter; large night-moths came in through the driving rain, and it was striking to notice that they remained completely dry in the process; small beetles posted themselves near the lamps and made short work of the many moths which swarmed around them. The zoologists were not the only ones to be very active, for there were other members of the expedition whose hunting instincts became aroused. True, every now and then there were protests from those who were sitting reading or writing, and who could not understand why a couple of beetles had to be trapped just on their book or on their letter, or why they had suddenly to sit absolutely still to allow themselves to be "de-mothed". The same evening, as well as next morning, many hours were spent on labelling and packing the catch.

Besides all these activities there were quite enough events to divert us, even though we would very willingly have done without such emotions. For instance, one day we heard the Twin Pioneer circling above the clouds over the valley without being able to make radio contact; it was obvious that there was widespread radio interference, as we could not get in touch with the airfields either. It was one of those anxious moments when all that we could do was to wait and see what happened; things were bound to come out all right in the end, but it gave one a helpless feeling to be unable to do anything. On 17th May the Twin Pioneer arrived and Venema flew down to Tanah Merah to try to speed up the transport of supplies, and to see how the sick pilots were getting on. Two days later the plane set off with three passengers from the Sibil Valley to Hollandia; the aircraft took off and slowly climbed to 10,000 feet to get over the mountains. Suddenly it began to make a queer noise and a trail of blue smoke issued from its port engine. Watching with binoculars we could see that the propeller had stopped, and the Twin Pioneer was returning to land in wide sweeping curves. We had no fire extinguishers at the landing-strip and all we could do was to post a number of policemen along the runway with shovels, to put out any fire that might begin as the plane touched down, but fortunately things did not reach this point. The Cessna aircraft of the Missionary Aviation Fellowship flew in a mechanic who inspected the motor; one cylinder had burst and the oil was full of bits of metal (we used a butterfly-net as a filter to discover this). This meant that the motor would have to be replaced—not an easy task on a landing-strip without any equipment. The operation involved a great deal of to-and-fro traffic; the Cessna landed several times with mechanics and tools, and even Sibil now became an international airfield; the new engine was delivered by an aircraft of Qantas, the Australian airline. Using tree-trunks the police-constables set up a working platform and a hoist under the guidance of Kroon. The dud engine was attached to the tackle, and the holding bolts removed; then the aircraft was pushed backwards and the motor lowered slowly to the ground. The installation of the new engine was more difficult, since while it remained suspended from the pulley tackle, the plane had to be pushed by hand into such a position that everything fitted properly. This was a troublesome job, but it was achieved and the aircraft was ready to fly again in within a week. The police, the Muyus and some Sibillers had a stiff job with the hoisting and assembling, but they were people with a sense of humour, and found the whole affair very amusing.

Just when we thought that everything was running smoothly—both helicopters were flying again along the Digul route, and Venema had reached Katem on his return journey to the Sibil Valley—there came another piece of bad news; all three pilots and one of the mechanics had been taken off to hospital in Hollandia suffering from jaundice. In all it was between six and eight weeks before we could get the work going again. Remarkably enough, this new check did not make the expedition members downhearted; in fact, rather the contrary. Now that the transport of supplies either by helicopter or by Twin Pioneer had been stopped by circumstances, there was every reason to reconsider the plans thoroughly once again. Venema would have to stay in Katem for the time being; this was a nuisance, because he was the right man to deal with all sorts of problems connected with flying. The original plan was maintained in so far as the geological group was still to set off from Katem along the Ok Iwur in a northerly direction, towards the Antares Mountains; moreover, this group was to prepare the way for the helicopters and for the other parties. A period of three months had originally been allotted to this operation and to the investigation of the Antares Range, and by now, on 25th May, one and a half months of this period had gone by without any progress being made with the plan, because it had not been possible to bring up supplies to Katem in time. Almost all the expedition members were at Mabilabol, and what equipment had been brought up was there too; it was therefore more logical to drop the Katem-Antares plan and start out from the Sibil Valley instead. The solution to the problem of achieving rapid and adequate provision of food supplies was to have them dropped from the air, and Brongersma decided to do this. On 2nd June, the Catalina amphibian of the Netherlands New Guinea Petroleum Company made an air-drop of 3 tons of food, and a day or two later the Dakota owned by De Kroonduif brought in another four tons. Telegrams were sent to Holland to ask for extra funds, and Venema was informed of the modified plans. The Foundation Council asked for more details and Brongersma went down to Hollandia to talk to the Netherlands on the phone. The approach was surprisingly successful; we were granted a credit of 100,000 guilders to charter extra aircraft for the supply operation and to hire bearers. Next morning all the participants sat around the radio in Mabilabol, waiting to hear what had been the result of the telephone conversation. Brongersma did not know whether he was allowed to announce the amount involved or not, since the whole of New Guinea was listening in. To the disappointment of the eaves-droppers, he expressed himself in the following terms: "If you chaps take the new plan that I left on my desk, and add the bearers' wages to the flying charges, you can put another 100,000 guilders on top of that and then take 40% off; that'll tell you how much money's available." Whoops of triumph from Mabilabol were heard over the radio, and that evening the general public in New Guinea did after all learn the amount involved from the press reports. Having talked everything over in Hollandia, Brongersma returned to the Sibil Valley accompanied by a new visitor to the camp; this was Mr. J. Klaarenbeek, LL.D., who was to write articles about the expedition for the illustrated papers. Mean-while, Venema had reached Mabilabol. The first helicopter arrived on 18th June, followed six days later by the second, which flew in to operate from Sibil. They were to provide support for the groups working in the field. The future looked rosy, and we could now get down to the task of exploration.

5

The Sibil Valley

IT WAS ONE OF THOSE RARE, LOVELY MORNINGS WHEN THE SKY WAS bright and virtually cloudless. The first rays of the sun slanted over the high mountains in the east, tingeing the ridge—and later the slopes—of the Digul Mountains a reddish-copper colour, although this did not last for long. The sun climbed higher, the light became harder and more yellow and the reddish glow disappeared; soon the whole valley was flooded with bright sunlight. The landscape was a patchwork of varying tones of green; dark tints in the woods which clothed the mountain slopes contrasted with the light green of the canefields all along the river. At many points columns of smoke rose from the woods, clearly indicating where the inhabitants' settlements were.

The ridges and summits of the mountains stood out clearly against the blue sky. These were the Orion Mountains to the north, the Digul range to the south-west and the Tamal in the south, while in the east a range of hills closed off the valley. In the north-west we could see—very much foreshortened—the easternmost outlier of the Juliana Mountains, with the Dirksz Summit (named after Augustijn Dirksz, who had visited S.W. New Guinea in 1678 and 1679 in the ship *Pisang*).

Long before white men penetrated into the mountains, survey measurements had been made from various points in the lowlands to determine and plot the position and height of mountains as accurately as possible; the principal ridges and summits were given names. The military expedition which reconnoitred along the Digul in 1909 and 1913 gave the name of Star Mountains to that part of the central mountainous region which runs eastward from the Juliana Mountains right into Australian New Guinea; the ridges and summits of this region were named after stars or constellations, such as Leo, the Orion Range, and Betelgeuze in the vicinity of the Sibil Valley.

76

11. (1) Houses in Kasengabib.
(2) Sitting round the fire in the evening, at Ebabding.

At the point in the west where the Digul and Orion Ranges run together, the Ok Sibil rises. "Ok" is the Sibil word for water and is also used as a general name for rivers. The river follows a very winding course eastward through the valley, and finally disappears into the ground.

On its way the Ok Sibil collects the water from a number of tributaries which all run down the slopes of the Orion Mountains, that is, from the north. There are no tributaries on the southern side of the river, since the broad south-western section of the Sibil Valley is a dry

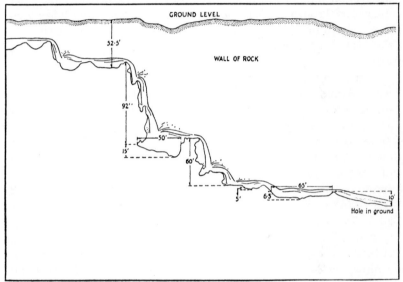

Fig. 3. Section of the cleft in which the Ok Sibil disappears into the ground.

karstic region; what rain does fall disappears into the ground and no rivers are formed.

The level of the water in the river varies very considerably. When it has rained fairly heavily in the west of the valley, the Ok Sibil becomes a wildly-rushing river of muddy water, while torrential rain can cause it to break its banks. If, however, the weather stays dry for several days at a stretch, the stream dries up and leaves only a few pools in its bed, separated from one another by banks of sand or gravel. To the east of the air-strip, the Ok Sibil has cut a deep cleft in the ridge of hills which shuts off the end of the valley. As long as the river continues to flow, its

12. (1) Woman and baby at Kukding.
(2) Interested spectators; the carrying-nets contain potatoes.

waters rushing wildly through the cleft, no one can reach the place where the river disappears underground. Great clouds of spray hide this point from view. After three days without any rain, on 29th June, Surgeon-Lieutenant Tissing, Marine-Sergeant J. A. de Wijn, Marine Scharff and the pilot Menge managed to climb down about 50 yards into the kloof. The waters of the Ok Sibil here fall over a series of steps or terraces into the depths of the kloof (Fig. 3) ; in each of these rock steps the rushing water has created potholes by whirling round and round the pebbles carried along in the current, and even in a time of sustained drought these potholes contain water. At the end of the kloof, the water disappears through a hole in the ground some 10 feet across. It had been assumed that this underground river probably comes out somewhere in the East Digul, but it was not known where. This problem was now to be solved.

Verstappen travelled from Mabilabol to Songgam on the East Digul, while Marine Timmer was posted by the Ariemkop spring. Early in the morning Nicolas and Tissing threw a quantity of dye into the Ok Sibil, as close as possible to the point where the river disappears. About 4 hours later Verstappen—at Songgam, about 10 miles away—saw coloured water flowing out of the rocks into the East Digul. The outflow of the Ok Sibil was discovered. Timmer stayed till midnight at the spring at Ariemkop, but there was no coloration of the water at all and this spring is thus clearly shown to have no connection with the Ok Sibil. The well-known karstic phenomenon of underground river-courses is found frequently in this district; to the west of the kampong at Betabib the Ok Atem and Ok Aisyek also disappear into the ground.

Along the slopes of the Orion Mountains and of the Tamal, we found remains of old river terraces—large flat areas on which the villages have been built. To the south of the base camp, on the other side of the valley, lay the village of Tulo, with the village of Kigonmedip at some distance towards the west; on our side of the valley were the villages of Kasengabib and Betabib, and to the north-east of the camp, Kukding. These were the nearest villages to Mabilabol and it was the inhabitants of these kampongs who came to the base camp every day to work, to look on and to eat. Farther west were a number of other villages, but in the early days our investigations did not carry us so far.

Our camp at Mabilabol was quite frequently visited by the inhabitants of the surrounding villages. In speaking of them, we called them "Sibillers", and there is nothing against this so long as the name is used for the people who live in the Sibil Valley; just as we talked of the "Ok Tsyoppers", the people who live in the valley of the Ok Tsyop, or called the people from the Ok Bon Valley "Ok Bonners", although all these people belong to one race. To the language we gave the name Sibillish, since we learned to know it in the Sibil Valley, but it is in fact spoken over a wide area, in the valley of the Ok Tsyop, along the valley of the Ok Bon and also in the Kiwirok Valley, some 15 miles as the crow flies away from the Ok Sibil and to the north of the central watershed. We learned a good deal from the people who visited our camp about their appearance, their clothing and their ornaments. The Sibillers are of small build; the men reach an average height of 59.85 inches, and the women one of 54.25 inches, so that they are, according to the anthropologists, still rather too large to be called pygmies. Their diet is not particularly good; it is rather monotonous, consisting principally of batatas and keladi (sweet potatoes and *Colocasia esculenta*) and as a result they suffer from protein deficiency. In spite of this, they look quite healthy and this is probably due to the fact that they do not suffer from cascado, a disease in which the skin peels off very badly and which is of frequent occurrence in the population of the much lower-lying region of Katem, and among our Muyu bearers from the lowlands. Framboesia (yaws) is also of rare incidence. Malaria occurs sporadically around Mabilabol, and the only cases which arise must presumably be attributed to the Muyus, who have imported the malaria parasites from the lowland. In villages a long way from the base camp we found no traces of malaria at all. Tuberculosis does not seem to have reached here as yet.

The skin colour of the inhabitants varies very widely. Most of the Sibillers are dark brown, but exceptionally light-coloured individuals are also found among them. In addition, it is not always easy to determine the true colour of the skin, which is frequently masked by a layer of dirt. It is true that the children play in the water, but washing or bathing is not precisely a daily occupation of adults. A few of the Muyu bearers who have become acquainted with hygiene in their lowland homes and have married Sibil wives had begun by washing these ladies very thoroughly in the river to a fine state of cleanness. Men and boys frequently decorate themselves by smearing their faces and part of their trunk with a mixture of red earth and pig fat; pig fat is forbidden to the women, but they still apply red earth in coloured stripes on their forehead and cheeks; sometimes even the babies are decorated with red earth (see Plate 12 (1)).

The black, curly hair of the local inhabitants can sometimes have a reddish tinge, and in certain cases this seems to be the result of a vitamin deficiency. The hair is worn short, and only in the case of a few women does one find longish tresses hanging down from their heads. Frequently small lumps of clay are kneaded into the hair and some of the boys have the whole of their head covered with a thick layer of clay. Lumps or crusts of clay worn on the head do not exactly give them a neat appearance. Some of the men wear a beard in which lumps of clay have also been worked in. Lice thrive luxuriously in the scalp, hair and beard, and it is nothing uncommon to see a man being relieved of some of his lice by a friend. Frequently beard hairs and some of the scalp hairs are pulled out. Pieces of strip steel were very much sought after in our camp to make tweezers with which hairs could be extracted. Razors too were at a premium, and we were very surprised to see how a razor was handled with bare hands, and beard and scalp hairs shaved off without using any shaving soap, yet without any wounds being caused at all. A tuft of hair on top of the head is left since this prevents the strap of the "mem" (carrying-net) from slipping backwards.

The clothing worn by the Sibillers is very simple. The women carry fore and aft a little apron of rushes ("wunom") tied with a girdle round the middle. These little skirts are short and consist of several layers one on top of another. They often give the impression much more of a rough scrubbing brush than of an elegant skirt. Even the smallest girls wear one of these aprons, which in this instance will consist of one or two layers of reeds. Small boys run about completely naked, but when they reach (as we estimate) about six years of age, they wear—like the men—a penis gourd ("bong"), made from a hollowed-out calabash and fastened round the middle with a cord. In other parts of the mountainous region, for instance near the Wissel Lakes, the men wear straight gourds, which are worn upright, in which position they are held by a second cord higher up the body. The Sibillers have all kinds of remarkably-curved calabashes which stick out in front. On festival occasions the men will wear a gourd surmounted by the beak of a hornbill (Rhyticeros plicatus). Each man wears a black cord, known as the "bilminong", around his middle; these cords are some 30 feet or more in length, being wound around the body many times. The cord is woven from six strands and has a herring-bone pattern. Sometimes they wear a girdle which carries a row of dogs' teeth. These seem to be particularly precious ornaments, which perhaps also have some

13.   Man from Ariemkop, wearing the kamil; the strands are not covered with a layer of clay, as with the kamils from Kigonmedip or Tomkadin (see Plate 8); a cord carrying dogs' teeth serves him as a girdle.

magical significance, since they were not to be bought, not even at the price of one of our steel axes—a particularly valuable article in these regions. To all our requests for these girdles, we obtained the answer "alut", i.e. taboo, and they could not be passed on to anyone else. No Sibiller—man, woman or child—will be seen without a "mem", a carrying-bag woven out of thread. The mem is an absolutely indispensable piece of equipment. Food is carried in it and other possessions as well; mothers use it for carrying their babies, but not until they have laid a couple of large leaves in the bottom, because the pattern of the fibres used presses on the child's flesh in none too kindly a fashion; piglets are also carried in this way. For ordinary use, the carrying-bags are simple, but some are very finely decorated with birds' feathers; here and there would be a feather or two of a Bird of Paradise or a whole series of flight-feathers of a species of buzzard (Henicopernis longicauda).

Although clothing is pretty scanty, it is supplemented by a great variety of ornaments. Small, finely-woven leg- or arm-bands are made by the men. For weaving they use a bow or a special type of portable loom. With a long thin bone alternate threads are lifted, while another thread is drawn through them; an oval, flat piece of wood is used to keep the woven material tightly pressed together. It is very common for men to wear arm-bands decorated with pigs' tushes, frequently four or six of them, set one above another and fastened between two vertical sticks. A loop of twine fastened to one stick is bound round the arm and hooked up behind the ends of the other. Generally an arm-band of this kind carries a hanging chain of Job's Tears, the pseudocarps of a kind of grass (Coix Lacryma-Jobi) which are already provided by Nature with a hole through the middle for threading. At the end of the chain is the tail of a striped opossum (Dactylopsila sp.; perhaps also Dactylonax sp.) or of a native cat (Satanellus sp.).

Various types of ornaments are worn about the neck. The simplest of these is a broad ring made of the wing feathers of a cassowary; the pointed top of one feather is stuck into the hollow bottom end of the next. Three such feathers form a chain, and sometimes their bottom ends are reinforced against breaking away by a little woven strip around them. In addition these rings can be decorated with a small length of a pig's tail or a pair of the red or yellow beaks of small parrots. Even more decorative are the pigs' incisors worn in strings by many of the older men. Whether this is simply an expression of

14. Groups of men outside the iwool at Tulo.

riches or a sign of respect (e.g. in the case of the keeper of the iwool, the ritual men's house) is not yet clear. Children and men do wear a necklace consisting of two large pigs' tushes, with one or several cowrie shells between them, though necklaces made up entirely of cowrie shells also occur quite frequently. These shells, which are negotiable currency in many of the mountainous regions, are even a part of the bride price in this district. Some of the neck ornaments are obtained by trading with other tribes. For instance, there are necklaces of freshwater mussels, brought up from the lowlands to the south of the mountains, probably from the Red or Blue Digul; the evidence that this trade extends from the lowlands to the south coast, via various tribes, is the fact that a fragment of a large sea-shell (Turbo marmoreus) was worn by one Sibiller on his necklace. Women frequently wear bands made of a strip of rattan with strips of the yellow bark of an orchid (Dendrobium) woven around it; bands of this kind are frequently about 14 ft. long, and are wound about eight times around the neck.

Many of the men have the lobe of the ear bored and stretched so as to take a whitewashed disc of bamboo; they often also carry a piece of wood or a roll of tobacco leaves in the same place. Sometimes the lobe of the ear breaks through and both sides hang down like two little cords below the ear. If a man does not wear a disc of bamboo in the ear and the dangling, hanging edge of the lobe bothers him, he simply winds it around the rest of the organ. Our friend Bomdogi was modern; in one ear he wore a tin which had contained adhesive plaster, while in the other he had a large white ear-ring which had been given him by the Governor's wife, and he was justly proud of the distinction conferred thereby. Anything that we imported and for which we had no further use was readily used as a decoration, so that there was a boy running around with a label which bore the legend "Guaranteed for a year" on a string around his neck, while a man had stuck on his chest a label with the word "Fragile".

There are three kinds of nose ornament. As in many other regions of New Guinea the inter-nasal septum is pierced. Through the hole is passed a bamboo rod or a piece of white stone ground into a kind of torpedo-shape, with one or two red bands around each end. In addition the side walls of the nose may also be pierced. A small stick or a bone, e.g. a rat's rib, is then poked through each side of the nose; generally these "antennae" hang down at an angle, but if the wearer begins to laugh they start dancing about merrily in the air. Finally, it is often the practice to make high up on the bridge of the nose yet another pair of holes held open by little sticks placed in them. A piece of shell may also be fastened on top of the nose, or, in more modern times, a brightly-coloured button is used. One of our friends attached to the top of his nose the round card from a tin of cigarettes, with a red button on top of it. It made a very bright decoration on the man, but he had to squint frightfully in order to look around the edges. The most attractive ornaments used on the bridge of the nose are the heads of rhinoceros beetles, which are fastened to little sticks, next to each other on top of the nose. Sometimes a bright feather—which may be one of very many varieties—is added.

The men often wear a head-dress of cassowary feathers, those from young birds being light brown in colour and those of older birds black. The feathers are bound in little bundles which are fastened next to each other and tied to the head-band by a woven ribbon of twine. Coloured feathers may be added between these bundles; thus one frequently sees a single feather of the Greater Bird of Paradise (Paradisaea apoda), two feathers of the King of Saxony's Bird of Paradise (Pteridophora alberti) or the long tail feathers of the long-tailed lory (Charmosyna papou) as a head-band decoration. Less frequently the head-bands are made of the striped skin of an opossum (Dactylopsila sp.).

As the young men reach marriageable age, they wear for a period of time the "kamil" in their hair (see Plate 8 and 13). The kamil is a large club-shaped attachment bearing a smaller, similar club, fastened to the hair with clay. It consists of a good hundred strings made from bundles of small strips of the leaves from a species of screw-palm (Pandanus), which are wound about with more strips of the same leaves. Tufts of hair are twisted round each other and some of these streamers are attached to a string of the kamil by winding them together with the strips of leaf and sticking the whole lot together with clay.

Close to the end of each string, the covering strip is wound round and round, and thus each bundle becomes much thicker. These thickened parts of the strings produce the bulbous part of the club, which after first thickening, then tapers towards its tip, in which a short round stick is inserted. The bulbous part of the club is covered with a layer of tree bark, covered in turn with a winding of thin cord. The whole kamil is coated with red clay, a transverse band of black dye being generally painted across it. Where the strips of screw-palm leaf are spread out over a wide area to be joined in with the hair, there is a broad, widening area of clay. Separate strands of hair (from 14 to 16 in number) are used to attach a second, much smaller lot of clay to the head; this lies on top of the large club of clay and jumps about as it hangs down. At the farther end of this small club is fastened a bunch of feathers, sometimes with a suspended chain of Job's Tears. According to the place from which the wearer comes, the shape of the kamil varies; the men from Ariemkop have a much thicker and fatter kamil (Plate 13) than those from the villages in our region. A man of the Bonsigi tribe which lives to the north of the Antares Mountains—who visited us en route to Tulo—had a very slender kamil. The Bonsigi kamil has a small club of the same length as the large one, this small club being made from a flat piece of wood wound round with cord (Plate 8 (2)). In the Sibil kamils, the small club is always much shorter than the large one; sometimes a flat piece of wood is inserted in it, and sometimes it is entirely made of bundles of strips of leaf, like the large club. The kamils in the Sibil region are heavy, and weigh between $2\frac{1}{2}$ and $4\frac{1}{2}$ lb. The Bonsigi kamil weighs very little more than a couple of pounds.

The preparation of this extension of the hair is carried out in a special hut situated outside the village; the women are not allowed to be present during the ceremony, but once the kamil has been attached, the young man goes directly to show himself to the women in the village. However, he may not enter the iwool with it, because then the keladi crop would not prosper. That this ornament has a particular significance in connection with the bearer's eligibility for marriage is clear from the name which obtains in the Sibil district; the large club is called "korayma", literally the female, while the small club is called "imyayma" the male. As far as we were able to discover, the kamil is not worn only on reaching marriageable age, but also later. Several of the older youths were seen with the kamil; it is not impossible that they continue to wear it as a sign that they are about to get married. It would appear that there was a time when the kamil was also obligatory among the Muyus, who live to the south of the mountainous region and who are also related to the Sibillers as far as language is concerned.

It is still possible but pretty rare to see a Sibiller working with a stone adze; nowadays he uses a steel axe, earned by working for it. But even with a stone adze it is possible to fell large trees, as Corporal Bril demonstrated during the clearing of a helicopter landing-strip. The

15. Women catching tadpoles in the Ok Sibil.

stone adzes are obtained by the population of the Sibil Valley by trade with other tribes living farther to the north-west in the mountainous area. They themselves put the haft on the adze. For this purpose a piece of tree stem bearing a side branch is cut; the side branch serves as a handgrip, and the adze is bound fast to the section cut from the trunk, by bands of split rattan. These stone adzes are carried over the shoulder (Plate 3); the stone part of the adze rests on the shoulder-blade, and the handle hangs obliquely downwards in front of the breast. Every now and then the adze has to be sharpened. When this is necessary a large, smooth, hard stone is sought in the river, to serve as a whetstone. A piece of limestone is knocked against this until the whetstone is covered with a coating of fine dust; the dust is then worked into a paste with water and the sharpening of the adze can begin. It is rubbed to and fro over the whetstone, just sufficiently long to make the edge of the adze sharp again.

For working in our camp a fully-grown man could earn two boxes of matches per day, receiving in addition to this, after twenty-seven days' work, a steel axe. There was no such thing as income tax in these cases where payment is made in kind. The period of twenty-seven days was chosen, because the Sibillers could count up to that number. Their body is used as an abacus (Plate 21), beginning with the left-hand little finger, moving along the arm to the head, over the right arm and downwards to finish up at the right-hand little finger:

Left		Right	
Little finger	1	Eye	15
Ring finger	2	Ear	16
Middle finger	3	Shoulder	17
Index finger	4	Shoulder joint	18
Thumb	5	Upper arm	19
Pulse	6	Elbow	20
Forearm	7	Forearm	21
Elbow	8	Pulse	22
Upper arm	9	Thumb	23
Shoulder joint	10	Index finger	24
Shoulder	11	Middle finger	25
Ear	12	Ring finger	26
Eye	13	Little finger	27
Nose	14		

16. Delek (from Kukding) sitting on a helicopter float.

In counting, the words for the cardinal numbers are also the names of the parts of the body. Thus the word "sirong" is the word for ear and also the cardinal number 1 2 ; if we are talking about the right ear, the word tabar is added, and "sirong tabar" is the right ear and also the cardinal number 1 6. This method of counting was very easy for us, since without knowing the words we could indicate numbers and make it clear that we would give a small mirror for four frogs. This was done by showing a mirror, adding the words "kolson burotai" (bring frogs) and at the same time bending over the little finger and the other fingers up to the index finger on the left hand. When a man had worked for twenty-seven days, and had thus come to the end of his counting capacity, it was made clear to him he could work for another eight days (which entailed counting up to his left elbow) and receive a large steel axe in place of the small one.

There are not many musical instruments. On one occasion we did see a jew's harp, with which the player can make a soft humming noise, the mouth serving as a sounding-board in the process. This instrument has a very wide distribution; similar jew's harps are found among the Negritos in Pahang on the Malay Peninsula, as well as among numerous tribes on the island of New Guinea. Each village has several drums, which play an important part in the festival celebrations. The drum in the Sibil area (known as the "wot") is roughly cylindrical or hour-glass-shaped and the open bottom end is slightly smaller than the top end; these drums are sometimes decorated with carving, and occasionally painted with coloured bands of red clay and chalk. The skin of the drum is made from the skin of a lizard (Gonyocephalus sp.); across the middle of the drum-skin runs a strip which carries relatively large keeled scales: this is the belly skin of the lizard, and on either side of it the scales become smaller. Abuldalogi from Betabib gave us a demonstration of the tuning of a drum, in which operation the stretching of the skin is of the utmost importance. The degree of tensioning varies with the humidity. In this case, the skin was clearly too dry, and a couple of pieces of sappy plant stem were put inside the drum; this was then held upside down and shaken, so that it could take up a good deal of moisture. The drum was then beaten and since the result was still not as desired, shaken again. There were four or more lumps of clay on the skin, and these seemed to be of some importance in producing the tone. Abuldalogi rubbed some sweat and some fat off his body, using them to make the clay somewhat softer; the lumps were shifted slightly and after each change the tone was tested again. Finally, he appeared to be satisfied. The drum was held in the left hand, with the top end held slightly tilted, and the drum beaten with the finger-tips of the right hand, to show what a fine full note this "wot" could give.

We could only find one object which had any connection with healing (medicine is certainly not practised here): this was a leg-shield made from the shell of the soft-shelled tortoise (*Pelochelys bibroni*). People who are in pain rub or scratch this over the body and it is claimed that the pain will then disappear. These plates come from the lowlands to the south of the mountains, where the soft-shelled tortoise occurs in the large rivers, such as the Digul.

Having now learned to know our Sibil neighbours by the visits they had made at Mabilabol, it was clearly time for us to make a visit to their villages.

First of all we went to Kigonmedip, guided by the government officials Sneep and Herberts. It was a pleasant journey for an afternoon walk, and eminently suited for a first trial. A pair of Sibil boys went with us to carry our cameras. Our path lay first of all across the airfield and then through the reed-beds along the river's edge. It is quite remarkable to notice how we always tried to keep our shoes dry and clear of mud; of course, we never succeeded and it only made the journey all the more tiring, but almost everybody tried it notwithstanding. The narrow path between the cane was a soft pudding-like mass of thick black mud; to keep out of this dirty mess, you would try to pick out the dry edges of the path, first on the left, then on the right, until the moment when you suddenly slipped, losing your footing and finishing up in the mud. After this, walking was a great deal easier because you no longer needed to look out so carefully where you were going to put your feet. It was no good trying to keep dry either, because after about ten minutes the road took us through the Ok Sibil; the water was not deep, but was still high enough to fill our shoes completely. The little Sibil boys who walked with us hopped through the water with considerable agility; we took it rather more quietly and carefully watched where we were putting our feet so as not to measure our length in the water. Then the track ran through another reed-bed, this time along the edge of the higher, southern river-bank; here it was necessary to walk very carefully, for every now and then a piece of the bank had broken away, and a misplaced step would involve a fall of six feet or so. Then once again the track ran through the river, to cut off a bend, but here the water was deeper. It actually reached above our knees, and did so just at the point where we were able to pick out the right places to step so as to avoid the even deeper parts; what is more, the current was quite a considerable hindrance. Walking in water-filled shoes and with streaming wet trouser-legs was not particularly agreeable, but we soon got used to it. Our path then ran through the wood, where the tree-roots projecting above the ground made walking more difficult again. Here and there a tree had been felled, so that the trunk lay along the path. It was possible at these places to avoid the mud by walking on top of the trunk. This was no trouble at all to the Papuans; they just ran along it with their bare feet quite quickly. For us it was often a problem, the stem being smooth and slippery, and it was difficult to keep our balance. As long as the trunk lay on the ground and there was no more risk than that of dropping a few inches into the mud, matters were not too bad. Moreover, this was a cause of considerable delight to our Sibillers, who are extraordinarily fond of laughing. If, however, the tree-trunk served as a bridge over a dip in the ground, it was more troublesome for us to cross it. Some of us chose the safest way, even though it was not the shortest, and dropped down into the little depression. That involved rather more effort—with the drop and the climb out on the other side—but it was not half so risky. As we climbed higher, the track improved; it ran through low shrubs and had a natural paving of pebbles. True, it was narrow and deeply-worn, so that we had to put our feet carefully one in front of the other; what is more, after a shower of rain it became transformed into a miniature brook with stretches as slippery as glass. In this way we came to the first houses in Kigonmedip; apart from the actual village, there are a few "suburbs", which lie a little way away. The actual village consisted of five houses which formed an almost complete ring around a small flat space; on the side facing towards the open space they were connected by a low fence of tree-trunks laid horizontally. The houses were round or oval, standing on piles, with the floor two or three feet above ground level. The walls consisted of laths set vertically and fastened in place with strips of rattan. The roof—made of branches, leaves and cane—projected beyond the house and there was generally a small plank bench set underneath the overhanging eaves, where one could sit in the dry even in rainy weather. Each house had two entrances: a square hole, set at some height above the floor level on the side facing the open space, and forming the men's entrance, and a large door reaching to the whole height of the house, by which the women, children and pigs entered at the back. Each house had a fireplace where the roots were roasted ready for eating. The fire was generally kept in, even at night, and it is nothing unusual for one of the inhabitants of the hut to put his arm or his leg into the fire in his sleep. The greasy smoke produced by the firewood seems to make the roof completely water-tight. Each of these houses was a home for one family. One of them lay completely in ruins; an adult inhabitant had died, the house had been abandoned by the surviving occupants and the others had simply let them go off.

Inside the enclosure, on the side where the circle of dwelling-houses was not complete, stood the ritual men's house: the iwool. Only the initiated men and boys are allowed to enter this building, and even then only those who belong to this iwool society; an initiated man who belongs to another iwool society, e.g. to that of Betabib, is not allowed to enter the iwool in Kigonmedip. It is, however, true that some vil-lages have links of a historic or family nature. Thus, further to the west lies the village of Ebonatera, which began as an off-shoot of Kigonmedip and possesses its own iwool, but the men from each of the villages may visit the iwool in the other. As uninitiated people, we were not only not allowed into an iwool, but were not even permitted to look in through the door. In this respect we were, as Bomdogi once expressed it, still children under age. There is probably not a great deal to be seen in the iwool; in any event, pigs' fat appears to be stored there, as this com-modity clearly plays an important part in their life. The word for pigs' fat may not be pronounced in the presence of women.

To the left and right of the rear wall of the iwool one always finds a few shrubs with red leaves (Cordyline sp.). We do not know what part they play in the life of the Sibillers.

Sometimes there is a second house on the open place, the "bogaam", where men from other villages are allowed to enter. There is also a fireplace in this house, and it seems to serve as a sort of men's "smoking room". When the inhabitants of the village are working during the day in their gardens, there is always an old man left in the village to watch over the iwool. The men either sleep with their family at home, or in the ritual men's house.

Apart from these men's houses, women's houses also exist; here the women withdraw on special occasions, such as the birth of a child. This women's house, known as the "sogaam", stands outside the village and is forbidden to the men. The houses are shut up with laths when the occupants go out, and this is also done at night. During the day there is not much life in the village, because everybody is out working in the gardens. This meant that the anthropologist, the ethnologist and the linguist could carry out their research work only when they were in camp near a village; in the evening, or early in the morning, when the inhabitants were at home, they were able to gather their data.

When we made our first visit to Kigonmedip, only the iwool-keeper and a little boy were at home. They were most hospitable, and offered us a couple of roast sweet potatoes, and we gave them a few cigarettes as a gift in return. The one thing that we had to be very careful about was not to leave any remains of food in or near the village lying on the ground; this is forbidden here, as it brings very bad luck. There was not a great deal of life in Kigonmedip. Since a bank of clouds was driving up from the west along the slopes of the Tamal, sprinkling us with a fine drizzle, we turned back along another, shorter route. On the way we visited one of the suburbs of Kigonmedip. Here the houses were not arranged in any kind of pattern and there was no iwool. The drizzle had by now given way to a heavy shower and we took shelter under the eaves of the houses. Most of the inhabitants were at home. The men chatted with Sneep and Herberts; the women and children were unable to contain their curiosity and sat at a little distance, watching us with considerable interest. It appeared that we presented an amusing spectacle, because there was a good deal of laughter among them. An old man was kind enough to exorcise the weather for us. He took up some ash and blew it in the direction from which the rain was coming, busily reciting something all the while. This did not help very much, because as we continued our walk, it began to rain a good deal harder. Here and there the track led through pools of mud, where we sank up to our knees in soft, black slime. It was tiring to have to drag one leg out of the mud while the other continued to sink deeper. We were somewhat stirred to hear Sneep say to Herberts that he had never known this path to be so dry before, and he added as an encouragement for us that this was one of the best tracks in the whole mountain range; this was a very "stimulating" thought. We continued to flounder on, climbing up extremely slippery slopes and then passing through the river again on our way back to Mabilabol; at the speed at which Sneep and Herberts covered the ground it was indeed only three quarters of an hour from Mabilabol to Kigonmedip, but on all subsequent occasions we were careful to make due allowance for the fact that there was a difference between "a government official's quarter of an hour" and our fifteen minutes.

We made frequent trips like this during the early part of our stay. They were exceptionally suitable as preliminary training for the longer treks which were to follow, and for the expedition members who had come from Holland to New Guinea for the first time, it was very good to become accustomed to walking in this climate in such a manner.

The villages were all built on the same principle. Each iwool society has its ring of dwelling-houses set around the open space, where the iwool stands, and in addition, the suburbs; these are groups of individual houses which lie at the most half an hour's walk from the main village. There were only differences of detail; thus the iwool at Tulo was surrounded by its own low fence, and next to the door there hung a row of pigs' lower jaws. Not many people live in such a village; Kigonmedip has only one hundred and fifteen inhabitants. Although a man is allowed to marry more than one wife, this seems to occur in fact quite rarely. Of the twenty-five married men in Kigonmedip only three had two wives apiece.

Thus the population live widely scattered in small groups. This is particularly due to the infertility of the ground on which the gardens are laid out. The principal crops cultivated are batatas (sweet potatoes; *Ipomaea batatas*) and keladi (*Colocasia esculenta*). The sweet-potato gardens lie on the slopes, and the keladi gardens are generally lower in the valley. The normal diet consists of batatas—known as "boneng"; keladi, here called "om", is eaten at certain ceremonies only. To make a garden, a section of wood is cleared as cleanly as possible. The large trees are left standing; a fire is lit around the trunk to kill them. The dead leafless stem keeps virtually none of the light from the ground and it saves a great deal of work to let them stand in this way. Such groups of bare trees can be clearly seen in the aerial photographs, and before we arrived, it was a puzzle for us to know what these trees were; the solution is simply that they are trees in the gardens which have been killed in this way.

A garden of this kind cannot be cultivated for very long, because the ground rapidly becomes exhausted. A new garden has then to be laid out; the old garden lies fallow for about twenty years and the forest vegetation takes over again. Where sweet potatoes have to be harvested every day, the gardens are as near as possible to the houses, and each village or suburb thus needs a large region, occupied by gardens under cultivation or which are to be planted at some time in the future. The gardens are cleared by everybody working together and fenced around to keep out the pigs, but the garden is then parcelled out to individual owners. Each member of the community—man, woman or child—has his own piece of ground which has to be worked and he has a right to the harvest. It is only the very youngest children who do not yet possess their own garden. Batatas or sweet potatoes may be planted without any special preparation, but the planting of keladi is subject to clearly-defined rules and ceremonies. For instance, a man who has eaten the fruit of the screw-palm (Pandanus) during the day must not enter the keladi garden, as otherwise the crop will not grow. It was not clear to us how far the cultivated land of a village extends, but sometimes gardens are laid out at a distance of an hour's walk or more from the village. Betabib, which is about three-quarters of an hour's walk west of Mabilabol, to the north of the Ok Sibil, was laying out a new keladi garden on the southern bank of the river opposite Mabilabol.

The roots are roasted in the hot ashes of the fire. They are then only superficially cleaned of ash; this has the advantage that the consumers also ingest a certain quantity of salts. In addition to roots, the Sibillers eat almost everything that they can lay hand on in the way of animals: marsupials, rats and mice, lizards, frogs, caterpillars and dragon-fly larvae. The women and children use their carrying-net as a fishing net and catch tadpoles which are eaten raw. There is very little in the animal kingdom which is not eaten. Pig's flesh is only eaten on festival occasions. In addition to this all kinds of fruit are eaten such as pisangs (bananas) and the fruits of the screw-palm (Pandanus sp.). There are not many eating implements; spoons are made out of the shoulder-blades, or even more frequently out of the pelvis bones of pigs. The latter are the most attractive; the iliac bone constitutes the actual spoon, while the ischium serves as the handle. The Sibillers have no pottery; indeed, pottery is unknown in the greater part of Netherlands New Guinea; only near the Sentani Lake are pots baked out of clay. Our empty tins and bottles were consequently very much sought after.

Black pigs are encountered in all the villages. There is no actual stock-raising practised here. The boars run wild in the woods, and in the villages one only finds sows, gilts and piglets. In the morning the pigs all leave the village and go out in the surrounding area to forage;

17.   (1) Cicada (Sawda sp.) 1½× enlarged.
    (2) Tree kangaroo (Dendrolagus dorianus subsp.) Antares.

in the evening they return to take up their place in the house, and sleep in the huts with the occupants. Sneep had bought himself one of these Papuan pigs, called "Bertie", which ran around freely in the daytime but would return home as it became dark. It was a comical sight to see Bertie on the way home; first of all he would appear somewhere or other out of the reed-beds, run for some distance and then stand completely still, after which he would run a stretch, and then again stop still; in this way he would run up the hill and into Sneep's house. Here there was a pan of rice waiting for him, and he would completely empty it with a good deal of noise. He would allow Sneep to give him a good scratch every now and then, but he was not very taken with all the newcomers; it had become far too busy in the district for Bertie and it later turned out that he also went and slept outside. In an attempt to improve the pig stock, a European brood sow had been imported, but the attempt was unsuccessful since, as we have said, all the breeding boars run about quite freely in the woods and methodical improvement of the race is therefore impossible. This European pig had had a fine pig-sty built for her but every now and then she would break through the fence and would give us a great deal of fun as the Papuan police-constables and bearers tried to drive it back again. The animal was very strong and the men were scared stiff of it. Finally, it was allowed to run free for a few days; it could not do a great deal of damage in the district, except to turn up our paths.

There are not many dogs in the Sibil Valley; only once did inhabitants with a dog visit us. This probably explains the great value placed upon the string of dogs' teeth; it would take quite a number of animals to provide the teeth for a string of this kind (Plate 13).

Our scientific research began in the eastern section of the Sibil Valley. The first expedition members to set up a camp elsewhere were the linguist and the ethnologist, Anceaux and Pouwer. They settled with two police-constables and an interpreter in a little camp near Kigonmedip. The constables would look after the various camp activities and keep an eye on the camp while the two research workers were about their business in the village or in the gardens. They were to stay there for a week and had taken supplies of food for that period with them. It was, therefore, no little surprise to the leaders when a report was received four days later that the food was almost finished. Although the quantity they had been issued with had been fairly generously calculated, and a runner had been sent up every day with a fresh loaf,

18. Family from Tumabib (West Sibil).

new stores were despatched. Later Anceaux and Pouwer came back with a considerable excess of supplies; it turned out that they had been using one case as a chair to sit on, and—not having looked at it—they had not found their stocks of rice.

With the assistance of an interpreter, a Muyu who could speak the Sibil dialect, Anceaux began to assemble data about the language. Lists of words were drawn up, the conjugation of the verbs recorded and the sentence structures studied. All the data collected were then checked in conversation with other people. The spelling of the words occasioned some difficulty, because the pronunciation tends to vary. Thus some of the people would say "yambulgi" (small) while others would pronounce it "yamburgi"; the letters "l" and "r" are freely interchanged here. In addition, it would sometimes happen that new words were found in strange ways. On the day when the supplies were dropped from the air to the base camp for the first time, Anceaux climbed up into a small tree to have a better view of the landing-strip, but the sapling was not strong enough and he fell out of it, happily without any hurt. From the remarks of the bystanders Anceaux was able to find a word which was new to him for the act of falling. It seems that the Sibillers use a different word for falling from a certain height from that for falling over from a standing position.

The other members of the expedition also tried to learn something of the language and in doing so made use of a list of words which had been drawn up by Hermans when he settled here at the time that the landing-strip was first prepared. We had to accustom ourselves to the idea that "nè" did not mean No but Yes, and that the Sibil word for No was "dò", "dòyo" or "adò"; "sigip" meant enough, "magison" more, and "burotai" is the word for to bring. This vocabulary was already quite adequate for a trade in animals; frequently one could hear the cry: "kolson, awotson burotai", which means: "frogs, lizards, bring". If too many of one sort were brought then the word "sigip" would be employed while if we wanted more then we had to say "burotai magison" (bring, more); if then we added a few names for the animals and, if necessary, the further remark "yambulgi" (small), or "dalogi" (big), business ran very smoothly indeed. When we met strangers out in the field we would say "kaga kaga mok-mok" (kaga = man, mok-mok = good) which is as much as to say "good folk", and we would then ask "abib kopma?" (where do you come from: literally, "house or village, where?"). It was not necessary to talk a great deal when doing business; we simply needed to show what we offered as a reward and if it happened to suit our customer, he would then raise his eyebrows for a completely sufficient answer. It was striking to see how the Sibillers and whites could carry on an animated conversation without either understanding one word of what the other said. A certain amount of prudence was in fact advisable, because strange misunderstandings might arise. This was experienced by one of the expedition members who wished to take a photograph of a woman. She understood something quite different, and some time later a few rather excited men came to complain. With the help of the government officials and the interpreter, whose name was Kotanon, this misunderstanding was speedily settled and the offended parties soon ran off laughing. In our trading we frequently needed the help of the government officials to fix the prices. If we were to pay too much and flood the markets with objects which were valuable to the Sibillers, this would result in a devaluation which would not make life any easier for the local inhabitants. This had happened in the past elsewhere in the mountainous regions, where an excessive quantity of cowrie shells had been brought in as a means of payment; the result was a devaluation of the "money" and it was necessary to look for a new "coinage". We used as our currency: beads or buttons to be worn on the nose or strung on a necklace, plastic drinking-straws to be worn through the nose-perforation, safety pins to be worn in the ears, razors, boxes of matches and tobacco. We employed biscuits as small change and our large items of currency were knives, machetes, axes and coloured cloths. Matches were very much in demand; they saved the inhabitants a great deal of trouble in lighting fires. Previously they had used for this purpose a very long piece of rattan, which was wound round a piece of wood and very rapidly drawn to and fro until the wood began to glow; this piece of rattan was carried as a broad woven armband when going on a journey, but in our district this aid became completely replaced by matches.

Pouwer took a census of the people in the village. He noted down their names and tried to determine their relationships; who was married to whom, what their parents were called, how many children they had had from their marriage and how many were still alive. The local inhabitants did not know the dates of birth, but frequently a pretty accurate estimate could be made by indications such as: "this child was born when the landing-strip was laid out" or "we'd only just planted that garden at the time". Pouwer also studied the distribution of the garden land among the different inhabitants, how the planting was carried out, and whether there were special regulations to be observed, or whether there were particular ceremonies which preceded the harvest, and so on. It was a time-consuming task, because, apart from the fact that repeated checking was necessary, the research workers first of all had to win the confidence of the population. There is nothing better suited for doing this than to camp in the vicinity of a village, so that one can be with the people during their normal daily occupations. Moreover, they did not restrict themselves to one visit, but the camp was set up near Kigonmedip on several different occasions. In the intervening period the data were collated, classified and studied at Mabilabol, because working at a table is always a good deal easier than when sitting on a can.

The many conversations that Pouwer had with his informants brought up all kinds of interesting points. For instance, one Sibiller replied to the question as to who was his father-in-law by saying: "Oh, but he was eaten up a long time ago!" Clearly, cannibalism was practised in this district in the past; it even seems to have occurred sporadically during the last twenty years. A man would be killed and eaten as a deliberate insult to the village where he lived, and the consequence would be war. At the present time, war does occasionally break out, but nowadays the reason for it is different.

During our stay in the Sibil Valley a war was waged between the villages of Sagsaga and Lewengbon (to the west of Betabib). When compared with the great wars which we know, a Sibil war is more like a sporting event, although people do die in the process. The cause of this particular fight was the death of a man in the village of Sagsaga. Nobody believed very firmly that he had died of natural causes, but much rather that his death was due to witchcraft. There must therefore have been black magic in the affair, and Lewengbon must be sheltering the culprit. Something naturally had to be done, and Sagsaga called upon men from a friendly village to help them destroy the keladi gardens belonging to Lewengbon. The keladi gardens were chosen precisely because keladi is eaten at all kinds of religious ceremonies. The people of Lewengbon considered themselves to be innocent and were deeply offended, so that the only solution was to fight. There is no question of falling upon the villagers by surprise, and the women and children are in no danger at all. In accordance with Sibil custom both sides agree when the war

19.   Dance festival in Kigonmedip.

is to begin. The two parties together clear the battleground and the fight can then begin. Participation is not limited to the two warring kampongs, but men from villages friendly to one or the other of the combatants may take part. Thus Kigonmedip was also invited and we learned of the war, since Pouwer and Anceaux heard reports of the fight. Rolling on the ground with laughter, a man from Kigonmedip related how one of the opponents had been injured by an arrow in an exceedingly painful spot. This association of other villages in the affair also explained why we found so few Sibillers in Mabilabol; it was said that they were working in the gardens but they had naturally gone to the fight, too. The government official could not tolerate war anywhere in his area and thus that afternoon a patrol set out consisting of Sneep, Nicolas, Tissing, Kotanon the interpreter and four constables. It happened that this afternoon the weather was very bad and there was therefore no fighting. The men in Lewengbon were very brightly decorated, as is always the case on formal occasions and festivals; their faces were painted red with pigs' fat and red earth. It was not denied that a war was going on and there were even two wounded men. To render the fight impossible, all the arrows were confiscated (as long as they were not too carefully hidden). The villagers were, however, allowed to keep their bows—very precious articles, which have to be imported to this district from the Muyu area, and also needed for hunting. Next day news came via Kigonmedip that the war was nevertheless going ahead. The Lewengbon people were humiliated that it was of all things their arrows which had been confiscated, because they were really the challenged party. If they did not take up the fight again, they would become a laughing-stock. A new patrol, led by the government official Dasselaar,

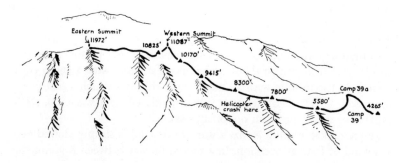

20. Antares from the north, showing the route taken by the climbing party, ▲—camps.

therefore set out to see what the situation was. It was found that a new battleground had been prepared and this time Sagsaga had made sure that a "home match" would take place. The men from Lewengbon were dancing themselves to a standstill on the old ground, and were also waiting for reinforcements. Kukding was represented but Betabib had not arrived. After a little talking, they seemed ready to lead the new patrol to the second fighting-ground. There they found the men of Sagsaga with their associates, busily preparing for the fight. It is always an open question how the parties will react to interference in cases of this kind. The best thing is to make a rapid and impressive appearance on the scene, and so Dasselaar with his two constables rushed on to the field accompanied by Kotanon, with his arrow to his bow. Completely flabbergasted, the men of Sagsaga lowered their bows and arrows, and the day was saved. Dasselaar had now time to address the men and to make it quite clear to them that the Government was most strongly opposed to their waging war. A number of the men slipped away, while others hid their arrows as carefully as possible, but ultimately Sagsaga too delivered up a considerable bundle of arrows which were confiscated, and the police found more in the shrubs. It was then decided that peace was to be made, and so the war was brought to an end (for the moment at least, since it broke out again some weeks later). Betabib was angry with us, because Pouwer had set up a camp near by and that prevented them from joining in. The intention in a war of this kind is to continue until both sides have lost an equal number of killed; if the number becomes rather high, the combatants may in certain circumstances be prepared to have an armistice, in the hope that the party with the lower number of killed will find that one or two of its wounded will die, thus making the "score" even. Only bows and arrows are used in the fight. There are special arrows for use against men, just as the hunters employ special arrows for pigs or for birds when hunting. Some of the fighters had protected themselves by wearing a sort of cuirass woven from rattan, probably imported from the Muyu region. In one of the villages we discovered another imported article used in fighting; this was a round flat stone with a sharp edge, pierced in the middle with a circular hole through which a haft could be passed. This turned the stone into a highly efficient war-club, easily capable of smashing in an opponent's skull.

The remarkable thing is that a war of this kind is simply viewed here as a kind of festival occasion. In a preceding war between Kigonmedip and Tulo, the difficulty arose that Tulo had too few fighting men. In order to be able to help, and yet to remain neutral, Betabib shared its men with the two sides. True, it was agreed beforehand that the men from Betabib would not shoot at fellow-villagers fighting on the other side.

Once Pouwer had won the confidence of the people, he managed to hear the local account of the origin of mankind.* A large white rock ("tum") which lies somewhere in the vicinity of the Dirksz Summit became pregnant but was unable to bring forth a child. Then an earth-worm ("upi") begat a child on itself. First of all small earthworms were born, and subsequently the first man, followed by the first woman. From these two human beings, the entire human race descended, and they have spread out over the Star Mountains (to the Sibillers this region constitutes the whole world). The mother worm died, and therefore all her descendants are mortal and died too.

The first white people to reach the Sibil Valley, during a search for gold in 1939, were regarded with complete amazement; the local in-habitants were even frightened of them. Their great white bodies and the precious and strange things which they brought with them were enough to cause them to be considered as very special beings. They were connected with the great white rock of the creation story, and thought to be the children of the rock and so were called "tum tenna" (tum = rock, stone; tenna = child), even as they themselves, the local inhabitants, were "upi tenna", worm-children.

The rock still stands there and is therefore immortal, and its des-cendants—the white men—were also considered to be immortal.

Later, during a visit to the Ok Bon region, Pouwer was asked in all seriousness whether he would die. The affirmative answer, together with the information that his father had already died, produced a cry of surprise from the listeners. When visiting another village, he was introduced with the remark: "His father is dead." This discovery of the mortality of the whites may well have reassured the Sibillers and their relatives; it is always a somewhat risky matter to have to do with immortal creatures, ghosts and the like.

De Wilde, the physical anthropologist, also began his research in the region around Mabilabol. His measuring instruments had not yet

* J. Pouwer: "Zij en Wij". (They and us) *Nieuw Guinea Koerier*, Year 1, No. 194. 1959.

arrived, and he had for the time being to make do with taking finger-prints and palm-prints. The pattern formed by the lines on the skin is not important solely as a means of identifying people (because the pattern does not change during the whole lifetime of an individual), but also because the frequency of the different types of pattern in a particular population is a characteristic of the race to which these people belong. By taking finger-prints and hand-prints from a large number of people, one can obtain information which is valuable in determining the relationship between the Sibillers and other Papuan tribes. Initially we suffered from a shortage of paper, but we soon dis-covered that the backs of calendars which had been given to us in Hollandia, or of the minute sheets of the Council meetings which we received from Holland, were very suitable for making prints. To the annoyance of the occupants of the camp all the calendars vanished from our houses, while to the great joy of the leaders of the expedition a great deal more paper disappeared which they would otherwise have had to keep. The name and dwelling-place of every Papuan whose prints had been taken was written on the sheet, so that the data could later be supplemented by adding his body measurements. Two men are needed in order to learn the name of a Sibiller. He himself never pronounces his own name, and a friend has to do it for him. Probably this is because he is frightened that some spirit or other will gain control over him if he pronounces his own name. It was difficult for us to remember the names of all the people, even of the men who regularly visited our camp. The Survey Department employees working here have found a simple solution to this problem: each Sibiller accompanying a party on a journey is given a number painted on his chest. They have found only one objection to this plan, namely, that to the Sibillers this decoration was so attractive that they were very willing to let themselves be numbered, without having any intention of going on the trek. Once the number had been painted on, the fellow would disappear and not be seen again for some days.

Once De Wilde's instruments had arrived he was able to start his anthropological studies. A large number of measurements were made of each Papuan, man or woman, such as: body length, length and breadth of head, length and breadth of nose. In addition we noted data about the colour of the skin, the hair and the eyes, the type of implantation of the hair, etc. All these characteristics were important to obtain a good description of the race to which the Sibillers belong, and of its relationship with others. As time went on the number of measurements to be taken was reduced because some of them were difficult to make. Thus we could not determine their sitting height. The person to be measured in this position has to sit upright with the head in a particular position, and this seemed to be difficult to achieve. The local inhabitants are accustomed to sit hunched up with the head bent somewhat forward and we were rarely successful in getting them to adopt the proper posture. It was also difficult to get them to give us a lock of hair. They were frightened that the man who possesses this lock of hair would be given a particular power over the person who had given it to him.

The Government official Herberts sometimes tried to inculcate hygiene into the Sibillers, and to reduce the number of lice, by clipping them bald. This the Sibillers were very willing to have done, but they would take all the hair away with them very carefully, to the disappointment of the zoologists, who had looked to obtain a rich harvest of lice.

De Wilde was assisted in his work by one or two marines. While he was busily occupied measuring, one marine would write the data down; another could also establish the colours, by the use of a colour chart and also take the prints (Plate 26). In this way quite a number of people could be examined in a short time. This was of considerable importance when such investigations were to be carried out in more remote villages. De Wilde would set up his camp near by, and was obliged to study the population either in the afternoon, when they came back to the village from the gardens, or before they left again next morning. At the beginning he carried out his work together with Dr. Romeijn, the Government medico, who also wished to examine the population. It had originally been the intention that only one doctor would accompany the expedition, and that he would always remain at the base camp, to provide medical attention for the members of the expedition, the marines, the police and the bearers; in addition, bearing in mind the rather busy aerial traffic, it was a good thing to have a doctor near at hand should an accident occur. Shortly before the expedition began, a second medical man was added to the expedition —Dr. Tissing; both doctors were thus provided with more freedom to do field work. Romeijn made a study of the incidence of framboesia (yaws), but as has already been said, this disease does not occur very frequently here.

For several months a specialist in the study of blood groups, L. E. ·Nijenhuis, worked in the Sibil Valley. He had already investigated in the Netherlands blood samples from Papuans from various regions in New Guinea, but the difficulty was that it was either impossible, or at least very difficult, to determine a number of the blood groups. For certain groups it is essential to have fresh blood; the long time required to transport the samples from the centre of New Guinea to the Netherlands could bring about changes in the samples, so falsifying the analysis of the blood. The blood of a large number of Sibillers was studied, not only the normal blood groups—such as A, B, AB, O—and the Rhesus factor, but also certain other factors. The frequency of occurrence of these groups gave important indications as to the relationship of the Sibillers with other tribes. Nijenhuis's work kept him at the base camp, because his equipment was not very easy to transport. A refrigerator had been brought in for his use, but this was also appreciated by other members of the expedition, and he also had an incubator and a number of cases of equipment. In general the Sibillers were quite willing to allow a couple of drops of their blood to be drawn off. Nijenhuis watched out for every new face, and hustled the man to his work-table; the victim would be rewarded with a cigarette, a button or a plastic drinking-straw. It subsequently turned out that some of our visitors did not particularly care for this investigation. Some of the men from the valley of the Ok Bon who had visited Mabilabol were not willing to be measured after that; they had lost their confidence. Nijenhuis went himself to Tulo, Kigonmedip and Betabib to fetch blood samples, and the specimens collected by Romeijn from villages farther off were brought into Mabilabol by helicopter. In this way the blood from a great number of people from different parts of the valley was investigated. The expedition members were willing victims, being most anxious to seize this opportunity to have a detailed study of their blood groups. One had to have a certain disposition towards this sort of thing, because the general leader of the expedition was told—with a completely serious face—that he was a "negative zero" (Blood group O and Rhesus negative), while a respectable visitor was told that his blood looked most like that of a Mandobo (a tribe from the lowlands near Tanah Merah).

Reynders, who had already spent a short time in the Sibil Valley (lodging with the Government officials) went out every day. He had chosen a Muyu to help him collect soil samples. Using an earth drill, samples of the weathered soil were taken, and holes dug to enable him to study and photograph a section through the successive strata. The purpose of these studies was to record the constitution of the soil and its relationship to the rocks from which it was formed. The soil samples were kept in bags. Since they had to be dried, a shelf with a small roof over it was built; this was known in our camp as the "herring-stall". When Reynders was out on a trip, this structure was taken over by the zoologists; they stretched out there a vertical white sheet illuminated by two desk lamps, thus obtaining a movable screen close by the camp, on which they could of an evening trap the insects attracted by the light; in this way they gathered great numbers. But the collecting of animals was not only a night job. Considerable additions were made to the specimens during the daytime. The Sibillers were continually bringing material, and the specimens had to be preserved. Before the food supplies were parachuted in, the cane fields on both sides of the airstrip had been cleared, driving out a great many frogs and lizards, which were brought to us by the little Sibil children. There was a tendency for them to bring in the small kinds because there was not so much meat on these; on one single occasion a large frog was brought and we paid a higher price to encourage the gatherers. In addition, snakes were obtained from the canefields, principally specimens of a species of ringed snake (Natrix) and of Stegonotus modestus. We collected only one venomous snake in this district: Micropechis ikaheka; the specimen was found by Surgeon-Lieutenant Tissing along the path from Betabib to Lewengbon. The local inhabitants are very frightened of snakes, even of harmless kinds. They would bring them in to us with the head carefully tied up in leaves, and if one of us was walking with a (dead) snake into the camp all the children would run away.

Both women and children from Kigonmedip brought us small, almost black frogs with a pointed nose (Asterophrys minima), about an inch in length; this is one of the species (very numerous in New Guinea) which do not lay their eggs in the water, but in the ground or in the hollows of rotting tree-trunks. The eggs are comparatively large and very rich in yolk; they develop rapidly into small frogs; the life cycle of these species does not comprise a larval stage living in the water. The striking thing is that this species was brought from Kigonmedip, but did not appear to occur around our camp. One kind which was very common around the camp had the upper eyelids provided with a small, projecting horn (*Sphenophryne cornuta*) ; it has a brown back and a rusty-red belly.

The fact that we offered good prices for frogs and similar animals soon spread around the district so that we even had a man from the valley of the Ok Tsyop (one day's march away) who brought four frogs to sell; somebody also came from the village to the southwest of Ariemkop bringing frogs. These were very valuable acquisitions, since they turned out to be completely different species from those in the region around our camp. We kept a good number of each species, to enable us to study the variations in detail subsequently. Some of these kinds are very widespread in New Guinea, but from one place to another there are various slight differences in the characteristics. Only by collecting series and comparing specimens from other sites was it possible for us to get a clear idea of the value of these local differences; it is possible on this basis to distinguish races in many of the species, each of which has a restricted distribution area in New Guinea. We made further collections in all the places which we visited, so that we could determine the distribution of the species in the mountainous areas. The distribution can vary considerably from one place to another, and yet other species are met with at different heights in the mountains.

In addition to the sink-hole behind our camp, similar water-filled depressions in the ground occurred in other places in the forest, for example, along the track from Mabilabol to the kampong of Betabib. There were also a few sink-holes down in the valleys, at the foot of the terrace slopes. The valley pools had a thick growth of water plants along the banks; lying between the tall, slim Araucarias they looked like small picturesque fens. In one of the dry periods, the gulley along the path to Betabib dried up, but before it was completely dry we went over to see what animals lived in it. In many fresh-water pools and streams in New Guinea shrimps and small crayfish occur, and we enquired diligently of the Sibillers on this point. When we showed them a picture, they gave us the name "Ok Siep" (Ok = water, siep = louse) and they told us that such creatures were indeed eaten when there was a shortage of food. We pulled large clumps of the water-plant up with a rake, and set them on the bank to pick them over. The ok siep were then found to be the larvae of dragon-flies and damosel-flies; subsequently we were offered large quantities in exchange for buttons or water biscuits. On top of this there were a number of tadpoles (larvae of one type of tree-frog), water-bugs and whirligig beetles; but of shrimps there was no trace. We fished in other gulleys but the result was always the same; there are certainly no shrimps in the Sibil Valley. If possible, the fauna of the Ok Sibil is even poorer. There are no fishes at all; the only creatures we caught in this river were tadpoles and mayfly larvae. The tadpoles in the river were quite different from those in the gulley; they were adapted to living in rapidly-flowing water, being strongly flattened and provided with a strong suction disc on the mouth, with which they could attach themselves to stones, so anchoring themselves against the current. We were not particularly surprised that there should be no fish in the Ok Sibil. The rapidly-changing water level is probably a factor unfavourable to fish; on one day it is a wildly-foaming stream, but this gives way a few days later to an almost completely dry bed. Even on days with a certain amount of rainfall, the river is in many places only a few inches deep. The underground course of the Ok Sibil must also be a hindrance to fishes, crayfish and crabs reaching the Sibil Valley.

We did not see many mammals in the Sibil Valley. To some extent this is likely to be the consequence of hunting; rats and marsupials are considered a delicacy in this region, and they are caught whenever the opportunity offers. The fact that this does not happen daily is clear from the inclusion of a number of rats in the bride price. No rats occur in the Sibillers' villages; from this point of view, there is an exemplary degree of hygiene, even though this may not have been applied wittingly. The inhabitants only dig as many roots from their gardens as they need for immediate consumption, and there are thus no storage places which might attract the rats. Their food supplies are not so generous that there is a great deal over, and even if this were the case, it is burnt rather than left lying about; an evil-intentioned person who takes possession of left-over food can do a great deal of damage by sorcery. The scarcity of mammals and their great value as food meant that initially the local population were not very willing to offer these animals for purchase, but slowly we were nevertheless able to assemble a small collection. The food position has been improved for many Sibillers by the coming of the expedition; they were frequently able to obtain a good meal from us, and they could therefore quite well spare us a rat on occasion. In all, two sorts of rats and five marsupials were brought to us.*

One of the rats (Pogonomys macrourus) is a tree animal with a soft and
* The mammals were identified by A. M. Husson.

woolly pelt; the back is dark-brown to grey-brown, the belly clear white and the tail ends in a bald tip, which is used as a prehensile organ to hold on to branches. The other species of rat (Rattus leucopus ringens) lives on the ground; only in very young animals is the fur to any degree woolly, while the adult rats have soft straight hairs with stiff hard bristles between them. The back varies from almost dark-brown to black and the belly is grey; generally these animals have a white patch on the breast, which sometimes continues as a narrow band over the whole length of the belly. Among the marsupials is the pen-tailed opossum (Distoechurus pennatus), which has a tail bearing a row of long hairs on each side, giving it the appearance of a bird's feather; the coloured pattern on the head resembles that of the badger, with two longitudinal black stripes separated by a white stripe. In addition, there was also the dormouse opossum (Eudromicia caudata) and two sorts of opossum rats, one of them being a specimen of Neophascogale lorentzi. An even longer search would probably reveal yet other species. The local inhabitants wear skins of the striped opossum (Dactylopsila sp.) as a forehead band, and tails of the same animal are used as decorations on armbands; on one armband we also found the tail of a "native cat" (Satanellus albopunctatus). It is thus probable that these animals occur in the Sibil Valley, although it must be borne in mind that objects of this kind are also obtainable by trade with other tribes. We showed the Sibillers illustrations of tree-kangaroos and ant-eaters, but these animals are completely unknown here.

The bird world is more richly varied. (1). The large numbers of frogs which occur in this district provide ample food for three sorts of herons. We frequently saw above the woods across the river plumed egrets (Egretta intermedia) gliding away; sometimes they would walk over the air-strip or stand in the reeds near the gulley looking for frogs. A white-fronted heron (Nothophoyx novae-hollandiae) and a nankeen night-heron (Nycticorax caledonicus) are also found here, with a black bittern (Dupetor flavicollis); the occurrence of plumed egret, nankeen night-heron, and black bittern at this height (about 4,133 feet above sea-level) is interesting because all three species are well known as lowland birds. In the sink-hole lake there were little grebes (Podiceps ruficollis novae-hollandiae), which have nested there. On branches near the water we could often see kingfishers sitting (Halcyon sancta, a migrant from Australia, and Syma megarhyncha). The family of the honey-eaters,

* The identification of the birds was carried out by Dr. G. C. A. Junge.

which is characteristic of Australia and New Guinea, is represented by a number of species: *Melidectes torquatus*, which has an orange patch around the eye and a white throat, cut off from the breast by a transverse black band, the long-billed honey-eater (*Melilestes megarhynchus*) and several others. From the woods on the other side of the river we obtained specimens of white-eyes (*Zosterops fuscicapilla*), small birds with a dark-green back, a yellow-green belly and the characteristic white rims round the eyes, which give them their name. Particularly lovely birds are the pigeons, of which we found two species, both of them fruit pigeons: *Ptilinopus rivoli*, mainly green in colour, with a purple patch on the head, a yellow and white transverse band across the breast, and the belly green with a purple patch, and the larger *Reinwardtoena reinwardtsi* which has the head, shoulders, breast and belly grey, the back and wings purplish-brown, and the long tail brown. We often saw, sitting on the paling erected by the staircase which ran from our house to the godown, a small black little bird with a white stripe across the wings and a white rump; this was a species of stonechat (*Saxicola caprata*). Every now and then, in the forest behind Mabilabol, we found lories (*Neopsittacus musschenbroekii*) —small green parrot-like birds with red patches on breast and belly; the underside of the wings is red. The beaks of these lories are often used as a decoration for necklaces. A migrant from Australia—which remains in New Guinea as long as it is winter on the continent of Australia—is the bee-eater (*Merops ornatus*); we would frequently see these birds on the lighting wires in our camp, and they would suddenly fly up and return to sit in the same place. New Guinea is well known as the land of the Birds of Paradise, and they were not lacking there. Both the Greater Bird of Paradise (*Paradisaea apoda*) and the Queen of Saxony's Bird of Paradise (*Parotia carolae*) are found. Here and there in the forest we would find small hides used for hunting Birds of Paradise. The finely-divided yellow feathers of the Greater Bird of Paradise are very much used by the Sibillers as a headdress decoration and sometimes little feathers are used to decorate their carrying-nets. Bundles of feathers in bamboo tubes were offered to us to purchase. The male of the Queen of Saxony's Bird of Paradise is black and has a bundle of white feathers at each side of the body; behind each eye he wears three long feathers which have a little "flag" at the end of the long bare shaft of the feather. These birds have on their breasts a patch of feathers with a bright purple and green-gold sheen. The females of both species are much less brightly-coloured; they are so completely different in colour and so little eye-catching that one does not at first think that they could be Birds of Paradise. Perhaps a third species of Bird of Paradise occurs in the Sibil Valley—the King of Saxony's Bird of Paradise (*Pteridophora alberti*); sometimes feathers of this bird, consisting of a long shaft with a row of small bluish plumes at the end, are used to decorate head-dresses.

The old river terrace on which the base camp stood was partly covered with woods, but these were interspersed with large open areas, probably on the sites once occupied by gardens. True virgin forest is not found here, since the systematic clearing and burning practised by the inhabitants markedly affects the constitution of the forest. Apart from the tall slender Araucarias (*Araucaria cunninghamii*) there are numerous beeches (*Nothofagus*). The finest and largest trees stand on the slopes of gulleys and ravines which are not so suitable for laying out gardens. Between the trees grow tree-ferns, with long thin stems several yards long, bearing at the top a crown of finely-divided leaves. The Araucarias are absent on the opposite side of the valley on the slopes of the Tamal; in their place grows a species of oak which bears long, flat acorns

Lianas climbed upward over the trees and frequently hung down like stout ropes across the path. Many kinds of plants, such as ferns and orchids, grew on the tree branches, while on the rotting trunks of fallen trees there were clumps of red toadstools. The ground forming the terrace was peaty and marshy; the open regions were covered with mosses, lichens, ferns and stag-horn moss, alternating with various terrestrial orchids, and a species of ginger plant with yellow-edged red flowers. Here too, grew the young Araucarias, whose neat rings of branches recalled the small firs grown as pot-plants to decorate Dutch living-rooms. Between the shrubs grew numerous rhododendrons with large white flowers (Plate 10, (2)). In the very marshy spots, containing little pools of water, there was a species of bladderwort with yellow flowers, the leaves of which—either under the water-level or hidden in the moss—end in small bladders. Orchid-lovers could collect here to their heart's content; there were numerous fine species growing on the trees: orchids with waxy white blooms (Plate 10, (1)), species with yellow, brown-spotted hairy flowers, and others with purple blooms, and so on. It was not surprising that various members of the expedition planted small orchid gardens near the camp.

Very common around here were the pitcher plants (*Nepenthes* sp.), insectivorous plants with leaves which end at the top in an upright pitcher-shaped vessel. When the leaves are young, the pitcher is closed by a small lid, but once they are fully grown, the flap is raised; it keeps the rain out of the pitcher. The plant secretes a fluid which gathers in the bottom of the pitcher and digests the insects which fall into it.

The remarkable thing is that some creatures can resist the action of this fluid, so that in the bottom of the pitchers one finds mosquito larvae and fly grubs merrily swimming round and completing their whole cycle of development there. In our camp we had little or no trouble with mosquitoes, but consequently suffered a good deal more from them in the forests; thus these pitcher plants present a problem, being good breeding-places for mosquitoes, which, although they are not bearers of malaria, can make life very unpleasant. Two sorts of pitcher plants grew in the vicinity. One species grew on the ground (Plate 30 (2)), and had pitchers bearing two deeply-toothed ridges on one side. The other was a climbing species which grew over the shrubs, bearing large groups of pitchers which hung close together.

On the trunks of the Araucarias and on the branches of other trees we found ant-house plants (Myrmecodia), plants with thick, fleshy stalks which have a few leaves on the top; these stalks are covered with many spines and bear small white flowers. The striking feature of these plants is that there are openings in the stem which allow access to a network of cavities in which live colonies of ants. If you cut the stem longitudinally you can see a seething mass of ants trying to carry the pupae to safety in the remoter cavities in the stem.

Our two botanists, Kalkman and Van Zanten, had their hands full collecting all the species of plants. Kalkman concentrated on the flowering plants, which had to be dried between newspapers. The air here was so moist that this drying could not be done without artificial help. Two drying-stoves were set up, sheet-iron boxes each carrying a plate pierced by a number of holes; these were heated by pressure oil lamps, the plant presses containing the packets of herbarium material being laid on the grids. It was necessary to get the stoves to burn all night; if they went out, the packages would rapidly become wet again by reason of the great humidity of the air and the plants would be thickly covered with mildew. In order to obtain material for exchange with overseas institutes, eight specimens of each species were collected wherever possible. Each morning the plants were laid between fresh, dry newspapers; the old newspapers were then dried again ready for re-use. Once a packet of specimens had been completely dried, it was packed in tar paper (with formalin tablets as a protection against mildew) to keep out the moisture, and prepared for despatch. Van Zanten's special concern was with the lower plants: mosses, lichens and fungi. In the field he stored his material in plastic bags. Back in camp, the specimens were sorted over and drawings made of the fungi complete with notes of the colours; this was done to record their original shapes, because these plants can shrink considerably when dried. All the material was then dried over the drying-stoves in paper bags or cardboard tart-cases, and then made ready for despatch.

A route which attracted many people was the walk, or more correctly climb, to Um Buk, the valley of the giant pisangs (bananas). Between Tulo and Kigonmedip is a small valley where giant pisang trees grow to a height of forty to fifty feet, and with stems so thick that a fully-grown man cannot get his arms right around them. Actually, the fruits are small and full of large seeds; this was not an edible species of pisang, but since it was none the less of interest to research stations concerned with the study of the cultivation of the banana, a number of seeds were collected and sent off. The Um Buk also attracted the zoologists, because large numbers of snails (which are, incidentally, rare in the Sibil Valley) are found on the limestone rocks. In addition, there was a small cave in these rocks in which we caught some bats.

After short trips to places which could be reached on foot in an hour or two from Mabilabol, there followed longer journeys, some of which took us outside the Sibil Valley.

On 22nd April Reynders, Verstappen and Vervoort set off with Herberts, three policemen and nineteen bearers on a trip to the Ok Tsyop. The gear was standing ready by the scientific workers' hut, most of it in tightly-closed aluminium boxes, and the rest packed in water-proof sheeting. The carriers belonging to the aluminium containers, consisting of broad straps to be fastened over the shoulders, were con-temptuously pushed aside by the bearers. They made new carrying-straps of split rattan, which were passed around the forehead in a large loop, in precisely the same way as they bear their mem (carrying-net). This trip was eagerly awaited, because the Sibillers always enjoyed accompanying Herberts on a trek. At the last moment a very small Sibil boy tried to join the party with a water-bottle and a sweet potato as his only load, but he was unsuccessful. Kotanon, the interpreter, hung the water-bottle over the shoulders of an adult bearer and the boy was sent back.

The route first led over flat, muddy ground and then began to climb the wooded slopes. Every now and then a pithy remark would be heard as somebody stumbled over a tree-root or became entangled in a liana. Slowly but steadily the path continued to rise, until, after several hours, the party reached at a height of 5,580 feet a pass over the Orion Mountains. The view was magnificent. On the opposite side of the Ok Tsyop rose the Yagum Mountains, crowned with a ring of clouds;

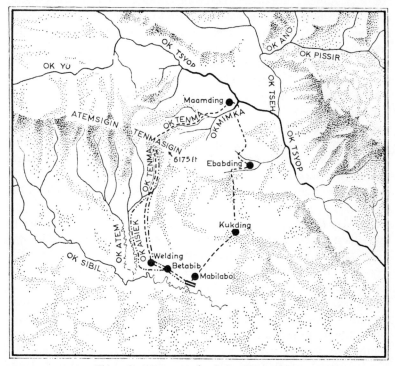

Fig. 4. Journeys over the Orion Mountains.
----, Reynders, Verstappen and Vervoort. -·-·-, biological group.

beyond could be seen other mountain summits and valleys.

The party now dropped down the north slope through the valley of the Ok Nung, to the village of Ebabding, where they set up camp. There was not much that could be done that afternoon, as a thick mist came down, reducing visibility to some twenty yards. The style in which Ebabding was built differed from that of the other villages; the houses were not arranged in a ring, but on opposite sides of a narrow street strewn with large stones. The inner surface of the house-walls, which were built of small tree-trunks, was covered with a layer of bark. But the houses were provided with two entries just like those of the Sibil Valley. There was only one exception—in a house occupied by three bachelors, which did not therefore have a back entry for the women's use; this house had only the normal men's entry about one yard above the floor. About four o'clock the women came home from the gardens, and in each house the fire was stirred up to enable them to roast their boneng (batatas). Some of the women went down to the river to fetch drinking water in hollowed-out calabashes. Herberts walked into the village to buy batatas for the bearers; payment was made in matches, which are very much prized here. That evening the villagers fraternised with their visitors. They sat in one of the houses around the fire to eat boneng; the guests had to shove over a bit when the pig came in, as he too wanted a warm spot.

The camp was a simple affair—a stretched tent-cloth under which the wind blew sharply. It was cool and each member of the party needed two thick blankets in order to be able to sleep well. Their wet clothes were hung up to dry over a small, smoking fire in one of the houses.

Next day the group continued its journey in fine, sunny weather to the village of Maamding. They paused for a moment on the Kungul Ridge (at a height of 5,745 feet). Vervoort collected insects here while Reynders and Verstappen examined the surroundings. They then followed the valley of the Ok Mimka; the view over the valley was of breath-taking beauty, but the depth of the valley itself, into which they had to descend, was fantastic. Herberts went down at a tremendous rate, sliding rather than walking; Reynders followed at a good pace behind him, but Verstappen and Vervoort took it rather more steadily. The last stretch of the descent led over a steep cliff of hard rock. Footholds and handholds had to be sought with care; where necessary the Sibillers gave a hand. The Ok Mimka flows foaming over great blocks of rock, and the party had some trouble in getting across the river. The Sibillers, each carrying a 40-lb. load, sprang nimbly from stone to stone on their bare feet and were amused at what was, in their eyes, the clumsy show put up by the Europeans. On the farther bank the party rested and prepared a good meal. They would have preferred to make camp here, but they were bound to continue as far as Maamding so that they could buy batatas for the bearers. They had barely arrived at the village when the mist came down again and, on top of that, it began to rain. Next day too, it poured with rain; it was useless to try to work, so there was nothing left for it but to stay in again or to visit the village. That evening everybody crept benumbed under the blankets. When they awoke on the fourth day, it was still raining steadily, but the mist had thinned somewhat and they decided to resume their journey. Wet clothes were put on again and the group, following a shorter route to the crest of the Orion Mountains, climbed over several mountain ridges and through the Ok Mimka and the Ok Tenma; this time they crossed the Orion Mountains at a height of 6,390 feet. From this point their route ran downwards into the valley of the Ok Sibil and then in an easterly direction to Mabilabol. As usual, the returning patrol announced its approach by a few signal shots, to which the Sibillers added their rapidly-repeated cry of "Wa, wa, wa . . ." A little later the occupants of the base camp saw a small group of soaked, mud-bespattered but contented figures arrive. After a cup of fresh coffee, the men put on dry clothes and then began to go over their discarded rig and their bedding with large quantities of dieldrex, an insecticide; it is impossible to visit any of the houses in the kampongs without bringing a number of fleas out. This disinfection must have been carried out either too late or not thoroughly enough, since those who had remained in camp had the benefit of the pests for several days thereafter.

*   *   *

Almost a month later Vervoort, Kalkman, Van Heijningen and Staats made a similar journey. As they intended to collect animals and plants, they needed a very full set of equipment, and thus had to have a good number of bearers. In addition, Van Sprang, the radio correspondent, wanted to accompany them on part of the journey and we engaged a special team of bearers to carry his film apparatus and his personal baggage. On 18th May a long column left Mabilabol: 5 Europeans, 3 police-constables and 43 bearers, the latter consisting of both men and boys. Since so many bearers were needed, we could not be too particular and quite a few youngsters were included in the group. These lads were very useful for carrying a small bag containing collecting material, but the "size" of the bearers did cause some difficulties in this instance; some of the youngsters were so small that they had to be lifted, load and all, over the fallen tree-trunks. The party did not progress very rapidly, because repeated stops had to be made for Van Sprang to shoot some more film. The route ran in a westerly direction, passed the villages of Betabib and Welding, through the bed of the Ok Aisyek to the Ok Tenma where they made camp at 4,920 feet.

The inhabitants of the Star Mountains have the curious habit of giving the same name to two rivers rising one on each side of a watershed. The Ok Tenma referred to here lies to the south of the Orion Mountains, while there is another Ok Tenma on the north side.

The camp was soon set up. In order to save weight, no camp beds had been taken along, but a raised floor, or para-para, was constructed from thin canes. It is possible to sleep well on such a platform when the para-para is made of fine, smooth, springy canes, but sometimes it is difficult to get the right kind and one then finds oneself lying with nothing more than a blanket between one's body and a layer of irregular knotty branches. Opinions about sleeping on the para-para were therefore divided. Vervoort was strongly in favour, while others hadn't a good word for the thing. At night the attempt was made to catch insects attracted by the lamp, but without much success, for there was a cloudless sky and the moon was shining brightly. The best time for such trapping is at new moon, with an overcast sky and preferably with a heavy shower of rain. On the second day the party remained in this camp to collect specimens in the vicinity, both in the river and on land. The next day the catch was carried to Mabilabol, when Van Sprang returned accompanied by one constable and seven bearers. Two local Sibillers were engaged to go on with the group as bearers. Unfortunately, this did not seem to be a successful idea, as after some time these new bearers had had enough; they simply set their loads down silently and made off. The party continued along a local track through the forest, and reached the river again at a height of 5,250 feet. They were able to walk uphill along the river-bed, which had been dry for a time, so that there was not much water. At about 6,240 feet they reached the pass over the Tenmasigin (the watershed between the southern and the northern Ok Tenma). One constable and several Sibillers began to look for a suitable camping site, and found one a little lower down on the northern slope. The operation of clearing trees and shrubs brought out a great number of frogs which formed a most welcome acquisition for the zoological collection; the species found were quite different from those found at Mabilabol. On either side of the watershed runs a narrow strip of virgin forest, where no regular clearing was carried out. It was decided to stay two days collecting in the vicinity, concentrating particularly on dragon-flies. During the evening of 21st May there was a certain amount of excitement, because a party of people was heard approaching. The Sibillers crowded together; they were not very happy, because the local inhabitants do not generally move about at night. Happily, it turned out that they were "kaga mok-mok", good people from the village of Maamding, who had a pig for sale. A large steel axe was offered for the pig, but did not seem to be sufficient. A small axe was added, and this clinched the deal. For the Sibillers the purchase of a pig was a great stroke of luck. Next day they stuffed themselves full of pork and sweet potatoes, and although they were unusually excited by the feast, they did not have much heart for working that day. The afternoon and evening were rainy, and this favoured the trapping of insects around the lamp. Camp was broken after five days and the party trekked back to the Sibil Valley over the watershed.

6

Katem

IN A LOOP IN THE OK IWUR, SOME 650 FEET ABOVE SEA-LEVEL AND CLOSE
to the point where this river flows into the East Digul, the Katem camp
had already been built before the expedition began. It was a large,
permanent camp with sizeable buildings to accommodate the research
workers, the marines and the police, provided with a large storage place
for supplies and a number of dwelling houses—built according to local
custom on poles—for the bearers and the guides. As was the case everywhere else, the Papuans were very keen to be near when anything special
was going on, and there consequently soon arose round the camp
houses of the Katemtaman—the people of Katem. Originally, it had been
intended to use Katem as the starting-point for a journey along the Ok
Iwur to the Antares Mountains, but the illness of the helicopter pilots
and the resulting inadequate transport of supplies forced us to change
our plans. Consequently, Katem was never occupied by the large company for which it had been built. It did, however, remain an important
intermediate station on the helicopter route. From this point it was
necessary for the helicopters to go through a pass to reach the Sibil
Valley—a pass which was often closed by masses of cloud; if this were
the case, the pilot would remain waiting in Katem until the weather
had cleared somewhat. Patrols making the journey from Mindiptana to
Mabilabol on foot, and which had had to camp for days under primitive
conditions, found in Katem a well-equipped camp before they began
the 3,280-foot climb to reach the valley. Various research workers made
use of the camp for journeys of exploration in the vicinity.

The Katemmers were less responsive than the Sibillers. They were
quite prepared to work for us in and around the camp, and were even
ready now and then to act as porters or mail-runners as far as Mabilabol,
but they would never stay there longer than was absolutely necessary.

If they arrived in Mabilabol in the evening, they would leave early next morning, sometimes even without having eaten the breakfast which was prepared for them. Although we had arranged with them that they would carry either letters or loads, they seemed to disappear before daybreak. The Sibillers were equally unwilling to go to Katem; it was always very troublesome to engage bearers for a journey there. The clothing worn by the men from Katem is even scantier than that of the Sibillers; instead of a decent calabash, they only wear a small shell from one kind of nut or another. While the Sibillers almost all have a smooth skin, the Katemmers frequently suffer from cascado, a skin disease of fungoid origin which causes the skin to peel off badly in small flakes; this certainly does not give them a very attractive appearance. But on festival occasions they were certainly able to decorate themselves quite as brightly: red earth on the face, chains of pig's teeth and a head-dress of feathers. The language spoken by the Katemmers differs from that used by the Sibillers and this must undoubtedly be a hindrance to contact between them. As far as diet is concerned, sago palms still grow at this low height above sea-level, and sago is the most important item on their menu. Where the soil is suitable, batatas and keladi are cultivated.

The track between Mabilabol and Katem was one of the most used paths in the region during the expedition. In April Police-Sergeant Kroon had cleared the landing-strips for the helicopters along this route. From Mabilabol the track ran through the Ok Sibil, continuing through the forest on the southern bank in an easterly direction, over the ridge which closes the valley at this point. Beyond these hills we entered a dry limestone region, where the water brought down in the very heavy rain-showers disappears into the ground. There are no small rivers here, and only one place where water can be obtained, near the village of Ariemkop, where the water rises above the ground, only to disappear again ten yards farther on. All groups travelling from Mabilabol to Katem or in the opposite direction were accustomed to make camp at the spring at Ariemkop; this was where they could find the water they needed to boil their rice and make their coffee. This last is perhaps the most important, because the making of coffee had to begin almost as soon as camp had been set up; without coffee life in the rimbu (jungle) would hardly be conceivable. Next morning the journey continued to Songgam, where the camp was set up high on the valley wall of the East Digul somewhat to the south of the point where the river comes out of a cleft valley. From Songgam the route went on past Selalabo to Katem; .here the valley became wider and there were broad river terraces stretching out towards the slopes. The track dropped gradually along the East Digul, but before reaching Katem there was another trial: the rattan suspension bridge. The Papuans are masters in making bridges over rivers. Over the East Digul near Dilmot was a suspension bridge approximately ninety yards long. Strands of rattan had been stretched between trees on either bank. Sometimes the foot-way of such bridges consists of a strand of rattan, but frequently it is made of a number of strands of rattan bound together. To the left and right of this bundle, which is used as the foot-way, two strands are set somewhat higher over the river, to serve as hand-ropes. These hand-ropes are connected to the foot-way by a large number of rattan connecting threads. Anyone walking on the bridge feels as though he is walking through a large V-shaped fish-net. If the bridge is very long, transverse rods are set between the hand-ropes at intervals to keep the V open at the top. If this is not done, and the bottom strand is pulled downwards by the weight of the man walking on it, the two hand-ropes are pulled together and the man is pinched between them. The two ends of the bridge are somewhat above the ground level, so that one has to mount a ladder to get on to the bridge. Walking over a rattan suspension bridge of this kind is not an unmixed pleasure, especially when it is raining and the bottom strand is as slippery as glass. It frequently happens that the weight of the people walking across the bridge causes some of the connecting strands between the foot-way and the hand-ropes to break with a snap; this brings everybody on the bridge down a little and the bridge itself begins to swing. The only thing that one can then do is to wait until the bridge has stopped swinging before moving on again. On long bridges, we had to bend down at intervals to get under the transverse bars, because these bridges are made for small Papuans and not for us much taller Europeans. The cross-bars also gave trouble to the bearers, who frequently had to carry a high-piled load, and they often had their burdens caught in these bars. Only one person crosses the bridge at a time. We were not the only ones who were frightened on occasion, as our bearers were scared too; you would stop in the middle of the bridge, and looking down from this point, would get the impression that the river was standing still and that it was the bridge that was moving. Stopping on the bridge delays the crossing, but it is much worse if the bridge starts to swing and there is a likelihood that

you might fall off. If a bearer became so frightened that he stopped in
the middle of the swaying bridge, his friends on the bank would take
drastic measures. With loud shouts and screams they would throw
stones at him until he was so frightened that he would pull himself
together and quickly run across to the other side. If you have to cross a
bridge of this sort with a large group of bearers, it will take a couple of
hours or so, as each man requires from three to five minutes to make
the trip. If the weather is fine, this is not a bad thing, because it gives
the waiting bearers a good rest and they are able to bask comfortably in
the sun. In pouring rain, it is a thoroughly wretched business.

These suspension bridges, made by the local inhabitants with no
other tools than a stone axe, always filled us with admiration. Before a
bridge is installed, it is naturally necessary to wait for a favourable
opportunity; after a period of drought, when the river is not too deep
and the current not too strong, the builders have to wade through the
water carrying the first strands to the opposite bank. Once the bridge has
been completed, it does, of course, need to be repaired from time to
time, and this is what was often lacking. Whenever bridges of this sort
lay on our route, they were always checked by the police first of all, and
frequently they had to be strengthened, because our weight was so
much greater than that of the Papuans.

Police-Sergeant Kroon—accompanied by Marine Boon, several
constables and a number of Muyus—moved into the Katem camp and
prepared for the reception of Bär and Cortel's group, which was due to
arrive on 5th May. Superintendent Oosterman also left for Katem, and
had a stroke of luck on the way, since he was picked up by a helicopter
which deposited him at the camp. Oosterman took over the control of
the camp, to ensure that it would be ready by the time the research
workers arrived. For the time being there was no prospect of this; a
fault in one of the helicopters had delayed the transport of supplies
along the Digul. There was sufficient food in Katem for a small team, but
it was essential to maintain the group as small as possible for the
moment. Cortel and Kroon, with several constables and some of the
Sansapor bearers, therefore headed for Mabilabol, where the food
situation was considerably better. Bär remained in Katem and Reynders
seized the opportunity to travel there by helicopter. They were to go
together on a trip along the Ok Iwur. Bär was to look for a suitable
route for the helicopters and indicate where landing-places could be
made. Reynders would be able to carry out soil investigations in this

region. They left on 8th May. For a short while they followed a track through the wood until they came to the point where they had to cross the Ok Katem. On the map this little river was shown as an unimportant stream; in dry weather it could be crossed easily, and one would only just get one's feet wet in the process. But it had rained hard during the night and the Ok Katem was in full bandyir (spate); foaming wildly, its waters were rushing through the river bed. The group therefore had to make a bridge, cutting a tree for the purpose in such a way that it fell across the river. They chose a high, stout tree on the bank and it was carefully cut down. As it fell into the water with a great noise, the current caught its crown and the whole trunk was swept away. In carrying it a couple of hundred yards, the force of the current had broken the crown up very small. A new tree was therefore selected, but suffered the same fate. The third and fourth trees dropped into bad positions because they were bound to others by the creepers. In this way the group moved some distance along the river bank looking for new trees and trying again and again. The fifth attempt was successful; the branches of the trees remained firmly lodged on the opposite bank. The only difficulty now was that some part of the tree-trunk had finished up under water, and the river was rushing over it with great force. A couple of bearers plucked up enough courage to attempt the crossing and safely reached the other side; there they felled another tree, which neatly dropped on top of the first. After two hours the bridge was finished and the entire group was able to cross the Ok Katem. Meanwhile it had started to rain and they continued to trek through the forest in a drenched condition. It went on raining for four days and each afternoon they arrived at their camp soaked to the skin. Fortunately there is one particular thing at which the Papuans are especially clever, and that is making a fire, even if all the wood available is soaking wet. Once the fire was alight, everybody's one desire could be met—coffee. A good-sized mug of coffee and a cigarette can make life under a canvas tent in the jungle really agreeable, even in pouring rain! Of an evening the muddy clothes were washed and hung up to dry over a wood fire. In the morning the group would be able to put on dry clothes again, but—as Reynders put it—this meant that you would finish up with the colour and smell of a smoked eel. The drying of clothes was not an operation from which one benefited for long, because after walking for about half an hour everybody was soaked to the skin again by the rain. Here and there the path they followed led across the Ok Iwur and its tributary the Ok Irin, but rattan

suspension bridges were available for the crossings. They continued the
march for three days; the survey overseer Wattimena measured the
track, set his marks and thus plotted on the map the route they had
followed. Reynders collected a number of soil samples which were
taken along in cotton sample bags to be examined in greater detail
later. One of the most important finds in this region was the occurrence
of large complexes of *Agathis*. *Agathis* is a species of tree, related to the
Araucaria and consequently also to the pines; *Agathis* has no needles but

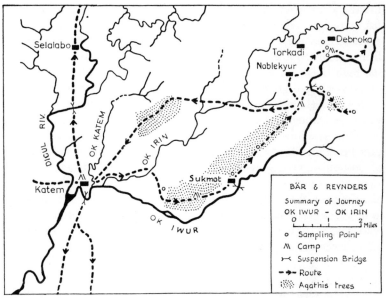

Fig. 5. Bär and Reynders' journey from the Ok Iwur to the Ok Irin.

bears large, broad leaves. The trees provide copal gum, a product
which is of economic importance because it is one of the substances
exported from Netherlands New Guinea. It was not to be wondered at
that Reynders observed during his helicopter flight to Katem a flock of
white cockatoos (*Cacatua galerita*). These cockatoos are very partial to the
seeds of *Agathis*. The Forestry Service wants to collect these seeds to sow
them again, but in many *Agathis* woods most of the seeds are eaten by
cockatoos, which can thus become a real pest. Bär had been in this
region before, and he was able to supplement his earlier observations.

After three days' journeying they reached the pre-determined goal, the watershed between the Ok Iwur and the Ok Irin, which lie very close together at this point; this was where the group camped. The forest blocked their view but the bearers knew a way round this difficulty. They cleared a number of trees, and then felled one tree, dropping it in such a way as to carry all the others with it. In this way it is possible to bring down a large number of trees without unnecessary labour. The return journey was begun on the fourth day, following a different route farther to the north. In general, it was common to have to cross muddy spots where one had to pick one's way over tree-trunks lying flat on the ground, but such conditions were quite exceptional here; for a whole hour they had to balance themselves on tree-trunks, jumping from one to another. Near Katem they found a few bark huts among the high trees; these huts were used by the Papuans for hunting the birds which feed greedily on the fruits of the neighbouring trees.

They were able to recover from their journey in the Katem camp, where Superintendent Oosterman had prepared a first-class meal. This delicious cooking was the reason for the objections raised by the expedition members who had to stay in Mabilabol against the departure of Oosterman, because wherever he had charge of the kitchen, the meals were very much tastier. A long stay in New Guinea and very wide experience in the rimbu (jungle) had made it possible for him always to be able to serve up something quite special. The expedition members who visited Katem were full of praise when they spoke of the "Oosterman Hotel".

*   *   *

Reynders made a few more short trips in the region around Katem and along the western side of the East Digul. Along the slopes of the mountain range, samples were taken at various heights and he also studied ground sections. The stocks of cotton bags containing samples lying out to dry at the Katem camp grew steadily. There was no more work here for Bär; he had already studied this region before, and the reconnaissance along the Ok Iwur asked for by the leaders of the ex-pedition had been completed. Supplies of food at Katem were not yet sufficient to maintain a large group and there was no point in keeping more people here than was strictly necessary. In addition, Cortel and the Sansapor bearers of the geological group were in the Sibil Valley, and a journey to the area which lies north of the central watershed was

more important to Bär than a longer stay in Katem. He therefore decided
to trek to Mabilabol, together with Lieutenant Nicolas, who had been
brought up from Kawakit by helicopter. They were able to engage
eight Katemmers as bearers, and they therefore arrived in the Sibil
Valley on 19th May. The expedition members called this journey "Bär's
hunger trip", not that he had suffered from hunger for one reason or
another, but because a newspaper reporter had written about this
journey under the heading: "Hunger forces Bär to return", forgetting
that there was no question of a return, but rather the completion of the
journey from Tanah Merah to the Sibil Valley. For those who saw Bär
arrive at Mabilabol well-nourished and lively, this press report was a
source of much amusement.

The eight Katemmers who had come with Bär wanted to get back
home as quickly as possible, and Verstappen went with them. Although
eight bearers is not a large number, he was at all events able to make the
journey. He did not take any of the police with him, because each
constable who went along would need a bearer for his spare clothes and
equipment, to say nothing of the additional food required. The area
between the Sibil Valley and Katem was completely peaceable, and
there was not the slightest risk in making this journey without protection. He was, however, provided with a rifle, because it looked good
and it might be possible for him to supplement his supplies of meat en
route. His personal equipment (spare clothes, instruments, medicines,
etc.) were pressed into a tin box, and made up an adequate load for one
man. The other bearers carried a light tent, with a few pans and some
food. The more food he took from Mabilabol, the longer he would be
able to operate independently. It would be possible to buy batatas in
the villages on the way to supply the bearers, against payment in salt,
matches and tobacco. In the early morning of the 30th May, Verstappen
set out with his eight Katem bearers. He was not able to understand
them; the few Sibil words which he knew and the international language of signs would have to serve for communication. He set up his
first camp near Ariemkop and reached Songgam on the East Digul on
the second day. He was not the only person to spend the night there, for
on the same day Reynders and De Wilde arrived from the opposite
direction. De Wilde was travelling with about twenty bearers from
Mindiptana, and this was a good opportunity for Reynders to accompany him back to Mabilabol. The three men therefore camped together
at Songgam and were thus able to exchange all the latest news. Reynders

and De Wilde reported on the delay in bringing in supplies caused by ·the illness of the helicopter pilots Zijlstra and Van den Bos, but they were also able to relate the achievements of Menge, who had made various flights to Katem on his own to bring in supplies. Verstappen sketched the situation at the base camp, and gave an account of the trouble with the Twin Pioneer, which had let them down a couple of times by reason of leaky oil and petrol leads, and was now standing on the airfield at Sibil with a faulty motor. In addition to these disheartening reports there were also some items of stirring news: Venema had gone to Tanah Merah to speed up the transport of supplies, and there was the possibility of new plans of carrying out work from Mabilabol first of all towards the north and east, etc. It was a very agreeable evening and even the pouring rain was not able to spoil their chat. Next morning the two groups set out on their respective routes; Verstappen continued along the Digul to Katem, while Reynders and De Wilde finished their journey to the Sibil Valley via Ariemkop in one day. Reynders, who was a quicker walker than De Wilde, went ahead with a few bearers and, when De Wilde reached Ariemkop, the coffee was ready and preparations for a good meal were being made. The last section of the journey presented a good many difficulties, because they were only just beginning to climb the pass and they had to reach a height of 4,133 feet (the height above sea-level of the Sibil Valley).

The pessimists made out that on the journey from Katem to Mabilabol you did not have to climb 3,000-odd feet, but without doubt 6,500 feet, because after climbing for a short while it was necessary to go downhill again for a stretch. The track was difficult and there was one point where the group had to climb a rock face. De Wilde took a false step and injured his foot, an injury which compelled him—to his great annoyance—to rest for a time at the base camp.

Meanwhile Verstappen had crossed the large suspension bridge near Dilmot with his bearers, and walked cheerfully into the camp at Katem, where Superintendent Oosterman received him with a fresh, steaming cup of coffee, as was the custom there. Here too, Verstappen found ready listeners to all the news which he brought from Mabilabol. Communication between the base camp and Katem was not yet very frequent, and the occupants of the camp were very glad to have somebody arrive with news. While they were sitting on a rough wooden bench enjoying the view across the Ok Iwur, a shy Papuan approached, offering a striking stone for sale. It appeared that he had found this stone to the south of

Katem in one of the terraces along the East Digul. We found on close inspection that this was a most important find: it was a fossilised vertebra. A few weeks later it was sent by airmail to the Netherlands, to Dr. D. A. Hooijer of the Rijksmuseum van Natuurlijke Historie (National Museum of Natural History) at Leiden, who identified it as a fossil thoracic vertebra of a crocodile (*Crocodylus* species). This was the first find in New Guinea of a vertebrate animal from the Pleistocene era. Further investigations at the place where the Papuan said he had unearthed this vertebra were fruitless, but somewhere in the bank of the East Digul or along one or another of its tributaries there must be a deposit which contains fossils of this kind. It must be left to future explorers to find this deposit, but if it is discovered, it will provide important data regarding the early fauna of New Guinea.

Verstappen began with a number of journeys in the vicinity of Katem of one or two days' duration, examining the river terraces in the region and so obtaining important information about the development of the river system. The terrace deposits were examined to determine what minerals occurred in them, in order to enable us to draw conclusions as to the origin of the material of which the terraces were made and from this in turn to discover the previous course of the river. Verstappen required little assistance on these short journeys, so that he was generally accompanied only by a small group of Katemmers, boys of ten or eleven years of age, who carried the little pan for lunch—which consisted principally of food out of a tin—a small kettle for the coffee, a few sample bags, a machete and an axe. Thus equipped, the little procession would set out in the morning at about seven o'clock, usually in drizzling rain, which accompanied them as they penetrated into the forest, and they would return to the camp about midday, in blazing sunshine, no less wet than when they left in the morning, but loaded with bags containing soil samples. The samples would be washed out in a flat bowl and examined with a magnifying glass to determine what mineral occurrences they showed.

The bearers' wages paid to the youngsters consisted of a handful of biscuits and a box of matches. "Tong", as matches are called in this part of the mountainous region, are an excellent commodity for making contact. The clumsy methods previously used to make fire have now become obsolete, and it is thus no longer a very serious matter if the fire goes out. It is a puzzle how these people who do not possess watertight pockets manage to keep their matches dry; they were always able to use them to start a small fire however hard it rained. On 23rd May the monotony of camp life was broken by the arrival of a helicopter. Although the weather did not seem so favourable early in the morning, it cleared up sufficiently later for Zijlstra (making his first flight after his attack of 'flu) to fly with Venema right through to Katem. When he had set his passenger down, he immediately flew back to Kloof Camp to fetch Escher, who had occupied himself there with washing river sand to see what minerals it contained. Ninety minutes later Zijlstra was back in Katem with Escher, and Menge brought in the second helicopter with a cargo of rice and tinned meat. Plans were made to bring up food and petrol from the Kloof Camp to Katem as quickly as possible, and also to locate the mechanics at this point with their equipment.

To keep up to date with what was going on in the world, Portier, the marine belonging to the communication service, sat next morning listening to the conversations between Mabilabol and Tanah Merah. He took off the headphones with a resigned gesture and sighed: "Helicopters knocked out." "They won't fly for eight weeks now," he added, in explanation. He had just received the report that the three flyers and one of the mechanics had gone down with yellow fever. There now followed a busy time for him and for Marine Koster at Mabilabol as Brongersma and Venema each gave their views of the future. While Katem was able to carry out telephone conversations very reasonably with the signal office of the marine barracks at Hollandia, Mabilabol was not so successful in this. Consequently, the reports were transmitted in morse. Both in Mabilabol and Katem the marines stood turning the generator handles to provide current for the transmitters, an excessively tiring operation, particularly when three-hundred-word telegrams had to be sent. For a moment communications threatened to break down altogether when one of the generator handles in Mabilabol broke; the handle-turning team were decidedly cheerful at this, but they had not reckoned with the technical skill of Corporal Goedhart, who repaired the thing in very good time. Once again the telegrams began to pass to and fro. As a matter of prudence, work was begun at Katem on clearing a stretch of forest, which might serve if needed for the dropping of supplies, but it did not come to this. After mature consideration Brongersma had decided for the moment to do without trips which started from Katem. The camps at Kloof Camp and Katem had adequate supplies to hold out for a time with their small populations. Kloof Camp was actually quite amply stocked up and, if necessary, supplementary supplies could be brought up to Katem from the Sibil Valley. Since Kloof Camp relied entirely on helicopter communications and in consequence nothing was known there of the new developments, the Missionary Aviation Fellowship was asked to send over a Cessna light aircraft to drop a message. This machine would at the same time be able to drop some letters at Katem. The mail and the messages were packed into a biscuit tin, and weighted with a fresh loaf; a roll of adhesive bandage was used to provide the package with long streamers to facilitate its recovery should it fall into the undergrowth.

Lieutenant Nicolas, who knew both camps, sat next to the pilot ready to drop the tins overboard. First they flew to Katem, where the package landed precisely in front of the door at Venema's feet. The three marines and two policemen forming the team at Kloof Camp were expecting a helicopter; instead they saw a small aircraft appear low over the trees, and, after sweeping round in a curve, drop a canister on to a sandbank in the river. In this way everybody was informed of the most recent developments.

Two men in Katem were not very concerned with the revised arrangements: Verstappen and Escher, who calmly went on with their exploration. They continued to go out together, collecting samples which were subjected to provisional examination in the camp. In Kawakit and near Kloof Camp, Escher had discovered magnetite (magnetic iron ore, Fe_3O_4) in the debris carried along by the River Digul and they were now about to try to find where this had come from. They made a one-day journey to the lower course of the Ok Bouw, which runs into the East Digul north of Katem, with the intention of sampling at this point deposits in the river, as well as those forming the river terraces. They found no magnetite in the washed samples taken from the Ok Bouw; however, some was present in the sandbanks of the Ok Iwur, and the concentration of iron as such was also particularly high. It was logical to conclude from this that the magnetite originated in the Antares Mountains, where the Ok Iwur rises; this was later confirmed by an investigation on the spot.

A search for gold carried out in 1938 and 1939 in the Katem region had given rise to expectations that gold might be found in the district. The marines, who became bored in the camp from time to time, since there was not much going on, seized upon this opportunity to divert themselves. They sat with their washing pans along a gravel-spit or sandbank washing handfuls of grit and mud, until all the silt had been removed. They then dried the residue over a small fire and removed the iron present by means of a magnet. This removal of the iron was always a source of wonder to the Papuans. They would watch with great interest the magnet being moved to and fro over the gravel, causing the little particles to jump out and adhere to the magnet. This magical phenomenon called forth from them a long-drawn "Ieee" of surprise. Meanwhile, it had become clear that the gravel consisted largely of magnetite, since there was not much material left after this treatment. Every now and then a yellow gleam would arouse some excitement, but no gold was found, not even a trace!

After a short stay, Escher trekked to the Sibil Valley to join the geologists who were about to leave for the Antares Mountains. Cortel went from Mabilabol to Katem to fetch down some equipment which Bär had had to leave behind there.

Verstappen left for two weeks on a journey to the region east of Katem. His equipment was simple: a small shovel, a hammer, a flat pan for washing out his soil samples, a few sample bags, a compass, and an altimeter were all that he needed for his field work and taken altogether this did not constitute a full load. With a modest outfit of this kind the group could be quite small, a factor which considerably increases the speed with which a team can cover the ground. It is always a cause of delays if one has to make use of a large train of bearers, even though this may be necessary on occasion; above all, if there are any rivers to be crossed, it takes hours before all the bearers have got to the opposite side. The party was accompanied by Constable Wefmayagai, a Papuan from the south coast. He was not only responsible for the safety of the group, but was also to take charge in constructing the camps and was to oversee the distribution of the bearers' loads. Eleven men from Katem went with the party to carry the camp equipment and the food supplies. They were also to serve as guides during the first part of the journey. A Muyu who answered to the impressive name of Kosmos went with the party as cook and interpreter; he was able to converse with Verstappen and Wefmayagai in Malay, and could also make himself understood to the Katemmers in his own Muyu. On 3rd June the group set off along the route which had already been used earlier by Bär and Reynders; first of all they went along the Ok Irin, later crossing it, and then proceeded eastwards to the small kampong of Sukmot, where the first camp was set up. From this point they continued on 4th June in a north-easterly direction, steadily climbing until they had reached a

21. Counting.

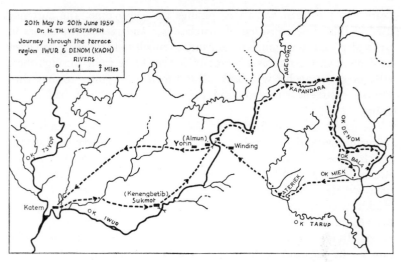

Fig. 6. Verstappen's journey along the Iwur and Kaoh Rivers.

point just over 2,130 feet above sea-level, where the village of Almun had stood earlier. The village had disappeared—a not very uncommon occurrence; the inhabitants had left, taking all their goods and chattels with them, and had settled elsewhere. The river here dashed wildly between great blocks of rock, so that it was impossible to wade through it. Because of this the local inhabitants had made a rattan suspension bridge, and the camp was set up close to it, so that Verstappen could from this base work on both sides of the river; for this purpose he set aside a total of three days. Roughly one hour's walk to the west of the bridge lay the kampong of Yorin, and at the same distance to the east the kampong of Winding. Winding was in a particularly beautiful situation, on a slope where the forest was broken up by gardens. In clear weather there was a fine view from this village across the Ok Iwur to Katem, and even further, to the ridges of the Digul Mountains; in New Guinea, where for days on end one can walk through the forest with no view at all, a prospect of this kind is very surprising. Yorin and Winding were, it is true, small villages, each consisting of roughly four houses. The inhabitants had their gardens on both sides of the river and there was thus a good deal of traffic over the bridge each day. From this point of view the camp was well placed strategically, as it enabled the expedition members to purchase from the passers-by food for the

22. Anceaux, the linguistic expert, talking to a Sibiller.

bearers in the form of batatas, pisangs and sugar-cane. The currency used in this trade consisted of matches, salt and razors. The razors in particular were very much in demand, so much so that Verstappen even used his own reserves as a means of barter. As he came through these villages again on his way back, all the men were going around with shining clean-shaven heads and faces, while he himself had a fine beard.

The inhabitants of Yorin and Winding were close friends, and frequently visited each other. Sometimes there were dance festivals, which were held alternately in Yorin and in Winding. The people attending the festival could be seen approaching from the camp; the men had their faces well covered with red earth and fat, and wore a headdress of cassowary and Bird of Paradise feathers and necklaces of pig's teeth. Since only one man could go over the bridge at a time, the others always stopped for a little chat. During the time that Verstappen camped by the bridge, the people from these two villages learned to know the Katemmers so well that some of them were even invited on one occasion to a dance festival. When Verstappen continued his journey on 8th June, he could with a clear conscience leave behind a Katemmer who had fallen ill to recover in Yorin. For the rest there was, however, little contact between the people of Katem and those of this region, and the Katem bearers did not know the way around here very well. Now that the business of making acquaintance had gone well, four men from these villages were ready to accompany the party on the journey as guides. The camp was struck, the bearers' loads distributed and the group—now increased to a total of seventeen—trekked along the eastern bank of the Ok Iwur towards the north.

To begin with there was still a track which might be dignified by the name of a path, but this soon turned off to the south and it was then necessary for the party to make its own track. Yard by yard the undergrowth had to be cleared to make a small path. There was no view, but the noise of the rushing river made it possible for them to orientate themselves roughly, while Verstappen checked the direction by means of his compass. The party then dropped steeply down towards the river and continued along the bank or in the river-bed. It was certainly not an agreeable walk. The undergrowth was thick and there were a number of thorny bushes which made progress very difficult; on top of this, it was pouring with rain. At this height leeches were numerous and they did not allow the chance of having a good meal to escape. On bushes along the path or on the floor of the wood they would wait for their prey. The first men to pass would be safe from their attentions; but the shaking of the ground (together, perhaps, with the men's odour) would stir them into activity. It was an interesting spectacle for those who were able to escape from them. Attached firmly by means of their rear suckers the leeches would stretch as far forward as possible, rearing upwards and searching around by moving the forward end of their bodies in circles, or else creeping towards the path. They move very much after the fashion of a looper caterpillar. The body is stretched out, the front sucker is attached, and the rest of the body then drawn up, during which operation the creature arches its back in a high loop until the rearmost sucker is attached to a point close beind the front sucker; the leech then stretches its body out again and the whole cycle begins anew. Leeches can travel quite quickly in this manner. They do not grow very large; when fully extended they are from one and a half inches to two inches long and only about half an inch thick. It was fascinating, but also somewhat unnerving, to see the army of leeches lying in wait along the track ready to attack, waving to and fro as they sought for their prey, or rearing up their backs as they approached from all sides. The optimists seemed to think that after a day or two of drought the leeches would hide under the fallen leaves and remain inactive; but they generally came back disappointed on this score and only noticed their mistake once some five or six of the creatures were busy sucking the blood from their veins. Good suitable clothing (shoes, socks, long trousers and puttees) did give a certain amount of protection, but the leeches are always capable of finding a gap through which they creep, even if there is nothing better to hand than the lace-holes of one's shoes. In this case they only have to climb up a little further until they are able to penetrate through to the skin. Good protection is provided by rubbing dimethylphthalate into one's shoes, socks and trouser-legs, but the dose has to be repeated at regular intervals, since the chemical can readily be washed away in the laundry or when the clothes are wetted in pouring rain.*

* Dimethylphthalate also has the advantage of keeping mosquitoes at a distance, and of deterring the mites (kutu maleo) that cause a disagreeable, very strong irritation known as scrub itch, and is also objectionable to the mites which carry another disease known as scrub typhus or tsutsugamushi disease.

If a leech manages to reach a suitable area of the skin, it bores a hole into the skin with its jaws and injects into the wound a substance which prevents the blood from congealing. Only when it is completely satiated with blood does the leech let go and drop to the ground, where it rests for a period to digest its meal. The boring of the skin is not felt by the victim, who generally notices that he has been attacked by a leech only when the creature has let go and he feels a thin stream of blood flowing over his skin. The substance which stops coagulation of the blood causes the wound to go on bleeding for a long time. If you happen to be fortunate enough to be one of those people who roll their own cigarettes, you can put a cigarette paper on the wound; this will staunch the flow of blood, but you must not be surprised if some hours later when you wash yourself the cigarette paper peels away and the blood begins to flow quite freely again. A Papuan who sees a leech sitting on his leg will scrape it off with his jungle knife. The Europeans are generally more careful, as it is easy to produce a very ugly tropical ulcer if the leech is dragged away from the skin roughly, leaving any part of its sharp mandibles in the wound. An easy way to clear them from your skin is to drop a little tobacco juice on them or to touch them with a burning cigarette, as this makes them let go immediately. Again and again we asked ourselves how the thousands of leeches found in a tropical forest manage to find sufficient food, as there are not many passers-by and no large mammals occur here at all. It is also remarkable that, as far as is known, leeches do not transfer any diseases, in spite of the fact that their blood-sucking manner of getting a living is really quite as well suited for the purpose as are the habits of many insects.

Laboriously clearing their way, now and then scratching themselves on thorns and constantly plagued by leeches, Verstappen and his men continued through the forest. They marched on in torrential rain and after five hours of hard slogging they had only advanced about two and a half miles. The river was rising rapidly and was about to go into bandyir (spate); this made it impossible for them to use the route through the bed of the river, which had frequently been much easier, and they therefore had to make their way through the forest on the bank. When they had reached the mouth of the Agegoro, a tributary of the Ok Iwur, at about half past three in the afternoon, Verstappen considered that they had had enough and gave orders to make camp. Sticks were cut and the tent-cloths spread over them, while the cook set about his work. Once Verstappen had taken off his wet things and put on a dry kit (the last he had), and was sitting under the tent where the rain could not reach him, with Kosmos serving a mug of strong coffee and a good plate of rice, he felt really set up again. Life in the rimbu was not so bad after all!

Next morning (9th June) the party was on its way again by seven o'clock. This time the route ran in an easterly direction along the southern bank of the Agegoro and then along the Kapandara. Once again they had to clear, foot by foot, a path over many small but very steep hills, which had to be climbed on all fours. Fortunately, it was now dry; if it had been raining the slopes would have been slippery and dangerous. The average height above sea-level of this track was about 3,200 feet. On one occasion only they found traces of an old path; some years previously a patrol sent out by the administration of the interior had passed this way. As they advanced, the party stopped for a moment at intervals, as on the foregoing days, to enable Verstappen to take samples of the deposits in the river-bed or to chip specimens from the rocks along the banks. Each in its own bag, labelled with indications of the point where they were taken and the height above sea-level, the samples were packed into carrying-cases. The loads carried by the bearers thus stayed at roughly the same weight during the entire journey. As fast as the rice was eaten up and the tins emptied, the loads were made up again with samples of the river-bank deposits and with geological specimens. Apart from these short interruptions, during which the bearers sat in the clearing comfortably basking in the sun, the group trekked all day, until at about half past four in the afternoon they reached, in fact unexpectedly, the Ok Denom, as the upper course of the Kaoh (or Kau) River is called. This difficult stretch of the journey, to which Verstappen had assigned several days in his plan, had now been covered in one day. Pleased with this success, the party set up camp by the Ok Denom, and a meal was prepared. It had been a heavy day and everybody fell asleep immediately after supper. Although it started to rain in the meantime, this could no longer do any harm; everybody was protected from the rain by the tents and their blankets kept out the cold.

The terrain remained difficult for the next two days as well, i.e. 10th and 11th June, as the party advanced southwards along the western bank of the Ok Denom. The rocks crop out almost continuously along this river, which is therefore of particular interest to the geologist. One disadvantage was that there was not a bridge to be found anywhere. .The water was too high, and the current too fast, for them to be able to wade across; had they had taller bearers and a sufficient number of ropes they might perhaps have succeeded, but it was too risky to attempt a crossing with the little Katemmers. There are virtually no inhabitants of this region and there were thus no local paths. Only once did they encounter Papuans in the valley of the Ok Denom; these were two men who had some freshly-pounded sago under a penthouse roof, and later they were joined by a woman with two children. The guides from Yorin and Winding were only just acquainted with this area; they were most unwilling to continue farther east, and Verstappen therefore had no alternative but to follow the course of the Ok Denom. The eastern-most point which he reached was only about six miles from the border of Australian New Guinea, but he was not able to fulfil his ambition of exploring right up to this boundary. On 12th June they continued from the Ok Denom through the valley of the Ok Bala and the Ok Miek to the valley of the Ateriek. This was an unnerving enter-prise for the bearers, because the region belonged to the territory of another tribe, and they did not like the idea of going onto somebody else's ground unless trading had enabled them to have frequent contact with the tribe living there. Also, in a district without villages the bearers had to eat rice, and the supplies carried by the party were thus rapidly used up. They therefore commenced the return journey—trekking upstream along the Ok Tarup. On 13th June they reached Winding and Yorin again. Here the guides left them and the sick bearer, who had meanwhile recovered, joined the group again. On 14th June they returned to Katem by a route farther to the north, crossing the upper course of the Ok Irin on the way. All the members of the party were very glad to be back in an inhabited region; for days on end they had marched through silent forest, with screeching cockatoos and scraping cicadas as their only neighbours. Verstappen reflected that it did you good to talk to a man again, even though you only just understood him. On his return he entered Katem Camp with a large stock of samples, his trousers torn to ribbons, and wearing a most impressive beard. The samples of the river deposits were washed, dried and packed, and—after the primitive meals in the forest—Verstappen regaled himself on the food offered him by Oosterman. The bearers were paid off, each receiving an axe or a machete, and returned to their homes content.

It was at Katem that Verstappen was told of the extra funds which had been made available, of the supply-dropping flights to the Sibil Valley and of the groups which were on their way to the valley of the Ok Bon. Warman, the new chief pilot, had arrived from Holland to replace Zijlstra, who was still in hospital at Hollandia with jaundice; Warman had already flown once to the Sibil Valley, so that Venema had been able to return to Mabilabol on 9th June. Two pilots, Van den Bos and Menge, had recovered and were at Tanah Merah; consequently, helicopter operations could now begin again. When he found that he was unable to engage sufficient bearers in the Sibil Valley, the head of the Survey Group—Van der Weiden—had gone via Hollandia and Tanah Merah to Mindiptana, where he had engaged one hundred Muyus, with whom he was now on his way to Katem. This group, reinforced by the addition of Verstappen, continued from Katem to the Sibil Valley, where they arrived on 20th June. In addition both the helicopters attempted the journey to the Sibil Valley, where they were now to be stationed permanently. Warman and Van den Bos, together with Nieraeth and Mr. De Bijl (the Inspector of the Burger Luchtvaart), reached Katem on the 14th June; here it was discovered that the rotor blades of one of the helicopters had deteriorated so badly that it would have been an unjustifiable risk to fly on to the Sibil Valley. After a stay of a few days (because of bad weather) the other helicopter went to Mabilabol to fetch new rotor blades, and to bring up another mechanic, Bekker. As the repaired helicopter left for the Sibil Valley on 24th June, silence fell on Katem. Oosterman stayed behind with a small team of marines and police, while a little survey group occupied the camp for the purpose of carrying out an astronomical fix and of mapping the region immediately surrounding the camp. Of an evening the marines and survey officials collected the insects attracted by the light; this enabled them to send interesting consignments to Mabilabol, where the zoologists were very glad to have such supplements to their collections.

On 3rd July De Wilde flew by helicopter to Katem, which he intended to use as a base for a number of trips. Superintendent Oosterman was able to provide him with twelve Katemmers as bearers, and so he set out on 5th July, accompanied by Marine Van Hirtum and Constable Rumpaidus. To the south of the confluence of the Ok Iwur and the East Digul, they crossed the river by means of a rattan suspension bridge, continuing along the western bank of the East Digul in a northerly direction. Some of the inhabitants of this region still live in tree-houses (rumah tinggi—literally "house high"), which are built about

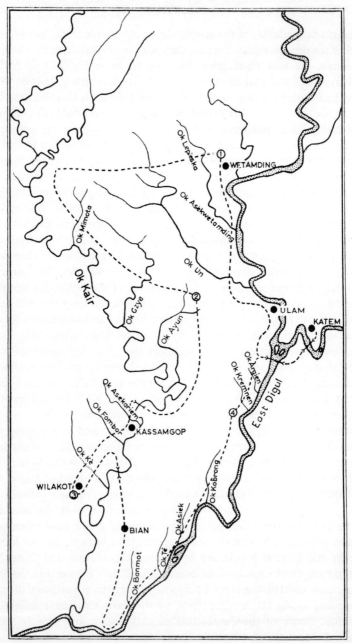

Fig. 7. De Wilde's route to the Ok Kair district; ①...④ Camps;)—(Bridge.

fifty feet above the ground in the branches of trees. Sometimes a single large stem supports the structure, and sometimes the house is built on a number of smaller adjacent trees. Several families live together in such houses. This fashion of living high above the ground gives the occupants a considerable degree of security against attack. Close by the bridge, De Wilde found the rumah tinggi known as Ulam. There was only one man at home and he readily allowed himself to be measured. In torrential rain the party then continued their journey to the settlement of Wetamding, built on a hill. This village consisted of three houses, closely resembling the Sibil dwellings in form, but built on piles about five feet high, in contrast to the houses in the Sibil Valley, where the floor is about one foot above the ground. They made their camp close by Wetamding; eleven of the inhabitants of the village submitted to the anthropologist's examination. There were many small rivers in the region and the party had to wade through the water again and again in order to proceed; however, this was not very serious, because everybody was soaking wet from the ceaseless rain. From Wetamding De Wilde turned westwards, with the intention of discovering whether there were more people living to the west of the Ok Kair, which is the most important river in this district; it is fast-flowing and has an eastern bank formed by a sheer cliff, about 130 feet high. There was no bridge, and it was impossible to make one, so that there was no prospect at all of crossing the river at this point. So there was therefore nothing for it but to follow the course of the river southwards. In the middle of the forest they camped by the Ok Kombremoga, a small river in which there lay enormous hard lumps of clay. Next day the group continued in a southerly direction and finally came upon a rattan bridge over the Ok Kair; this bridge was thoroughly repaired by Rumpaidus and the bearers, before they crossed it. To the west of the river they found two settlements, Kassamgop and Wilakot, each consisting of a large house occupied by more than one family. They set up their camp hard by Wilakot. The inhabitants of Kassamgop had accompanied them so that De Wilde was able to measure the population of both settlements at once. Between Kassamgop and Wilakot the Ok Ke flows into the Ok Kair. The Ok Ke is a small river which comes down from the Ariem Mountains and flows underground for a while, just before flowing into the Ok Kair. The latter river is the larger of the two and, according to our way of thinking, the river flowing from the confluence towards the south—towards the East Digul—ought to be called the Ok Kair, but the local inhabitants call this lower part of the course the Ok Ke, as they also do the small tributary. From Wilakot the party's route followed a north-easterly direction which took them again over the small Ok Ke to a second suspension bridge across the Ok Kair, and thence southwards to the rumah tinggi called Bian. They had to abandon their plan of crossing the East Digul hereabouts in order to trek further to Zigibi, the two bridges which had been here three months before (Bär had used one of them) having disappeared, swept away by a bandylr. The only possibility was to proceed northwards, to the bridge by which they had crossed the East Digul on the outward journey. On 9th July, De Wilde returned with his group to Katem; their numbers had increased en route, because quite a few people from the settlements through which they had passed had accompanied him. The group was in very good heart in spite of the constant rain. On the last day of their journey they saw crowned pigeons in the forest (Goura scheepmakeri); these are large bluish-grey birds which wear a crest of finely-ramified feathers. They have a purplish-brown breast, and their wings are marked with two transverse bars—one purplish-brown and one white. They are poor fliers, living on the ground and taking to the trees or bushes when disturbed. The feathers of the crowned pigeon used to be very much in demand, especially the crest feathers; to preserve the stock, the birds are now protected. The protection regulations do not apply to the Papuans; to them, the crowned pigeon is an excellent supplement to a diet so poor in animal protein. The numbers they shoot are not very great, so that there is no threat to the continuance of the species. De Wilde also brought with him a sketch-map marked with the names of a number of rivers and small streams. True, he himself said that the map was roughly drawn and that the scale was not always correct, but none the less it meant that he had collected geographical data which would be valuable to those who were later to travel in this region.

The weather hindered the operation of the helicopters. Van den Bos had got through to Katem on 4th July, but was unable to reach his actual objective, which was Kloof Camp, and in addition he could not return to the Sibil Valley. It was only on 8th July that Warman succeeded in flying to Katem and Kloof Camp, and Van den Bos also made a flight to the latter. They brought in equipment—tents, among other things—needed for operations in the mountains. The weather remained bad and made it impossible to carry out any more flights to

Katem or Kloof Camp. This was unfortunate, because it meant that Katem did not receive the large supplies of food which lay waiting in Kloof Camp and which De Wilde was expecting to receive at Katem. There were not sufficient reserves available in Katem for a journey of several weeks along the Ok Iwur, following the route which Bär and Reynders had employed. De Wilde therefore decided to go to Kloof Camp on foot with a team of bearers to fetch supplies. It was fortunate for him that the radio link between Mabilabol and Katem was not working very well and that the leaders did not know of his plan, as they would most certainly have objected to it. To reach Kloof Camp they had to pass through the Wambons' territory—a tribe with which Bär and Cortel had certainly not had any trouble—but which had to be approached with care. Bär and Cortel had avoided all villages in the region, but it was precisely to such villages that De Wilde wanted to go, where no white man had ever set foot before him. When the leaders heard that De Wilde had left for Kloof Camp they could not do much more than to hope that the trip would go off without any trouble, and that the hard going would not cause his knee, which he had injured earlier, to bother him; fortunately, however everything went off very smoothly.

On 11th July De Wilde left Katem; on this occasion, a marine and two police-constables accompanied him. On the first day they marched in pouring rain for six and a half hours, camping at Wekotsigobi, where it became frightfully cold in the evening. Next day they continued southwards through the valley of the Ok Wop, which flows over a limestone bed rich in fossils. On the way they visited the villages of Aptalabip, Lumabip and Sagorabip; here the people all live in tree-houses. There was no question of any aggressive behaviour; on the contrary the people were very friendly and freely submitted to being measured. The region was very rich in snakes; two or three were killed every day on the path, but unfortunately the party had nothing with them with which to preserve the bodies. The guide was not familiar with the region beyond Sagorabip and De Wilde therefore decided to trek to the west, because that was the direction of the East Digul and this would enable them to orientate themselves afresh. The last village they passed was Nipki and then, on 14th July, they reached Kloof Camp. Here De Wilde met quite a number of Wambons, who were even willing to allow samples to be taken of their hair. The marine who accompanied him had fallen off a rock into the Ok Wop and had hurt his back. He also had a badly inflamed toe, which made walking difficult for him. One of the police-constables had a badly swollen knee, while the other suffered from a continual fever. It was consequently by no means a luxury that the party enjoyed by resting at the camp for two days. On 17th July they began the return journey with more bearers than the outward trip, as a number of Wambons offered to go with them to Katem. De Wilde returned to Katem in good spirits, with 1000 lb. of food and with measurements and anthropological data from 142 people. On arrival however he was faced with a disappointment; his journey along the Ok Iwur was not to be made. One helicopter had been lost and the other was needed to support the groups in the Sibil Valley and in the valley of the Ok Tsyop. The route to the western part of the Sibil Valley had been reconnoitred and, with the means available, the expedition could do a great deal of useful work if its activities were as far as possible carried out along one line. Moreover, the health of the police detachment in Katem was not good enough to allow constables to be sent off on trips immediately. Superintendent Ooster-man had left, since there was nothing more for him to do there now that Katem was no longer an important base for research teams. The expedition leaders consequently decided to dispense with any further exploration in the vicinity of Katem. De Wilde therefore returned, measuring as he went.

From this time forward Katem served only as an intermediate stop-ping-place for groups that were trekking farther afield. Reynders passed through in the early part of July with fifty bearers who had been engaged at Mindiptana; Anceaux came by as he was returning to the Sibil Valley from the south in August. In September Pouwer trekked back to Mindiptana with the survey group bearers; it was a good opportunity for him to carry out ethnological studies in the Muyu region on his way. At the end of the expedition Menge and Bekker landed in Katem with the helicopter which was on its way back to Tanah Merah, and Corporal Bril went through with the expedition bearers; he took the camp equipment back with him to Mindiptana. This was the end of Katem as an expedition camp.

7

Kiwirok

TO THE NORTH OF THE CENTRAL WATERSHED, SOME FIFTEEN MILES AS THE
crow flies from Mabilabol, lies the Kiwirok Valley, a place to which the
Sibillers sometimes go, while the Kiwirokkers visit the Sibil Valley
from time to time. When the air-strip was made, the Sibillers became
rich people, by earning steel axes. The Kiwirokkers married their
daughters to inhabitants of the Sibil Valley in order to obtain steel axes
for themselves as part of the bride price. This is why some Kiwirok
women were found in the Sibil Valley. It was even claimed that there
was a man with one wife in the Sibil Valley and another in the Kiwirok
Valley; this was clearly quite practical, since it gave him a roof over
his head and food and care in both places. Thus trading relations gave
rise to family links, so increasing the interchange between the two
regions. Dragt, a government official, had already made one journey to
the Kiwirok Valley, and had reported that it was a particularly difficult
trip. Sneep was willing to go; he was very keen on making trips and was
not attracted by sitting round in the government post any longer while
so many others were setting out on their travels. At the beginning of
May he had a unique opportunity to go to the Kiwirok, because the
Sibillers were sending a trading mission to buy tobacco there. If Sneep
were to accompany this party, he would have guides with him and there
were sure to be a couple of Sibillers who would be willing to act as
bearers for an axe or a jungle knife. However he had to obtain the agreement of the expedition leaders, because the Resident of Southern New
Guinea had laid down that the government officials were only to make
trips outside the valley if this was in the interests of the expedition. The
entire contingent of mobile police based on the Sibil Valley had been
attached to the expedition, and the leaders therefore had to agree to
sending three constables with the group. Thus Sneep set out on 3rd May

to the silver house to put his case. This journey could be of service to the expedition by providing a reconnaissance of the route to the Antares Mountains and the Kiwirok Valley, regions which were of special interest to various research workers. But there were also objections. A good number of the police-constables were already out in the field with different groups and it was necessary to maintain sufficient strength at the base camp at all times; in addition, there always had to be several constables available to accompany the crash crew in the unwished for event of a helicopter getting into difficulties. Moreover, Herberts, the second man at the government post, was to be replaced by Dasselaar and it would be a good thing for continuity of government functions that Sneep should be at Mabilabol at that time. The expedition leaders would have preferred to put the journey off for a few weeks until the whole operation had gained more impetus. The whole matter was turned over and discussed. Sneep quite rightly pointed out that it was far from certain whether he would be able to get bearers and guides a week or two later, since the trading party would go whether he went or not; this was quite certain. He pleaded passionately and effectively, and thus obtained the permission he sought.

Next evening (6th May), a long column left the camp. Sneep, three constables, Kotanon the interpreter, and a whole group of Sibillers, even a few women who wanted to visit their families in the Kiwirok Valley, started off in a long line. The expedition members acted as photographers on this occasion; a great many photographs were taken and yards of film as well. Once the entire group had disappeared into the forest, as a farewell the Papuans uttered once again their loud, modulated cry. The Sibillers set a good pace. The route ran over the Orion Mountains and then followed a very steep descent to the Ok Tsyop; the river was crossed by means of a rattan suspension bridge (Plate 31). The first objective was to reach the Antares Mountains by travelling along the Ok Bon in an easterly direction. Sneep had already tried this once earlier, but had been unsuccessful on that occasion because heavy rains had swollen the Ok Bon so much that it was impossible to use its narrow valley as a route. This happened again this time, and it was therefore decided to make a detour to the north-east. The going was heavy; the party had to climb up steep slopes and then descend equally steeply on the farther side. This did not cause the slightest difficulty to the Sibillers, who moved rapidly and untiringly uphill or downhill like chamois, and although Sneep was accustomed to

this, the pace was rather too fast for him; the constables were also in
favour of a slightly slower rate. The trading party went on ahead, but
that evening they were all together again in the camp.

In spite of the great difficulty of the terrain, they crossed the central
watershed on the fourth day out (i.e. on 9th May), and then dropped
down through the valley of the Ok Etwi, a rather large river which they
presumed to belong to the rise catchment of the Sobger. However it is
not impossible that the Ok Etwi may be found to run into the Hoffnung
River, a tributary of the Sepik which flows in Australian New Guinea.
On the steep slopes above the Ok Etwi lies the little village of Atemagabib, where they camped. In this village, which consisted of no more
than six houses, Sneep met the trading mission, occupied in lively
bargaining. The inhabitants resembled the Sibillers quite closely, but
they informed the party that they belonged to the Kiwirok group,
with whom they also maintained very close relations. As is the case
everywhere in the eastern mountainous region, the local inhabitants
were particularly friendly to the "kaga wok", the white man. To prove
that he was real Sneep had to submit to being touched, to having his
arms and legs pinched and his hair stroked. His long, wavy blond
hair caused a long "Ieee" of surprise and admiration. Moreover, the—
in their eyes—tremendous height and robust build of this white man,
who stood far above their heads, was an exceptionally fruitful source
of awe and surprise for these mountain Papuans.

The batatas required for the bearers were bought against payment in
matches or pocket mirrors. The party only stopped one night in
Atemagabib and then continued its journey eastwards. After trekking
through the debris-filled beds of the streams and sliding over the muddy
steep slopes, they came to Kumulsiginabib. Here the party camped for
another night. The track then led along the Tayesigin (7,216 feet) as
far as the village of Tomkadin; this village stands on the mountain ridge
known as Tomka, which runs parallel to the northern Ok Bon. It is
here that one finds the phenomenon—to which we have already referred
—of the two rivers called by the name of Ok Bon; the southernmost
river of the pair rises in the Antares Mountains, and flows to the west,
eventually flowing into the Ok Tsyop, while the northernmost river
runs in a northerly direction and certainly belongs to the rise catchment of the Sepik. The mountain ridge which separates the northern
Ok Bon from the southern Ok Bon is known as Bonsigin; the people
living to the north of this watershed are called "Bonsigi" (and perhaps

also they use the name themselves?). The northern Ok Bon is a foaming brook, easily crossed by means of a crazy bridge constructed of branches and rattan put together by the Sibillers in under half an hour. It takes a certain amount of courage to cross such a bridge, which has a nasty surprise in store for anyone unfortunate enough to fall through it, but if this is the best that is available, then one has to get on with it. The path to Tomkadin led over numerous small landslips and over fallen slippery moss-grown tree-trunks. Again and again the track had to be cleared, a task entrusted to a team of very quarrelsome women, who went ahead, creating a great deal of row. Cold and tired out, soaked to the skin by the pouring rain, the party reached Tomkadin about four o'clock on the 12th May, in a sort of jogtrot, sometimes running down the slope of the Tomka. With great hospitality the inhabitants made a place by the fire in one of the houses for Sneep—a privilege of somewhat doubtful value, since a large number of fleas had also settled in this warm spot.

Next day the party rested. Early in the morning the inhabitants of the village were standing outside the camp. They were for the most part women and children, because a large number of the men had gone on a trading journey to Australian territory.

Tomkadin lies only some six miles from the frontier, but the inhabitants know nothing of the fact that there is a frontier running along the 141st parallel of longitude East. They are not in the slightest worried about it, and this really occasions no difficulties, since the region is not under government control; administrative difficulties will only arise when civilisation penetrates to this area. Their relations with their neighbours to the east appear to be good, because Sneep found in Tomkadin cloth, axes and machetes of Australian origin.

The inhabitants who had remained in the village also seemed quite ready to do trade, and there were many offers of food—principally keladi—in return for which they asked for matches. Sneep also began to exercise that auxiliary function which always falls to government officials in such areas: he bandaged wounds, applied adhesive plaster to minor injuries and gave injections when he found one single case of framboesia. There was quite a demand for bandages and plaster, because they gave a certain air of distinction to the wearers.

Sneep had moreover to hold each of the babies in his arms because the mothers cherished the hope that their children would later grow as big as he.

23. The iwool-keeper at Tulo.

A few of the young girls also tried to attain the same distinction, but they were firmly pushed aside by Sneep. It was a great disappointment that Sneep was not willing to give up one of his blond locks as a decoration. Had it been such an easy matter to persuade him, he would never have achieved such long hair, because all the members of the expedition had already tried at least once to get him to bring the shock of hair hanging around his neck to more normal proportions. This however was always met with considerable objections. According to Sneep his hair was one of his most important assets in making contact with the population, and if it were cut, he feared that a good deal of his reputation would be lost.

As a result of this trip people from Tomkadin later came to visit the Sibil Valley, among them a man with a kamil which was very much slenderer and lighter than those worn in the Sibil Valley (Plate 8).

From Tomkadin the route ran in a northerly direction, towards Bondipmakur, which was reached after a break-neck journey on 14th May. Here the camp was set up in the middle of a ring of some seven houses and, in consequence, the party was the object of continual interest. Once again food was offered in abundance. The principal "currency" desired consisted of matches, because they contribute to making life easier. Small mirrors were also very much in demand, but they were clearly regarded as being more in the nature of luxury articles.

As the first traces of dawn lit up the sky, Sneep was awakened by a noise and movement near the camp. Kotanon, the interpreter, came running up to Sneep with a shout, telling him that some of the inhabitants had arrived with a pig which they were willing to barter. After the usual noisy and quarrelsome haggling, agreement was reached that the price would be a small axe and a machete. The black pig, weighing about 90 lb., was killed by Sneep with a rifle-shot, to the undisguised amazement and excitement of the population, who were seeing the power of firearms for the first time. The creature was quickly cut up and roasted, the meat forming a welcome supplement to the scanty menu of rice and dried fish, enlivened with only a few batatas. It soon became a real festival meal, which the Sibillers also enjoyed.

The journey now continued in a westerly direction towards Kiwirok. Once again they crossed the Ok Etwi, but they now did so farther to the north, and the route then ran to a large extent through the valley of the Ok Yop (a tributary of the Ok Etwi). This time it was not the rain

24. Family from the Sibil Valley.

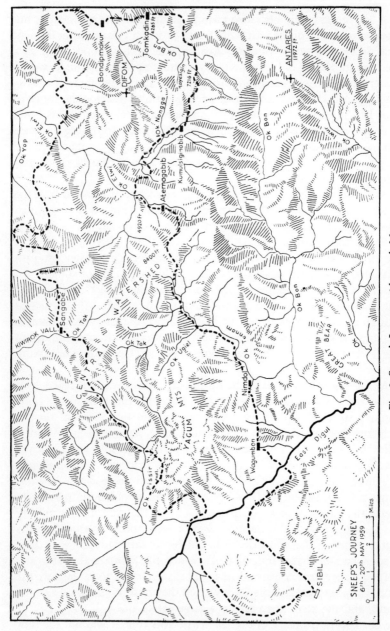

Fig. 8. Sneep's Journey, 6th—20th May.

that made progress difficult, but the blazing sun on the white stones which formed the bed of the Ok Yop, turning the entire valley into an oven. About five o'clock Sneep decided to make camp. That night there was a thunderstorm and rain. The Sibillers, who had as usual built a small protective roof of leaves, rapidly took cover from the torrents of water and climbed in, one on top of another, under the tent. Hardly had silence been restored and everybody had once again fallen asleep, when a tremendous din arose. Shrieking and yelling the Sibillers were pushing each other around in the small, tightly-filled tent. Cursing, Sneep got up very quickly and caught hold of his lantern. In its beam he saw a confused ball of dark bodies, arms and legs, which was obviously trying to get out of the tent, but which had fortunately not yet managed to break the strong tent-cloth. A police-constable was busily occupied trying to disentangle the ball, and to calm the men down. It appeared that one of the Sibillers had been frightened by a flash of lightning and had leapt to the opposite side of the tent, followed by another, who, it is true, did not know what was wrong, but thought it was much better to run away from the unknown danger. Thinking that the two were trying to flee from a bandyir, a third decided to follow them, dragging another couple with him, so that eventually they were all kicking with their bare feet at the tent-cloth, yelling with fear. There was not a great deal more sleep that night. The Sibillers could no longer keep quiet and tried over and over again to reconstruct the incident, with a great deal of laughter, in an attempt to make fun of each other.

It was a badly-rested and irritated government official who pulled his wet kit on next morning before setting off to Sangabe, the southern-most of the villages in the Kiwirok Valley. The inhabitants of Sangabe were not very responsive, and, even on subsequent visits, they earned themselves the name of being unfriendly, although they could certainly not be considered as hostile. This did happen even occasionally in the Sibil Valley, so that there might be here or there a village which would be rather more reserved in manner than elsewhere.

The group did not stay long in the Kiwirok Valley; they moved back towards the Sibil Valley in several forced marches of a day each, reaching their objective on 20th May. While they were still a long way off, their approach was announced by gun-shots and the loud calls made by the bearers, and the entire camp turned out to welcome Sneep back. He arrived just in time to say good-bye to Herberts, who had all the while been unable to leave, because of a fault in the Twin Pioneer.

Thanks to this reconnaissance journey—which, it is true, had not followed a route so close along the Antares Mountains as had been hoped—the expedition leaders now had at their disposal several important pieces of information about the northern mountainous area and about the type of people living there. The people to the north of the watershed speak a language which corresponds with that used in the Sibil Valley, and probably forms a dialect of it (Kiwirok dialect). In Tomkadin the people are bilingual, speaking the Kiwirok dialect and a language which is used in the adjacent Australian territory. It became clear in the next few days that the Sibillers had done good business, when they offered us numerous packets of tobacco (at the price of a steel axe). The leaves of the tobacco are packed together in a bottle-shaped bundle, surrounded by other leaves, and tied together with split rattan.

*   *   *

Bär, who had arrived in Mabilabol on the same day as Sneep, showed a great deal of interest in the route to the Kiwirok Valley. It was of considerable importance for his studies of the structure of the central mountainous region to obtain knowledge of the area to the north of the central watershed. Cortel and Escher were more interested in the Antares region. Part of the route, as far as the beginning of the valley of the Ok Bon, could be travelled by the three geologists together. Maps were examined, aerial photos studied, Sneep's advice was sought and detailed and exhaustive plans drawn up. The first thing was to prepare a series of emergency-landing strips for the helicopters from Mabilabol as far as the Ok Tsyop. The survey headman Wattimena was entrusted with this operation. He set off with a number of Sansapor bearers and a few police-constables, clearly marking the path as he went. The suspension bridge over the Ok Tsyop was repaired and reinforced so that it could also be used by the heavier Europeans. All these plans and preparations were based on the expectation that the helicopters would come up very quickly with supplies to the beginning of the Ok Bon; both Bär (heading for the Kiwirok Valley) and Cortel and Escher (en route to the Antares Mountains) must be assured that they could in an emergency fall back on a well-supplied camp on the lower course of the Ok Bon. But . . . the helicopters did not come, and for the time being they had to attempt to bring food supplies up to the Ok Bon by means of bearers. In addition, the funds of the expedition had to be strengthened. Brongersma was able to inform the inhabitants of the base camp that

25. (1) Women with painted decorations, at the polyclinic.
     (2) Two visitors to Mabilabol.

everything was in order on 6th July, speaking from Hollandia, where he had gone to get in touch with the Foundation back in Holland by telephone.

The first group left on the 8th June—consisting of Bär the geologist, Dasselaar the government official, two police-constables, Wattimena and fifty-three bearers (eighteen Sansapors, ten Muyus and twenty-five Sibillers). Although the number of bearers was high, it became clear that there were still not enough to allow Cortel and Escher to go with the party with all their equipment.

The Sibillers had been told to come early in the morning, and some of them had camped in our godown to avoid having an early morning walk from the village to the base camp. At the last minute all kinds of objects had to be packed into carrying-cases, and the fair distribution of the bearers' loads also occasioned some delay. But once this was over everything was ready and the column set off along the track which had been reconnoitred by Wattimena. At a height of 4,530 ft. above sea-level they reached the ridge of the Uteksigin, the easternmost region of the Orion Mountains. Here they made a short pause. In the depths below them flowed the Ok Tsyop, behind which rose the Yagum Mountains and the Great Bear. One of the bearers, who had scratched himself in the forest, was treated by Dasselaar with iodine to prevent infection, but there was no time for a long rest. There now followed the descent to the Ok Tsyop, a drop of 1,930 feet, which sloped at 25° in the steepest parts. In order to descend as gradually as possible, the group trekked slowly southwards, because the rattan suspension bridge lay in that direction. The camp was set up on the farther side of the river near the bridge. Next day twenty-six bearers went back to Mabilabol to fetch Escher; meanwhile the others cleared a landing-strip for the helicopters. All this activity attracted the attention of the inhabitants of the village of Wagumbon, who came along to take a look; some of the men seemed ready to go farther with the party as bearers. Dasselaar employed the stay to take a census record of the people of Wagumbon. This village contained an albino Papuan, who nervously kept himself hidden in the dark shelter; albinism does not seem to be very common here, and this was the only case which was encountered. Meanwhile Escher arrived on 11th June, bringing some mail with him, to the great joy of Bär and Dasselaar; he spent a day in the camp at Ok Tsyop, while the others trekked on to Nimdol where they cleared a landing-strip and set up camp. This was the thirty-sixth landing-strip

26. Marine Vlaanderen taking finger-prints.

en route from Kawakit to Antares via Mabilabol; the Nimdol camp was therefore known in expedition jargon as Camp 36. On 13th June twenty-nine bearers went back to bring up Escher, accompanied by Cortel, who had left Mabilabol on 12th June. Camp 36 was well situated; there were good supplies of drinking water and one could look as far as the western slopes of the Antares through the valley of the Ok Bon. It was at this camp that it had been decided to establish a store of food, and it was consequently assigned a permanent detachment of police and marines.

Up till now everything had gone well, although the continual travelling to and fro to fetch supplies had caused considerable delay. The helicopter route to Nimdol was finished and the group was now waiting for supplies to be carried up by air, since without them they could not trek any farther. On 14th June they kept an anxious look-out, but no helicopters came, nor did they come on the 15th. The geologists in Nimdol consulted together, and decided that Escher should go forward in the direction of the Antares Mountains with all the supplies that could reasonably be spared, while Bär, Cortel and Dasselaar stayed in Camp 36. A runner was sent to Mabilabol to inform the expedition leaders, and Bär added to this message the statement that the whole operation would have to be regarded as a failure if no supplies had been brought up by the 19th June. Although the weather in Mabilabol was fine and it seemed that the pass to Katem was open, it was clearly bad in Katem itself, from the fact that the helicopters did not come, however much Brongersma and Venema spluttered and shouted. The situation was indeed threatening to become critical and the only solution was to engage more bearers. Sneep told the Sibillers working at the base camp that bearers were needed, but no one came forward. Apparently the private war between Lewengbon and Sagasaga had blazed up again, and it was much more amusing to take part in that than to work. The interpreter Kotanon was therefore sent out to stir up the inhabitants of the surrounding villages—Kukding, Betabib, Tulo and Kigonmedip—to take service as bearers, but all in vain. Even a drastic increase in the wage was ineffective, although this was actually just as well; had we had to pay an axe for a two-days' journey, this would have brought about a serious devaluation.

On 17th June there was a second S.O.S. from Bär. Several of the Sibil bearers who had travelled with Escher and were on the way to Antares had deserted; if there were no supplies brought up that day, the geologists would be forced to start the return journey on the 18th June. Two Sibil ten-year-olds were willing to take to Nimdol a letter describing the situation and asking the party to hold out for a few days if it was at all possible. At ten in the morning the little messengers set off, and reached Nimdol at four in the afternoon; in the space of six hours they had covered a distance for which we had needed two full days with a train of bearers. On 18th June the first difficulty was overcome. First of all six Sibillers turned up and offered their services as bearers. Each of them was given a case containing 40 lb. of food to carry and they were sent out unaccompanied, so that we did not lose any weight by having to carry equipment. In addition the first helicopter at last arrived in the Sibil Valley, flown by Warman, the new chief pilot. The situation was discussed with him at great length and he then started off with Lieutenant Nicolas as his guide in the direction of the Ok Bon, to reconnoitre the route. They flew close up to the Antares Mountains which Escher had already reached, and where he had set up Camp 39. They also visited Bär in Camp 36 and left him two cases of rice. With the supplies brought by the six bearers he had enough to risk the journey to the Kiwirok, and he decided to do so using bearers alone. It would have delayed him too much to have to clear the landing-sites as well.

The stay in Nimdol had been of some use. A storage place for the supplies had been built, and accommodation for the members who remained in the camp was greatly improved. Dasselaar had visited the surrounding villages and had registered the inhabitants as usual. The largest village was Oksitbakon and at the same time the centre of the region, because it possesses an iwool. The inhabitants of other villages, such as Warip and Nimdol, go to Oksitbakon for dance festivals, and even the Sibillers go there to celebrate a festival on occasion. In addition to the iwool there are fourteen ordinary houses, three bogaams (men's houses) and a sugaam (a women's house). In the process of registering the inhabitants, the houses were counted and the occupants of each house noted down. This latter task is not very easy, because it can only be done properly if everyone is at home. During the day the people are working in their gardens, and sometimes there are members of the family who are travelling. There are also many difficulties which frequently arise in the recording of names, because no one willingly pronounces his own name. Warip has four houses, one bogaam and two sugaams. Nimdol consists of two parts, which are about twenty minutes' walk apart; between them the two districts of

Nimdol have seven houses, two bogaams and two sugaams. The ordinary houses are family houses, but a man who has two wives will frequently own two houses. Thus Sinonbirim was married to Ayutkonyimennip and to Ayutbirinip. The husband lived with the first wife and two children—Kitborip, a girl, and Aioknèdip, a boy—in one house, while the second wife lived in another house with her two boys—Tararweng and Ngibitweng. Kayangabee even had three wives: Bitbit, Tigagut and Oksengkon; Tigagut lived separately with her two children, while the other two wives—with two children and one child respectively— lived with the husband. Sometimes two families live in the same house; Pèban and his wife Kukyip with their two boys Bèbiki and Kotipki live together with Kuksaweng and his wife Yakonnip, and their son Diban. Sometimes the married couple live with the parents of one partner; in Oksitbakon, Kottir and his wife Pirinum live with his parents and their three younger children. If unmarried men do not wish to live with their parents or families they can enter a bogaam. Marital strife is not lacking; Kariput lives with her little son Kagoggi in Oksitbakon, while her husband had left and settled in another village as the result of an argument. One remarkable thing is that some of the children were named after neighbouring rivers: Ok Tsyop (a boy), Ok Tennam (a boy) and Ok Bon (a girl).

At half past eight on the morning of 19th June, Bär and Dasselaar left Nimdol on their trek to Kiwirok. They passed through the villages of Oksitbakon and Pasekulo, and then climbed gradually upwards along the mountain ridge known as Iyik. While they were resting for a short while at about ten o'clock, they looked back over the valley of the Ok Bon to see the helicopter—a small, glittering insect far below them, creeping along the dark-green face of the mountain, and disappearing now and then behind a low-lying wisp of cloud. A certain amount of excitement arose among the Sibillers, they dropped their loads, while some of them started to go back along the path they had just followed. Dasselaar called the agitated group to order.

"Where d'you think you're off to?"

The ringleader of the team began excitedly to give chapter and verse for their action. Now that the helicopters were coming up again it was clearly no longer necessary for them to carry all the supplies to the Kiwirok. Instead, they could leave everything here, and the helicopters would bring it on from here. They were going to run down to pass the message on to the pilot!

It took all Dasselaar's powers of persuasion to make them change their minds. Somewhat disappointed, they set off laboriously a little later.

After a gentle descent the track now rose again, taking them over a spur of the Indum at 7,710 feet. It was time to set up camp, but at this height there was no suitable place to do so on the southern slopes of the mountain. One of the first requirements for a camp site is that there must be water in the vicinity, but they had already entered a limestone area at 5,910 feet and there were no more streams. There was no point in going back, so they continued over the ridge, and here they found that luck was with them. On the northern side of the mountain the base of the limestone lies at 6,560 ft., and they only had to drop down barely 400 yards to reach a small stream, by the side of which they could set up camp. They had been marching for nine hours covering in that time a distance of nearly six miles, which is not bad going in the mountains.

On the second day (20th June) they did not progress so quickly; they took 7¾ hours to cover 3·1 miles—a little over 700 yards per hour—but the terrain was much more difficult. First they dropped down into the valley of the Ok Ugiel, and then crossed a mountain ridge heading towards the southern Ok Tak. The bed of this Ok Tak consists of noticeably soft sandy shale, so that walking was much more pleasant. The group followed the river until their progress was barred by a waterfall, 200 feet in height; here they started to climb towards the Taksigin, the central watershed (8,265 ft.). When Dasselaar reached the highest point, a few bearers were sitting astride the sharp ridge, with one leg in the valley of the southward-flowing Ok Tak and the other leg in the valley of the other Ok Tak which flows to the north. Just before the watershed was reached, several Kiwirokkers had joined the company and they advised Dasselaar to take off his shoes before beginning the steep descent ahead of them, precisely as Dragt had done on his trip. Bär was not very keen on this, and rightly so, since one needs to have thick callouses on the soles of one's feet to be able to walk barefoot over the sharp rocks. The first part of the descent was accomplished quickly because there were still dense undergrowth, together with a few stout trees which provided a firm hold, but this was followed by a stretch where there was very little vegetation and sloping at an angle of 50°. They made as much use as possible of the shrub-covered areas, and, where there was no vegetation they relied on ledges and irregularities in the surface of the rock. Fortunately there was only a short way to go over the patches without vegetation, and they soon reached a zone where there were sparse shrubs. At a height of 7,420 ft. they again came upon a path made by the local inhabitants, and finally set up a camp at 7,350 ft.

Thus the journey continued during the next few days over hill and dale. They principally followed the river-beds, because it was here that the rocks were laid bare, so that Bär was able to make his observations and collect rock samples. In Sangabe, the first Kiwirok village, which they came to on the third day, the population was not particularly responsive, as Sneep had already discovered. The camp did not attract many visitors; only a few men hung around all afternoon asking for tong (matches). Unfortunately they were not willing to provide batatas for the bearers in return. The Sibillers, to whom batatas were the favourite food, missed them very much indeed; true, they were able to eat rice, but they always found it an unfamiliar item of diet.

According to them, earlier patrols had never gone farther than this, and they thought it was time to be heading for home again. They also had another objection to this journey. The paths made by the local inhabitants generally lie along the mountain ridges, so that walking is easy, but Bär picked out precisely the river-beds, where they had to wade through the water and walk on boulders, or climb over large rocks. To the Sibillers this was no way to travel at all. That evening they talked it over with Dasselaar. "If the tuan dalogi (Big Master, i.e. Bär) wants to trudge through the river any farther, let him go ahead and do it with his kaga soronkis,* but at least let Dasselaar have some comprehension and return home with the Sibillers, there's no point in labouring on like this any farther." Dasselaar had to reason with the Sibillers for hours to bring them round to continuing in spite of what they had said; he reminded them that they would receive a steel axe provided that they accompanied the group on the whole journey. Next day the game started all over again, but soon after this they reached the village of Pelipbon, where the population was a little more friendly. The Sibillers were regaled with batatas and pisangs; this noticeably raised their morale and they decided to trek farther with the party.

* Kaga soronki = Sorong man, is the name given by the Sibillers to anyone working for the Netherlands New Guinea Petroleum Company, which is based at Sorong. In this case they meant the Sansapor bearers who had accompanied Bär.

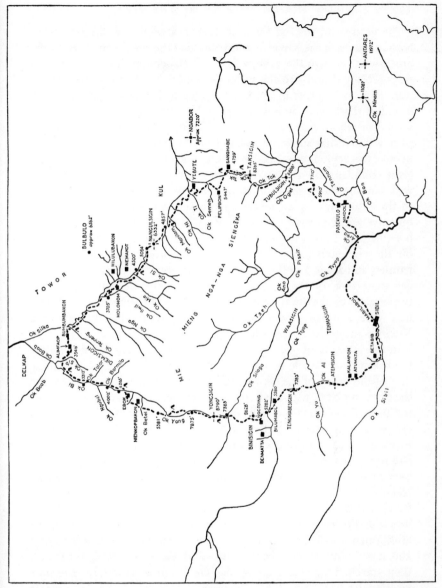

Fig. 9.
Bär and
Dasselaar's
route to
the Kiwirok and the
Ok Bi.

The group had trekked for four days in a northerly direction from Nimdol to reach the Kiwirok, and from here the route continued to the north-west through the valley of the Ok Nangul and over a mountain ridge—Nangulsigin—to the valley of the Ok Tahin. Here the Sibillers were ill at ease again; in the Kiwirok they had in fact been filled with fear, but there were at least people who could speak their language, several of whom had been in the Sibil Valley. Now they were in completely unfamiliar surroundings and no one yet knew by what sort of people the region was inhabited. On the other hand they did have great confidence in Dasselaar and this decided them to give way notwithstanding. Everything turned out very well, because the population of the Tahin was by no means aggressive; at the most they were inquisitive and curious to know what these foreigners had come to do here. Bär and Dasselaar were followed by dozens of Tahinners throughout the whole trek to the valley. They passed through several villages and hamlets and made a point of counting the houses everywhere, so as to get some idea of the number of inhabitants—information of great importance to the local government officials. In general, the villages here gave a much greater impression of poverty than those in the Kiwirok and those in the Sibil Valley.

In the interests of geological investigation the party did not follow the beaten tracks made by the local people, but followed a route along part of the valley of the Ok Mi; this is a river which has cut deep into the earth in places, with the result that there was a good deal of clambering to be done along the walls of the narrow valley. This was also the case when they returned to the valley of the Ok Tahin; the narrow ravine in which the stream runs could not always be followed and each man had to find his own way close to the sheer, terrifying rock cliffs. There seemed to be hardly anybody living in this area. On 27th June they reached the Ok Bi, deducing from the direction in which this river flows that it is one of the sources of the Sobger—a conclusion which was found to be mistaken when the break-through was made from the Sibil Valley to Hollandia. They had now been travelling for nine days and it was time to turn back to the Sibil Valley. On the return route they travelled upstream along the Ok Bi in a southerly direction, clearing landing-strips for helicopters at intervals along the route, in the hope that supply air-drops could be made to support the break-through to Hollandia. In the Bi Valley the Sibillers began to feel more at home again. They met old acquaintances and there was a great deal

27. (1) Party crossing the Ok Sibil, Vervoort on the extreme right.
(2) Column of bearers returning to Mabilabol.

of gossiping in which the Sibillers had a lot to say, by reason of their great experience in travelling. On 1st July they crossed the Yongsigin (8,790 ft.) which forms the central watershed at this point, and camped on the southern slopes at a height of 7,775 ft. It was a particularly chilly night, and the tent gave only moderate protection against the cold; at such heights it is really necessary to have a tent which can be tightly closed. The daily chore of putting on wet shoes and socks (they had to pass through water somewhere every day) was an exceptionally unpleasant job here. They had to cross another three mountain ridges: the Binisigin (8,626 ft.), the Tenumabesigin (7,383 ft.) and the Atemsigin (7,085 ft.), after which the group again reached the Sibil Valley, very satisfied with the results of their journey, on 4th July. The Sibillers returned home delighted with the axes which they had earned. Bär had collected a great deal of information which would give him a better idea of the structure of the mountains. In his report, Dasselaar was able to record a great many details about the density of population in the regions visited, and he could also be proud of the fact that the confidence the Sibillers had in him made them willing to follow him anywhere.

There was only one thing that was not solved, and that was the meaning of the name Kiwirok; most valleys are distinguished by the name of the river which flows through them, but there is no river named Kiwirok. It is also remarkable that the Sibil language is spoken in so large an area of the mountain district, even though there are a number of dialects.

Between Bär and Dasselaar there had grown up a friendship which promised very well for the major trip which they were to undertake together at the end of the expedition: the break-through to Hollandia.

28. The influence of civilisation; a ballpoint pen as a nose decoration.

8

Antares

THE MILITARY EXPEDITION WHICH IN 1912 CARRIED OUT SURVEYS FROM the hill country along the East Digul and the Kaoh, in order to fix the position of the summits in the central mountain region, gave the name of Scorpion Mountains to a range in what is now the Territory of New Guinea (at that time still German New Guinea); this range extends westwards into Netherlands territory and the expedition saw, at the western extremity of the range, a high peak (estimated to be 13,682 ft. in height), and named it Antares, after the brightest star in the constellation of Scorpio. This Mount Antares, which is in point of fact itself a mountain range with major and minor peaks, was one of the most important objectives for scientific research to be carried out by our expedition. The original plan, which envisaged reaching Antares by trekking up from the south along the Ok Iwur, had been dropped now that it was impossible to supply Katem quickly enough. Consequently, the route to be followed started from the west and ran through the valley of the Ok Bon. Two reconnaissances carried out by Sneep in this direction did not get as far as Antares, because the Ok Bon had been too heavily swollen as a result of the heavy rainfall. In Mabilabol the geologists, who were to prepare the route for other research workers, studied the aerial photographs and came to the conclusion that the Antares Mountains could be climbed from the west, and that it was even possible to mark out pretty accurately the route to be followed.

To support this operation (and also the trek to Kiwirok made by Bär and Dasselaar) Camp 36 was constructed near Nimdol, to serve as a half-way house, provided with a reserve food store on which the field teams could fall back if anything should go wrong farther along the route. On 14th June Bär, Cortel, Escher and Dasselaar waited in vain in this camp for the helicopters which should have brought supplies. They held a council of war and discussed the situation very fully. There was no point in the four of them continuing to wait at Nimdol and they therefore decided that Escher should trek on in the direction of Antares. He was given all the supplies which could in any way be spared and, in addition, Bär lent him a number of bearers for several days. On 15th June Escher left Nimdol with a police guard and bearers. Moving north from the Ok Bon he trekked in an easterly direction, clearing a helicopter landing-strip every mile or so along the route. One day later he had reached the foot of the Antares Mountains but with fewer bearers

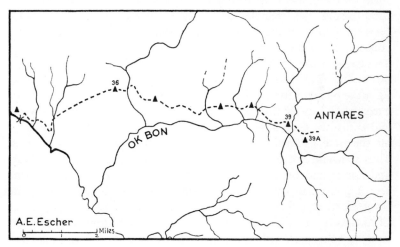

Fig. 10. The Antares route.
▲ Helicopter landing-places. The numbers indicate the camps.

than he had set out with. A number of Sibillers had had enough of this trip and quietly slipped off at night, to the sorrow of the remaining bearers, who had an extra four or five pounds apiece to carry.

The western outlier of the Antares Mountains is bounded by the Ok Bon and the Ok Minam. Close to the confluence of the two rivers, Camp 39 was set up, on the Ok Bon. There was not a great deal of level ground in this valley, and in consequence the huts for the research workers and the police were constructed on one bank and a camp for the bearers on the other. Small tree-trunks were used to make a primitive bridge which linked the two encampments. This bridge had to be repaired twice after sections had been swept away when the river rose rapidly as a result of a heavy fall of rain.

Up till now Operation Antares had gone smoothly, but as with all the other enterprises in the expedition, the group were waiting for the helicopters to bring up supplies. In this instance they really were needed, if sufficient stores and equipment were to be available in Camp 39 within a short time. The team of biologists was expected to follow directly after the geologists, and the former required a great deal of heavy equipment for the preservation of plant and animal specimens. If the supplies were to be brought in by bearers, it would require a great many of them, and even if they became available the consumption of food would rise tremendously. Bearers could cover the distance between Mabilabol and Antares and back in five days, but they would consume in food one-third of the total weight carried during the trip. To carry one ton of food to Camp 39 we would have had to send 84 bearers up from Mabilabol with a total load of one and a half tons. After the outward and return journey the bearers would have to rest for a day; all this meant that they could in fact make one such trip per week, and at that the team of bearers would have to maintain its full strength all the time—something which all too rarely happened in practice. Thus it would not be possible to bring in supplies by bearers alone, and Escher understood this very well. When he reached Camp 39 he sent a policeman back with the bearers lent him by Bär, taking the occasion to give them a letter to the expedition leaders: "The ascent of Antares is virtually only possible if supplies are brought up in good time by helicopter, with tents, warm clothes for the bearers, etc. I can only wait here until 25th June at the latest; if no helicopter has turned up by then, I shall be forced to return, leaving some of the equipment behind."

Fortunately it did not come to this; Escher's note reached Mabilabol by the helicopter which Warman flew to Camps 36 and 39 for a reconnaissance on 18th June. The helicopter support had arrived in the nick of time. It was not possible to fly every day; low-lying banks of cloud frequently hindered flights over the Orion Mountains or in the valley of the Ok Bon. From ground level in the Sibil Valley it was impossible to tell what the weather was like farther up in the mountains and Warman would take off every now and then, climbing to a sufficient height to obtain a view over the region behind the Orion Mountains. Sometimes he had to return without doing any good, and on other occasions he was able to fly through. He threw himself into the supply

29. Man from Tabiem (West Sibil Valley); a plastic drinking-straw serves as an extra nose decoration.

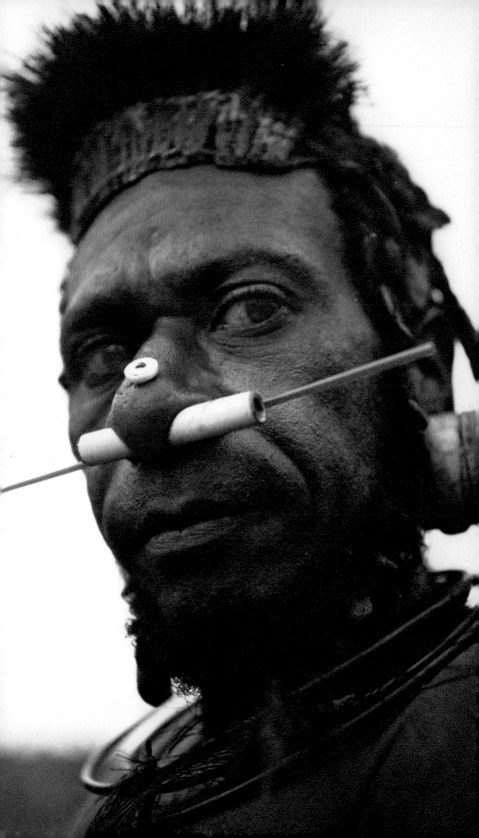

operation very energetically, making seven flights on 19th June, one on the 22nd and another seven on the 24th. In all he brought up two and a half tons of equipment to the two camps; the loads included pieces of equipment too heavy to be carried by the bearers and instruments requiring to be handled with great care. For the moment there were now enough reserves at the foot of the Antares Range to enable the teams to hold out for a while.

Meanwhile Escher had not been idle; having reached Camp 39 on the 16th June, he carried out a reconnaissance on the 17th to the western crest of Antares. At Nimdol people were not only looking westward, hoping to see the long-awaited helicopter, but they also gazed with excitement in an easterly direction through the valley of the Ok Bon towards Antares itself. On 17th June there arose suddenly on the western ridge a column of smoke; Escher had begun his climb and this was his way of signalling the fact. Unfortunately, his exploratory climb up to a height of 8,200 ft. had disappointing results: there was no water on the western ridge and this would present a considerable problem to a party of men intending to camp there. A few days later he made another reconnaissance by helicopter to see if there were another, better route, but this did not seem to be the case. They would therefore have to travel along the western ridge and carry water with them.

Now that supplies had begun to flow smoothly along the Ok Bon, Escher's peaceful life as the only inhabitant of Camp 39 was quickly disturbed. Soon a number of expedition members were trekking towards Antares: Verstappen and Nicolas, who were to try out the climb with Escher, the biological group (Vervoort, Kalkman, Van Zanten, Van Heijningen and Staats), a Survey team (Van der Weiden, De Jong, Gevelhof and Snackey), Van Sprang the radio commentator and Klaarenbeek the journalist. The exodus began on the 23rd June as Van der Weiden and his collaborators left Mabilabol together with Marine J. G. C. Hendriks and fifty bearers. For three days the weather had been unsuitable for flying and Verstappen and Nicolas, having already lost three days, did not want to risk an even longer stay in Mabilabol; consequently they set off with Van der Weiden's column. However, a long line of heavily-loaded bearers does not move very quickly and thus on the first day they did not even reach the Ok Tsyop. Verstappen and Nicolas, with a number of bearers, reached the crest of the Uteksigin about the end of the afternoon. They could see nothing of the beautiful panorama which Bär and Cortel had so much enjoyed. Everything was

30. (1) *Mearnsia* sp. in bloom (Antares, about 7,500 ft.).
(2) Pitcher plant (*Nepenthes* sp.) Mabilabol.

veiled in thick mist and it was useless for them to think of dropping down into the valley of the Ok Tsyop that day; darkness would have overtaken them, making the descent exceedingly dangerous. They camped on the ridge; here there was a small pool of muddy water, which was just enough to cook the rice. Van der Weiden camped lower down the slope with the rest of the bearers. A couple of the bearers from the first group had to be sent back to him because they were carrying the camping gear of those who had stayed behind. The expedition leaders were keeping a close watch on the requirements of the column, since the weather cleared up on the day following their departure and Warman was able to make a number of flights to Antares. He had to grin when he saw the men labouring over the heavy ground below him. Verstappen and Nicolas were now obliged to trek for days, whereas if they had only waited another day, they could have reached Camp 39 within an hour. They had also thought of this, and were quietly waiting at Nimdol on 26th June for the helicopter to catch them up and carry them to Antares. They very much enjoyed the short flight from Camp 36 to Camp 39. Between the dark-green valley walls the Ok Bon wound its way like a silver ribbon. There was not a great deal of water in the river, but where it rushed rapidly over the great boulders and between the huge blocks of rock, the white foam stood out clearly. Every now and then the stream broke into two branches which washed the banks of small green islands. On the valley slopes there were scattered a few Papuan villages; the oval roofs of the houses looked exactly like the shells of great sea-turtles. The gardens, hedged against the incursions of the pigs, showed up as cleared patches in the dense forest. They could also clearly see the emergency air-strips for the helicopters, with the built-up landing platforms. Directly in front of them the Antares massif towered high in the air, and they were able to see the steepness of the slopes which they would have to climb, the narrowness of the ridges that they would need to follow and the denseness of the vegetation. Everything was supremely beautiful, but it was also somewhat frightening when they considered that they would have to labour over that terrain with a small group of bearers.

There was quite a company waiting to welcome them, consisting of people who had left Mabilabol after them, but Escher immediately claimed their complete attention. The aerial photographs were brought out again and Escher described the results of his reconnaissance trips. The only practicable method was to make the climb from Camp 39 up to the western ridge, which would then have to be followed over its full length of more than seven miles to the summit. Supplies were made ready and packed into the aluminium carrying-cases. Twenty bearers were to take the three climbers as far as possible on the first day, after which fourteen of them were to return to Camp 39; the other six bearers would, however, accompany the climbers on the rest of the journey; these bearers were Muyus, who had been provided for the occasion with warm track suits and extra blankets, as it would be cold on the mountain. The equipment and the supplies of food which would have to be carried amounted, all in all, to more than six full loads; the bearers would therefore have to run a shuttle service, i.e. they would have to cover each leg of the journey two or three times to fetch all the gear up to the next camp. To use more bearers would have increased the food consumption yet further, and would thus have swollen the total weight to be transported; the gain would therefore have been slight. Moreover, Antares was covered with thick vegetation almost up to the highest summit, and the path would therefore have to be cleared; while one team was busy with this, the other could be travelling to and fro carrying up the barang. There were no villagers' tracks on Antares, and it was not possible to engage any of the inhabitants of the Ok Bon valley as bearers. To them the mountain was alut (taboo); the spirits of their departed ancestors live there and it is a place which is better avoided.

On 27th June the great day dawned. The climbers and bearers left Camp 39, accompanied for a while by some of the other research workers. The party carried eight days' supply of food including among other things Verkade emergency rations, which have a high nutritive value in relation to their weight. If everything went well, they expected to be back on 4th July.

Camp 39 was 4,265 ft. above sea-level, and they therefore had to climb from this point onwards. The first stretch was steep and the bearers could make only slow progress. They climbed up to 5,250 ft. and then dropped down about 300 feet to a cwm (basin) on the mountain, the bottom of which was covered with grass over an area of several acres; in one corner of this flat bottom lay a small pool, at which they filled two jerry cans with water to carry with them. The observers left the climbing party at this point. Van Sprang, who was not going any farther, gave the climbing party a ciné camera with which to record the most important events of their trip; he himself filmed the group as they trekked away over the grassy lawn and disappeared into the jungle on the far side of the cwm. That day the climbing party reached 5,580 ft., at which height they camped; fourteen of the bearers deposited their loads and happily set off downhill on the return journey. The three Europeans and the six Muyus were now left to their own devices.

Next day, the nine men trekked through the forest—a forest in which everything was covered with a thick layer of moss and which was filled with mist. This moss or mist forest made a deep impression on each member of the party. There were thick cushions of moss on the ground and on the trunks and branches of the trees. Fallen trees lay in disorder, sheeted in moss. Sometimes this thick green carpet grew on firm ground, but at other times covered deep holes. Creepers trailed downwards from the trees, and ferns and orchids had established themselves in the cushions of moss on the ground or on the branches of the trees. The rays of the sun rarely penetrate this far; the sunlight is generally diffused by the clinging mist. Once only did they hear the call of a bird, but apart from this the forest was silent; there was a silence broken only by the tinkle of the drops of water falling from the saturated moss cushions, or by the dull rumble of a tree, tired of life, falling to its last resting-place. The air was full of moisture and the smell of rotten wood. It was a fairy-tale forest, which led you to expect (as several expedition members said) that you might meet a goblin at any moment. This enchanted forest certainly made an impression on each of those who entered it but their appreciation of the atmosphere varied according to the length of time they had to spend in it. Anyone remaining in this forest for no more than a day, at the end of which he could go out again into the sun, would see nothing but the mysterious fairy-tale atmosphere, but those who had to march through it for days on end had rather a lower opinion of it. For them the chilly, moist moss forest became a depressing place and it was not surprising that the team of climbers would find no better comparison than that of a mildewy cellar. Every step had to be taken with great care, since the surface of the moss gave no indication as to whether it covered firm ground or was stretched a yard or more above the soil. Every now and then somebody would sink into the moss—sometimes six inches or so, but sometimes waist-deep. This was not the sort of terrain to be traversed alone, because a man could fall through the moss so quickly, even to a depth of several yards, where it was virtually impossible to get out again without help.

The climbing team advanced slowly—more slowly than had been expected. Clearing the path took a great deal of time. There was a good deal of climbing bamboo growing here, a plant with very elastic stems. These climbing bamboo plants cannot be cleared away by a strong blow, because this makes the stem bend and spring back. Each stem had to be held with one hand to enable one to cut it through. In places where climbing bamboo was found, progress was not more than two or three hundred yards an hour; elsewhere the undergrowth was still so dense that the party could not advance more than four or five hundred yards in an hour, clearing as they went. The progress per day was so slight that there was no point in shifting camp every day. For each camp they required one whole day to clear the track half-way to the place where the next camp was to be set up, so that they had to return to spend the night at the existing camp. Next day they cleared the remainder of the track and the bearers could then begin their shuttle service.

Another big problem was that of water supplies. If it rained over-night, then water running from the tent-cloths could be caught in empty carrying-cases; sometimes as much as four and a half gallons of water were obtained in this way. If it did not rain, it became much more diffi-cult, especially higher up the ridge. It was a risky matter to go farther without reserves of water; it was no good counting that it would rain the following night. This left them no alternative but to wring out the cushions of moss. True, the moss did contain a great deal of water, but it took hours and hours before they had managed to collect as much as two gallons. While two of the climbers were clearing the path and the bearers were trekking to and fro with their loads, bringing them up in stages to the next camp, the third climber was busy wringing out the tufts of moss. On those days the menu contained the item "Riz à la Forêt", rice cooked in brown, peaty water, with some tinned fish or corned beef as an entremet. "Nothing to write home about," was the climbers' judgment; the bearers laughed at this brown rice tasting of humus, but in Verstappen's mind it aroused visions of roast chicken.

After the first camp at 5,580 ft. other camps were set up succes-sively at 7,800 ft., 8,300 ft., and 9,415 ft. It was now that they en-countered a disagreeable surprise. The ridge, which initially ran west-east now turned towards the south-east, and the path was blocked by a steep cliff of moss-grown granite. This did not present any problem to experienced mountaineers, and Escher nimbly clambered up it, but there was no shadow of possibility that the heavily-laden bearers could climb up it. They therefore had to find a way round the obstacle. This was not easy, since the vegetation blocked the view and the cliff was invisible on the aerial photographs by reason of the thick forest around it. The only thing left for them was therefore to keep on clearing until they found a path. Eventually they found a likely route round the steep cliff, by a very steep track which they cleared along the south-western side. It had taken them hours to open this difficult route.

The Muyus behaved very well indeed. They did not belong to this district and therefore knew nothing of the spirits which inhabit the area, according to the Ok Bonners, but their objections to this journey into the mountains were of a very different nature. The high mountains and the steep rock faces filled them with fright; they were afraid that the mountains and rocks would fall and crush them. Again and again they had to be told that the mountain consisted of hard rock, and have the fact demonstrated to them to prove that it really could not fall down.

Where the underlying rock pushed out through the undergrowth, it was studied closely by Escher and Verstappen. The Antares Range consists principally of crystalline rocks. In ages long past the uppermost layers of the earth's crust were penetrated by a mass of molten magma, which crystallised out to form granodiorite. The high temperature of the magma produced very marked changes in the surrounding rock; for instance, limestone was transformed into marble by this process. The upper surface of the surrounding rock became completely weathered away, so that the granite and granodiorite rocks of the mountain core became exposed. Traces of the encasing rock are sometimes found on the slopes of the Antares Mountains, and among other rocks, these remains contain marble. The crystalline core contains a great deal of magnetite (magnetic iron ore), a fact which has to be allowed for when steering by compass, because the needle is strongly deflected by the mineral. Where the core crops out at the surface, it is also subjected to weathering, and the fine debris so produced is carried down by the rivers; the magnetite which Escher and Verstappen had found in such large quantities—in the Ok Iwur near Katem, farther south in the East Digul and in the Ok Bon—had originated in this core.

At a height of 9,510 ft. the dense forest died out. Here the party began to enter a region overgrown with shrubs, the twigs of which were so closely entwined that they formed a stout hedge which was certainly no easier to clear than the earlier undergrowth. An occasional tree grew between the shrubs, spreading its branches like a candelabra. Camp was set up in the midst of this shrub vegetation at a height of 10,170 ft. On the 4th July the party came out into an open area of grass at a height of 10,500 ft.; from here a small, steep ravine led to the western summit of Antares. On the day when the climbing party was expected back at Camp 39, the men were climbing this western summit. They pulled out their pocket altimeters and obtained a reading for the height of this summit of 11,087 ft. In accordance with an old mountaineering tradition, the climbers left behind them a token to inform subsequent climbers that Escher, Verstappen and Nicolas had reached this summit. They wrote their names on a sheet of paper which was then sealed in a plastic bottle; Lt. Nicolas added the Marine Corps badge, as a sign that a member of this corps had been one of the party.

The group trekked a little farther, and then the three climbers set up a small camp at 10,825 ft., in a depression in the ridge which links the western to the eastern summit. The bearers were sent back to the previous camp at 10,170 ft., where they would be less exposed to the bitter night cold at these heights. There were no trees at 10,825 ft., so that they had no branches over which to stretch their tent-cloths; instead they used the climbing ropes which they carried with them. The evening was very cold and the three men sat close together while they discussed their plans for the following day. The food supplies were almost exhausted. The little rice that remained was intended for the bearers, who were now being issued with plain rice and tea for their meals. The Europeans were eating emergency rations, a bar of chocolate and a tin of sweetened milk. They could spend one more day, but certainly not more, on the ascent to the higher eastern summit of Antares. If they were not able to achieve this on 5th July, they would have to abandon the attempt, since they barely had enough food for the return journey despite strict rationing. This last stretch of the journey was the most difficult, and they would have to climb the summit and return to the 10,825 ft. camp in one day. They decided that Escher and Verstappen, who were both experienced mountaineers, should make the attempt to reach the eastern summit via the narrow, steep ridge; Nicolas was to remain in the camp and keep a look-out. It was a decision which testified to a good team spirit, although it cannot have been a very easy matter for Nicolas to give up the chance of climbing the summit himself. But he left this last leg of the journey—which had to be covered quickly and called for mountaineering skill—to his friends, and proceeded to cover their return.

So on 5th July Escher and Verstappen set out along the ridge in an easterly direction, and they were very much relieved to reach the plantless, rocky area around the summit. Up to this point it had been tough going, but there had been no real mountaineering. Now their progress began to resemble to some extent the Alpine climbs which they had practised in Europe. There was no view, since the ridge and the summit were both covered by clouds. There were several small peaks along the ridge, and every now and then another higher point loomed up in front of them. If the weather had turned any worse, they would have had to turn back immediately; in any case they had to be back with Nicolas before dark, and night falls very quickly in the tropics. A couple of steep ravines which broke the ridge gave them a chance to exercise their climbing skill. At 2 p.m. they stood on the highest summit of the Antares, and pulled out their altimeters; the reading showed a height of 11,972 ft., that is, 1,710 ft. lower than the estimate made from the lowlands in 1912. Escher and Verstappen were not surprised by this, because before starting they had seen from the aerial photographs that the vegetation was continuous almost to the summit and that only a small section of bare rock stood out above it. If Antares had really been more than 13,120 ft. high, the bare region at the summit would have been much larger. They now literally and figuratively had their heads in the clouds, having succeeded in their attempt. For a moment longer they were assailed by a doubt as to whether they really were at the highest point, but then the clouds broke away for a short while and they were reassured: there was no higher point. They rested for a moment and took a few photographs, and then started to return at a good rate through mist and driving rain. They left behind a machete on the eastern summit as a token of their success.

Nicolas had been unable to watch the climbers during the ascent by reason of the dense mist. Would they succeed or would they come back without having achieved their aim—or would he have to go back alone next day? It is not very pleasant to be faced with such reflections sitting in a cold and wet tent without decent food, without cigarettes and without any means of passing the time. At 5.30 p.m. he heard the voices of Escher and Verstappen as they reached the camp; they had got to the top! Nicolas drew a deep breath of relief.

After a very cold night in which nobody got a wink of sleep, they began the return journey on 6th July. This time their progress was appreciably faster, as they were going downhill and the path was already cleared.

The biologists had occupied a new camp (Camp 39a) together with the Survey Department men near the meadow at 4,920 ft., and here too everyone was waiting anxiously for news of the climbing team. Excitement was just as great in Mabilabol, when it was learned that the climbers had not returned on 4th July, the day when they were expected. It was always possible that there had been a delay and that the food supplies were running out; it would have been a thousand pities if the group had had to return from a point so near their goal because of the shortage of food. Nobody believed that there had been an accident, because in such an event a couple of bearers would undoubtedly have come back with the message. Notwithstanding this, it was wiser to be ready for all eventualities. Surgeon-Lt. Tissing, a good walker with exceptional powers of endurance, went up to Camp 39 by helicopter and climbed from there to Camp 39a. He left on 7th July with a number of bearers, but he did not have to go very far. At 5,580 ft. he encountered the climbing team and they all went back together to Camp 39a, where the climbers were joyfully received and treated to a very special meal. You will understand that this was exceptionally welcome to the climbers and their bearers after days of stringent rationing. A runner was sent down to Camp 39 with a report which was passed on by radio-telephone to Mabilabol. As almost always when there was an exciting piece of news, wireless communication was bad. The only thing that they understood in Mabilabol was that the party had returned safely and that they had reached a height of 11,972 ft.; whether or not that was the summit was not clear from the message. Next day (8th July) Verstappen was brought back by helicopter to Mabilabol where he made a preliminary report. After this the news could be released to the world outside: the topmost summit of the Star Mountains had been climbed. Apart from this excellent athletic achievement, important information had been collected regarding the structure of the Antares Mountains; there were large quantities of magnetic iron ore but certainly no radioactive elements.

Once Escher, Bär and Dasselaar had left Nimdol, Cortel stayed on there with six Sansapor bearers to occupy Camp 36; he remained there until Marine J. G. C. Hendriks arrived with Van der Weiden's group and took over the guarding of the depot. Then Cortel too set off with his bearers along the Ok Bon towards Antares.

He had begun his investigations near Nimdol, to determine whether there were ores in this region. This was no dry job, because, as was the case with Bär, it was best for him to work in the river-beds where the rocks were laid bare. So Cortel had to wade through the water a great deal, and, as if that were not enough to make him wet, the rain soon did the rest. He examined the rocks along the river, knocking a piece off here and there—because a freshly-broken surface gives the clearest picture of the structure. With the aid of a magnifying glass he studied the samples to determine what minerals were present in the rocks. Later, back in Holland, thin sections were cut from these samples and ground so thin that they were translucent and easily examined under a microscope. At the same time, a chemical analysis was made, if necessary; some chemical treatment was already carried out in the field, since they had carried a small case of reagents with them. In addition to the solid rock, Cortel also devoted some attention to the boulders in the bed of the river. The current had swept these stones along over great distances and they thus revealed the deposits which occurred higher up the mountains. The river had also dragged along finer material—gravel and sand—which had sunk to the bottom. Cortel collected samples of this deposit, and washed them out with a small quantity of water in a flat washing-pan (actually, more of a flat dish), by moving the pan so that the water flowed gently in a circular pattern. In this process the water carried the lighter material along and he would very skilfully let a dash of this water drop over the edge of the pan together with some light particles. From time to time he would add a little more water and repeat the process until only the heavier particles remained behind. He would then pick out the coarse gravel by hand and examine the residue with his lens. By this means he could identify most of the minerals directly, but in a few cases more detailed examination under the microscope had to be carried out in the camp. Here and there Cortel had a groove dug in the soil along the river's edge, to obtain further samples.

First of all he examined the region around Nimdol and the Ok Tennam, which flowed east of the camp, in a southerly direction; the last stretch of this river had carved itself out a kloof, just before the point where it flowed into the Ok Bon. From the confluence, Cortel followed the latter river some way upstream, collecting rock samples, as well as samples of the deposits to be washed out. He carried out his work in the Antares region in the same way along the Ok Bon, the Ok Minam and many tributaries and streams—using Camp 39 as his base for this part of his research. He then climbed the slope of Antares to Camp 39a, thence descending another slope to the Ok Minam; on his way he investigated the beds of any streams which he encountered. Wherever the high temperature of the intruding magma had modified the surrounding rocks, ores might be present. He found marble in a number of places; this is probably where the local inhabitants get the material to make the ground, torpedo-shaped stones which the men

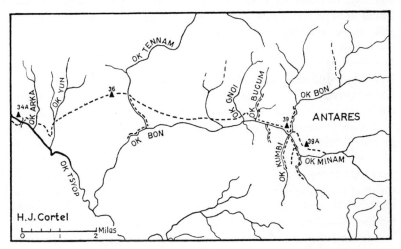

Fig. 11. Cortel's routes in the Ok Bon and Antares districts.

wear in the nasal septum. Between the marble and the granodiorites of the hardened magma there was a stratum of calcium-silicate hornfels in which he found crystals of garnet.

In the spring of 1939 the Netherlands New Guinea Mining Company (Mijnbouwmaatschappij Nederlandsch Nieuw-Guinea) had commissioned an investigation along the lower course of the Ok Bon up to a point roughly two miles upstream from where this river runs into the Ok Tsyop, with the object of determining among other things whether there was any gold in the locality. The report of this investigation had a hopeful note: "as was to be expected, traces of gold were indeed found".

The gradient of the river was however too steep, and the current consequently too strong, for this river gold to have been concentrated in anything like large quantitites. It is suggested that the origin of this river gold is to be sought in the mountainous region around Antares.* It goes without saying that Cortel paid particular attention to the possible occurrence of gold in or near the Antares Mountains, but the result of his investigation was decidedly negative. He found no gold, and later analysis failed to reveal even traces of the metal. Escher and Verstappen also panned samples in the valley of the Ok Bon with the same negative result. There was no gold in the region, neither was there any sign of other important minerals. Only magnetic iron ore was found in appreciable quantities, but it will be a very long time before this can be worked in such an inaccessible region.

For two and a half months the biological groups in the Sibil Valley had thoroughly investigated the flora and fauna in the area round Mabilabol, and there was not a great deal more to be learned there. Consequently Kalkman and Van Zanten the botanists, Vervoort the zoologist and Van Heijningen and Staats, the assistants, were happy to be able to move to Camp 39 on 26th June, so that they could work in completely new surroundings in which there occurred a number of species not present in the Sibil Valley. Camp 39 was situated at 4,260 ft. above sea-level and from this point of view was not very different from Mabilabol, lying at 4,130 ft. However, the landscape was entirely different. Here there was no wide valley with broad river terraces, but a narrow ravine dominated by the lofty peak of Antares. The forest along the river banks was, like that in the Sibil Valley, very much influenced by human intervention, since the inhabitants carry out regular clearings and burning in it. However, the slender scattered Araucarias which were so characteristic of the surroundings of the base camp were absent. In this region there were trees with sharp thorns growing on the trunk (Harmsiopanax), with thorny hairs on the twigs and leaves (Macaranga), and Dammaropsis kingiana (a tree related to the fig), whose huge leaves are used by the inhabitants as a roof-covering. As in the Sibil Valley, they found here species of grass growing several feet high, such as Ischaeum polystachum, together with balsams (Impatiens), marestails (Equisetum), etc. Along the steep slopes of Antares one can still find stretches of virgin forest, composed of a large number of

* De Groot, "De Ingenieur in Nederlandsch-Indië" (The engineer in the Dutch East Indies), Year 7, 1940, Section IV, page 132, fig 2.

deciduous trees, alternating with a few conifers (*Podocarpus*) and screw-palms (*Pandanus*). Orchids and ferns grow here in profusion, having established themselves on the stems and branches of trees.

Camp 39 was intended to serve as a half-way house, because the biologists were also going to work higher up in the Antares Mountains and would therefore be able to make use of the path which the climbing party had cleared. At a height of 4,920 ft., entirely surrounded by thickly-wooded slopes, was a grass meadow which formed a fine natural landing-place for the helicopters. This area of grass was separated from the valley of the Ok Minam (a tributary of the Ok Bon) by a steep ridge, on the spine of which the Survey Department party had built a camp for themselves and for the biologists (Camp 39a).

The houses were raised on short timber piles, thus ensuring that fewer animals could get in; the roof was covered with large brown tarpaulins. In front of the camp stood a flag pole bearing the Netherlands tricolour. Staats accompanied the survey group who had gone on ahead to build this camp, as the men in this party were good hunters and they would shoot animals which Staats could skin for inclusion in the collections. The bearers, who found no difficulty in climbing the steep slope, returned every evening to Camp 39, where there was more space and where it was not so cold. During the next few days Van Zanten and Van Heijningen left (on 29th June), followed by Kalkman and Marine Brandenburg Van den Gronden, on 30th June, both parties en route for Camp 39a. Vervoort remained in the Ok Bon camp for the time being, to collect specimens along the river and to keep an eye on the transport of equipment and supplies. Under the stones along the Ok Bon he found small crabs, snails and sow-bugs. Every day the Ok Bonners would come up and call at his camp: they did seem quite ready to collect animals, but as yet they did not seem inclined to do any real work, i.e., to act as bearers. The crabs were shown to them and they soon set about catching them with a great deal of zeal. These Papuans very soon twigged that for five crabs they would be paid the—to them—fantastic price of a small hand-mirror. This gave rise to a busy trade; again and again they would arrive with five crabs wrapped up in a leaf and receive their reward. Not until one consignment had been paid for was the next brought out of the carrying-net. When supplies became too plentiful Vervoort tried to reduce the price, but the Ok Bonners would have none of this. They preferred to throw the creatures away rather than agree to provide more than five crabs for one mirror. On this score they were tougher than the Sibillers, who were prepared to let the price come down if they could not sell their wares. In addition to the crabs they also brought lizards, snakes and tree-frogs; a rather large lizard with a brown back, spotted with beige and black patches, and a green belly (*Emoia cyanogaster*) was very common here. Apart from a few ringed snakes (*Natrix sp.*) one species of poisonous snake (*Pseudopistocalamus nymani*) was caught here, and a brown snake (*Boiga irregularis*) which lived in the bushes. In the river there were tadpoles with a flattened body and a large sucker mouth with which they could attach themselves to stones in the fast-flowing water; tadpoles of this kind also occur in the Ok Sibil and in other mountain streams. Using a fine-meshed net, Vervoort collected in the Ok Bon and the Ok Minam specimens of plankton— microscopically small living organisms which are carried along by the current. Dragon-flies were hunted all along the river-banks. Night trapping was not very effective in this area; it was cold at night and the group's stay there coincided with several of the rare clear nights which are not good for this kind of catch.

In the few days Staats spent in Camp 39 the following birds and mammals were collected: two species of honey-eater (*Melilestes megarhynchus* and *Melidectes belfordi*), a sparrow-hawk (*Accipiter cirrocephalus*) and a flower-pecker (*Oreocharis arfaki*), superficially resembling a titmouse. This flower-pecker has a black head and yellow cheeks and a yellow throat; the breast and belly are dark green, while the back is green and the wing-coverts are black with three large yellow patches. The inhabitants also brought in a species of rat (*Pogonomys macrourus*) which had also been collected in the Sibil Valley.

Towards the end of the Antares investigation, the inhabitants also contributed a living lau-lau or tree-kangaroo (*Dendrolagus dorianus* sub-sp.; see Plate 17 (2)). The hind legs of this animal are not as long as is the case with its large ground-dwelling relatives; moreover, it does not progress by means of great leaps, but gently hops around, with its forefeet touching the ground. The lau-lau climbs from branch to branch in the trees, an operation in which the big claws on both fore and hind feet are of great service. The tree-kangaroo is dark brown with a black stripe down the middle of its back, and it has a long, furry, beige-coloured tail. His thick head and little eyes give Lau—as he is popularly called—a decidedly stupid appearance. The animal was sent by helicopter to Mabilabol where it was accommodated in a fine kennel, to the great delight of the Sibillers, who repeatedly came to see it out of curiosity; tree-kangaroos are unknown in their district.

On 2nd July, Warman made a reconnaissance flight to Camp 39a; he found the grass strip a good enough landing-place, but considered that more trees would have to be cleared from the mountain ridge to enable the helicopter to approach and leave without difficulty. The work of clearing was speedily carried out and on 3rd July the helicopters were able to bring almost all the biological equipment from Camp 39 to Camp 39a. Vervoort and Van Sprang, the radio commentator, arranged to be set down at Camp 39a, while Klaarenbeek, the journalist, joined them later. Marine Roem remained at Camp 39 to man the radio.

The house for the biologists at Camp 39 was large without being really luxurious. As you went up the steps at the entrance, you came to a porch roofed with leaves, which tended to leak in a heavy shower of rain. The principal purpose of this porch was to stop the rain coming in to the remainder of the camp at the side; in addition, food supplies and equipment packed in tins could be stored here. In the single room which served as living and sleeping quarters and as a work place, a row of camp beds was arranged along one side, each provided with a klambu, while the other side of the room was occupied by a table and a bench of laths. Meals were taken at this table, Staats used it for stuffing the specimens of birds, Van Heijningen prepared his insects on it, the botanists piled up on it the plants they had collected but not yet mounted, everybody wrote letters at it and also drank coffee at it. The whole scene presented the familiar, sociable, but rather untidy mess always found where biologists are. The floor consisted of saplings, and this had the advantage of being easy to keep clean because the ash and cigarette ends would fall through. It was rather more annoying that all sorts of useful articles, like spoons or forks, would also disappear through the floor and be completely lost. Van Zanten had set his bed at the end of the living space, on the brink of the precipice at the bottom of which flowed the Ok Minam. The gulf did not disturb him in the least and he slept like a top. Of an evening, tree-frogs would climb up the sticks of the hut and establish themselves in his klambu. It was therefore Van Zanten's job, before he went to sleep, to catch all the frogs in his mosquito-net and deliver his prey to the zoologists. At the side of the camp, a flight of steps made of small logs led a little way down the steep slope to a point where a small platform hung suspended over the valley of the Ok Minam; this was the toilet. It must be said that in the daytime one had a very lovely view from this vantage-point, but if one had to pay a visit there in the evening, it was, to say the least of it, a highly frightening experience. One of the guests who visited Camp 39 for a few days and weighed nearly eighteen stone preferred to seek salvation elsewhere, rather than venture on that crazy structure.

A Papuan had accompanied the party as cook to provide for the commissariat. The meals were particularly simple and this cook did not succeed in introducing a great deal of variation. The occupants of the camp helped him, each in turn, and even ate the dishes prepared in this way with a certain amount of appetite; but for one of the inhabitants the smell of the food was sufficient to force him to depart somewhat hastily, and thereafter nourish himself with biscuits alone.

From Camp 39a the immediate surroundings were reconnoitred. The transition from the level grass to forest was in most places abrupt, but on one side it gave way to boggy ground dotted with a few shrubs, large and small, with a single taller tree among them. This vegetation was gradually succeeded by very marshy woodland, thickly grown with moss and epiphytic plants. In the peaty bog there grew rhododendrons and species of bilberry (Vaccinium). A great variety of orchids grew on the trees and shrubs. Here Kalkman was able to collect to his heart's content with Marine Brandenburg Van den Gronden to assist him. Armed with a machete they would clear their way through the bushes, looking out for species which were not yet represented in their collections. Wherever possible, several examples of each species were taken, in order to get a picture of the variability of the species and also to allow of sending specimens to other herbarium collections later. It was a hot and tiring job, this plant collecting, and it had to be followed by drying the specimens. Each had to be accompanied by field notes on the colour of the flowers and the conditions in which the plant was found (e.g. whether the plant was an epiphyte, i.e. a plant which grows on another plant, like orchids and ferns, which are so often found in the branches of trees). In the cases of trees and shrubs, of which they collected branches, the height was also recorded. It was important that, in addition to plants in full bloom, they should also collect specimens with developing or ripe seeds. Sometimes a tree had to be felled to enable them to get at the flowering branches. The large, fat fruits of the screw-palm (Pandanus) were cut up and sent by helicopter to Mabilabol, where they were preserved in a milk-can full of alcohol. The plants were laid between newspapers and the bundles pressed between two sheets of cardboard or metal plates. It was not possible to

31. Rattan suspension bridge over the Ok Tsyop: top, the bridge being repaired and strengthened: bottom, bearers crossing the bridge.

dry the plants properly in the camp, and the bundles were therefore soaked in alcohol, packed in tarred paper and sent down by helicopter to Mabilabol; here, they were subsequently set out between sheets of fresh, dry newspaper and dried on the drying-stove.

Van Zanten was delighted with the profusion in this region of mosses, lichens and fungi. Every day he set out carrying a number of plastic bags and came back with bales of moss. He too had to devote a great deal of time to preparing his material, to ensure that it would arrive in the Netherlands in satisfactory condition. In addition to this he took colour photographs of many noteworthy botanical specimens—in particular, some magnificent pictures of orchids.

The zoological group collected insects, amphibia, reptiles and birds. They not only netted fast-flying dragon-flies and butterflies, but also used a sweeping-net and separator-box. Many small insects which live in the vegetation can be caught by dragging a net through the plants. The difficulty is then to extract the specimens without letting the majority of them escape, because the net collects a mess of twigs, leaves and flowers. Van Heijningen would trudge across the ground with a ground-net, carrying his flap-box, a little wooden box with an opening at each end. A glass jam-pot was attached to one end, and the net rammed in through the other hole and shaken out, thus transferring all its contents to the box; this aperture was then closed by means of a flap (which gave the box its name). All the flying and creeping insects would leave the dark box and move towards the light, so that in a short time they were all in the jam-pot together. In this way a large quantity of small fry (among other things, little beetles, bugs and cicadas) could be caught in a very short time, all of which would otherwise have been missed; but it was precisely these small creatures which were so interesting as research material, because many of the species found among them are new to science.

Large tussocks of moss were pulled apart, revealing snails and sow-bugs. Vervoort felled screw-palms and looked for small creatures in the leaf axils. The valley-dwellers, who had initially had considerable objections to climbing the mountain, showed themselves less frightened by the spirits that lived on Antares now they had seen that the occupants of the camp had suffered no harm. Some of the Ok Bonners now regularly visited Camp 39a, and they continued to bring a few frogs and lizards. Staats went out hunting assisted by the survey team. Four species of birds were added to the collection; one was a

32. Valley of the Ok Bon, seen from Antares.

small species of cuckoo (*Chalcites lucidus plegosus*), which has back and wings of green with a golden sheen; the throat, breast and belly have broad transverse stripes of brown. *Pachycephala soror* is very beautifully patterned; the head is black and the back olive green, while the white throat is separated from the yellow breast and belly by the black transverse stripe. Only one mammal, an opossum rat (*Neophascogale lorentzi*) was caught. Small tree-frogs (*Hyla* sp.), dark green with black markings and a few whitish spots on the back, were found here in large numbers. Two other large species of tree-frog were rarer (*Nyctimystes papua* and *Nyctimystes humeralis*); the former was brown with large white-edged black blotches on the after-part of its back, while the latter was a uniform green.

The evenings in Camp 39a were chilly; banks of cloud used to come up the valley and blanket the region in mist. A good deal of rain fell here; there were days on which it poured the whole day through, so that there was not much else than to remain in camp—a depressing occupation. The meadow where the helicopters landed became a lake, which was over six feet deep in places. Probably such inundations have occurred repeatedly and thereby prevented the forest from invading this piece of ground. The helicopters were provided with floats, so that they could land as easily on the water as land. Taking off was, however, somewhat more difficult. The helicopter had to be moored fast, since otherwise, when the rotor started to turn, the craft would begin to rotate in the opposite direction. It was impossible to moor the helicopter here, since it had to be away from the water's edge before taking off, so that the whirling rotor blades did not smash themselves to pieces on the sloping ground or on a tree-stump. The only solution was for someone to enter the water and hold the helicopter in position. Vervoort was a master at this disagreeable task. He would swim round, towing or pushing the helicopter away from the bank, and ensuring that it did not begin to turn.

To get an idea of the state of affairs in Camp 39a Brongersma embarked in a helicopter on 5th July; this was on Sunday, and there was no radio communication, so that he could with a clear conscience leave the base camp for a couple of hours. It was a rather chilly journey, as the helicopter doors had been left open to enable him to take a few photographs from the air, and a cold wind blew right across the cabin. A certain amount of turbulence tossed the helicopter about quite strongly, but this soon ceased, after they had passed the first ridge of

mountains. Warman steered his craft through the valley of the Ok Bon
and a little way up that of the Ok Minam, and then made a sharp left-
hand turn over the camp and landed in the deep cwm. The slope
leading from the landing-base to the camp was steep and covered with
trunks and stumps of trees. A "path" had been made across this. Tree-
trunks had been laid along the slope and flat steps cut out of them to
facilitate walking; here and there a small flight of steps led to the next
higher trunk. For those who found it difficult to keep their balance on a
tree-trunk a rail had been provided—but this gave only moral support.
The thin strand of rattan which had been stretched between a few
vertical stakes flexed very markedly the moment anybody touched it,
so that those who trusted in the hand-rail without more ado fall off
the trunk. Vervoort, Van Zanten and Brandenburg Van den Gronden
had gone with Van der Weiden for a short trip to the Ok Minam, where,
among other things, they had caught a small snake. The rainfall of the
last few days had swollen the river and the valley was only just
negotiable.

Brongersma discussed with the men in the camp the possibilities of
penetrating farther into the mountains, and also the idea of sending
a patrol to provide any help that the climbing team might need. He
was not able to make his visit a very long one, because the clouds
might close in again at any moment, and Warman and he would have to
remain at the camp. Brongersma himself would not have had any
objection to this, because Camp 39a was set in particularly lovely
surroundings and he would have been very willing to spend a week
here. But his place was in Mabilabol, and after about an hour he therefore left the camp, which, despite the primitive conditions of life which
obtained there, gave him the impression of a holiday resort. At such
moments he would have preferred for a little while not to be the
leader of the expedition, but simply a member free to go trekking in the
forest. The weather was not outstandingly good and they consequently
decided not to visit Camps 39 and 36 on the way back. Brongersma had
to content himself with a distant glimpse of these camps and with a
view of the Ok Bon, which extended in the form of a long, continuous
stretch of rapids from Antares to the Ok Tsyop. The great sensation of
this flight was the last section, as one re-entered the valley of the Ok
Tsyop. The helicopter flew straight towards a vertical limestone cliff,
giving the passengers the impression that they would be smashed to bits
on it if the pilot did not climb any higher. It was a consolation to them

to think that Warman too was anxious to get over the cliff, an enterprise in which he was highly successful.

Two days later Vervoort returned Brongersma's visit and came down to Mabilabol for further discussions. There were not enough bearers to enable them to push higher up into the mountains. The Ok Bonners were certainly not prepared to go, and the expedition itself had few bearers available. The Sansapor bearers attached to the zoological group could not be made available and the other bearers were needed to open up a route through the valley of the Ok Tsyop in the direction of the Juliana Summit. Fortunately Van der Weiden was ready to provide temporary assistance, although he too was naturally not able to spare his bearers. Gevelhof of the Survey Group went with Brandenburg Van den Gronden higher up the mountain (on 9th July) to a height of 7,550 ft., where the climbing team had found a suitable place for camp. Here they intended to erect the new Camp 40 for the use of the biologists. To speed up the research work—since the idea was as many scientific workers as possible should move up in the direction of the Juliana Summit and the time set aside for the expedition was beginning to run really short—on 13th July Brongersma made a second visit to Camp 39a, where the biologists were still in occupation. The whole situation was discussed in detail and it was decided that a further two weeks should be assigned to continue researches in the Antares region. Marine-Sergeant De Wijn was sent to Camp 39a to see that the move to Camp 40 was carried out as quickly as possible. The new camp was virtually complete, and the helicopter landing-strip had been prepared. On 13th July Warman made a reconnaissance trip and found the landing-strip quite satisfactory; there were only a couple more trees which would have to be felled. To ensure better communication with Mabilabol, Marine Roem moved up Camp 39a with his transmitting/ receiving equipment. Everything looked hopeful; the biologists would now be able to work on making collections in two groups all the way from Camp 40 to the summit. The time at their disposal was not very long, but long enough for them to obtain important information.

On Wednesday 14th July Warman set off early in his helicopter to go to Antares. He was expected to be away for several hours, because he had to transport the maximum possible quantity of equipment and supplies from Camp 39 and Camp 39a to Camp 40. As the expedition members in Mabilabol sat down to their meal at midday, people gradually began to ask what was holding Warman back. Brongersma took a look at the sky; there was still some cloud behind the Orion Mountains, and it was therefore quite possible that the valley of the Ok Bon was shut off by cloud, making Warman wait for better weather. But then the shock came. Four o'clock was the time for the radio conversation between camps. Brongersma was listening with half an ear to the conversation between Marine Koster and Marine Hendriks in Camp 36, but he suddenly got to his feet very quickly when he thought he heard the word "Crash". He had in fact heard it, for the helicopter had crashed on the Antares Mountains, but Warman was happily uninjured. The accident must have occurred early that morning. The radio in Camp 39a was unserviceable, and a runner had been sent with all haste down to Camp 36 to pass the message on. Hendriks himself did not know precisely what had occurred. At all events it was too late that day to do anything about it. Brongersma stood discussing with Bekker, the aircraft mechanic, what they should do—whether to wait for further information or pass what they had back home to Holland. Slowly they walked down to the government station, where they discovered that someone was already dictating a long telegram for a radio transmission that very evening in Holland; it is a remarkable thing that set-backs always seem to have a greater news value than events which turn out well. Radio Merauke wanted to shut down and Brongersma had a lot of trouble in persuading them to accept another two short telegrams. One of these was addressed to Aero-Contractors, Warman's employers, to enable them to inform Mrs. Warman before she heard of the accident on the radio and to tell her that her husband was unharmed; the second was to the Department of Civil Aviation in Hollandia who would have to investigate the accident. As a safeguard, a further telegram was sent back to Holland via the Marines' communication system.

The second helicopter was at Katem, with Menge in charge, held up by bad weather. The message was also sent to him next morning telling him to fly back to Mabilabol once the weather made this reasonably easy, but above all to avoid any unnecessary risk, because the expedition would have more than enough trouble from one accident. Venema, who was at Tanah Merah, was also informed. It was a serious check, for the helicopters were just doing so well and it had already become clear that they were indispensable for the work of the expedition. There was a general feeling of depression at Mabilabol, and Brongersma therefore issued a dram all round as medicine against the shock and as an expression of general rejoicing that Warman was unhurt. This pilot had made many friends among the expedition members by his personality, his skill as a flyer and his perseverance.

Next morning Menge arrived by helicopter from Katem, following which Van den Bos went with his helicopter to Antares to fetch Warman. Meanwhile Venema arrived by Twin Pioneer. The two expedition leaders were just going up the slope towards the silver house, when they heard the helicopter approaching, so they went down again to the landing-platform. Everybody was very interested in Warman's return. The leaders were very anxious to know what had happened.

"Complete write-off?" asked Venema. Warman nodded: "Yes, a complete write-off," he replied. They did not say a great deal more at that moment, as the occupants of the camp were crowding around the pilot, to congratulate him on his safe return.

It was later that he gave them the full story: "The weather was fine when I wanted to land on the platform at Camp 40 at about half past eight; suddenly there was a squall which threw the helicopter forward, smashing the front of the floats against the edge of the platform. I bounced up in the air again, and before I knew where I was the helicopter was capsized and I was hanging head downwards in my seat. I still remember that my foot was caught, but I don't really know any more about it than that. I have no idea how I got out, but I do know that some time later I was standing on the platform looking at the wreck. When I saw how the helicopter was crushed, it gave me quite a fright."

"Did anybody else see it?" asked Venema.

"Yes, Brandenburg Van den Gronden of the Marines and Gevelhof of the Survey Department."

After the accident Warman travelled rapidly down to Camp 39a. As a result of the, for him, unaccustomed exercise—he had descended some 2,800 ft. in two and a half hours, slithering and sliding, and tripping over tree-roots—he was somewhat stiff; he had discovered all kinds of muscles whose existence he had not suspected. It was perhaps taking pleasure in somebody else's misfortune, but the members of the expedition enjoyed saying to him: "Willem, now you've got a bit of an idea what it's like to go on an expedition. You flying chaps like having a laugh when you look down from the air on us slogging over the ground, but now at least you're the first pilot to go on trek in the Star Mountains." Warman made it very clear that everybody should stick to his own profession and that he was not born to mountain climbing. Venema was occupied for the rest of the day taking statements from witnesses. He prepared a provisional report on the causes of the accident and had it transmitted to Hollandia; a communiqué was also issued for the radio and press. That evening they held a council of war, and discussed the extent to which this accident would influence the further course of the expedition. Flights along the route to the Antares Mountains would be made only occasionally; supplementary food supplies would be carried up, and one single flight would be made to fetch heavy pieces of equipment which could not be brought back by bearers. The research in the Antares region was to be continued by the biologists, but it would be impossible to allow them to extend the time originally allowed for the purpose; the members of this group would have to return on foot. Van Sprang and Klaarenbeek had been fortunate, because they had flown back to Mabilabol just in time. Camp 39a had been the highest point they were able to reach. Higher up in the mountains, the weight that a helicopter can carry on take-off is very small, and, as Van Sprang put it: "Unfortunately, you can't cut me in two, so I shall have to travel in one piece."

The reduction in the transport of supplies by helicopter would hit Reynders the hardest. He had left Mabilabol to go to Antares by a very long detour, and hoped on his arrival there to get supplies for a trip to the north. Unhappily this was now no longer possible. For the moment he did not know of this disappointment.

On 12th July—that is, two days before the accident—Reynders went by helicopter to Nimdol, where he met Marine-Corporal Bril, who had gone on ahead with a number of Muyu bearers. A day later they set out together; 27 bearers went with them to carry the camping gear and supplies. They travelled along the Ok Bon to Bon Makot, where this river flows into the Ok Tsyop. The level of the river was exceptionally high and the current very strong. They were unsuccessful in trying to lay a bridge of trees across the river, because the bank was steep and the felled trees dropped with their tops in the river, where the powerful current completely smashed them up. The only thing to do was to try again farther upstream, and there they fortunately found a rattan suspension bridge. This was in fact, in bad condition, but the bearers were sure that they could repair it. Thus, after a delay of a few hours, they reached the other side of the Ok Bon and set up their camp on the high bank, darkness having already fallen.

Bril was an ideal companion on a trek; he had a lively sense of humour and there was nothing he liked better than tramping through the rimbu. On this trip they did not eat tinned vegetables, as Bril had very successfully taken a course which taught him all about the edible things to be found in the jungle, and he picked leaves here and there, and served them up as fresh greens with the rice. From the Ok Bon the journey continued along the Ok Tsyop in a south-easterly direction and then up the Ok Imur towards the east. The weather was fine and sunny and they enjoyed clambering over the huge blocks of rock in the river-bed. Early in the afternoon they set up their camp near a waterfall 250 feet high. While Reynders studied soil sections along the slopes of the Great Bear (called Bi by the local inhabitants) and took soil samples, Bril followed a different pursuit. He was washing samples of sand from the bed of the Ok Imur, still in the hope of finding some gold; but once again this hope seemed to be vain. Reynders wanted to investigate two mountain ranges, the Great Bear and Andromeda, but it became clear that the time available was not sufficient. He therefore limited himself to working in the Great Bear Mountains where he could examine soil sections in the moss forest. He set up his camp after he had got over the summit (5,845 ft.), because there was no water to be found on top of the mountain. It was not an easy matter to light a small fire in the moss forest to cook a meal. All the wood was soaking wet, but he eventually succeeded with the help of a little paraffin. On 16th July Reynders and Bril reached Camp 39 where a disappointment awaited them. They learned that their trip could not continue farther north; there were not sufficient supplies in this camp to feed a group of twenty-nine men for a journey of several weeks' duration. The biologists were very pleased with the arrival of Reynders, since they could now at least move up into Camp 40 with the help of his bearers. Things did not move very fast, because some of the men took the wrong path, together with their bearers, and instead of climbing higher, dropped down towards the Ok Minam. They consequently made a considerable detour and reached the camp much later than the others. Along the track they found three play-nests built by bower-birds. The male bower-birds make a sort of dancing-ground where they parade before the females; the form and structure of these play-nests varies with the species. Here they were quite simple affairs. In the middle there were one or two small saplings, round which were piled up large numbers of dead twigs; around all this is the dancing floor, which is made of a layer of moss

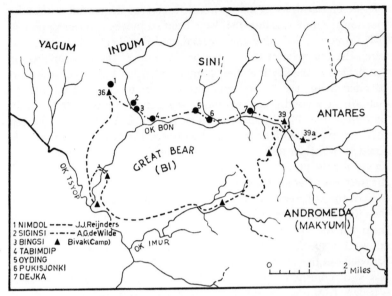

Fig. 12. Reynders' route from Camp 36 to Antares and De Wilde's route through the valley of the Ok Bon.

collected by the bird for the purpose. Around the edge of this dancing floor, which is about a yard in diameter, is a wall of moss some four inches high. Some of the moss is also heaped up around the saplings in the middle, a small hollow being made in this heap. Other species of bower-bird make much more complicated structures, in the middle of which is a bower consisting of two rows of twigs leaning against each other; they often decorate the dancing ground with brightly-coloured flower petals or with fruits which are set in little heaps according to colour.

On their way they came across the remains of two camps which Escher had set up on his first reconnaissance. For the last three hours they had to climb in pouring rain through the forest, where the climbing bamboo caused them a certain amount of trouble.

They had to climb on hands and knees, and often had to use firm handholds, and it was a good thing that they had stout gloves with them to protect their hands against the sharp thorns on the stems of the tree-ferns. Soaked to the skin and numbed they reached Camp 40, where

Marine Brandenburg Van den Gronden received them with boiling hot pea soup; rarely can this dish have been so justified in the tropics.

No time was lost after their arrival, and they began that evening to catch the insects attracted by the bright light of the paraffin pressure lamp. During the daytime, they hunted butterflies but found it difficult to catch them; the ground was too irregular to allow of following a butterfly at a good speed, so that it was better to wait quietly until a butterfly came close by and catch it with a quick swing of the net. Here too they worked with drag net and flap-box. The botanists explored the forest; it was their task to study its constitution, although they also had an eye for the ghostly appearance of the moss forest, where the tops of the trees were frequently veiled by mist. It was a very open forest, as the tops of the tall trees did not touch each other and sufficient light was therefore able to penetrate for small trees and shrubs to grow beneath them. Of the tall trees, species of Myrtaceae were the commonest; in addition a species of conifer—Phyllocladus hypophyllus, whose twigs are flattened out like leaves, while the leaves are reduced to narrow scales— was very common. Another species of conifer, related to Podocarpus, was less common. In the lower zone of vegetation two species of rhododendron occurred, one with light purple flowers and the other with dark pink flowers.

Around Camp 40 Staats collected a number of birds: three species of honey-eater (Myzomela rosenbergii, Oreornis subfrenatus and Ptiloprora guisei), two species of fly-catcher (Peneothello sigillatus and Microeca papuana) and a flower-pecker (Paramythia montium). Myzomela rosenbergii is a small bird with a slender, slightly down-curving beak; the male is black, with throat, neck and back of carmine, while the female is lighter in colour—more blackish-brown with light brown spots and with only a little red on the throat and on the tail-coverts. Ptiloprora guisei is much larger, but most unobtrusively coloured in slate-grey with whitish longitudinal stripes on the breast. Peneothello sigillatus is completely black with a large white blotch on the wings. Paramythia montium has a whitish head with a blue-black crest, a black throat and grey-blue neck, breast and belly, while the back and wings are green with touches of grey-blue on the scapulars.

The nights were very cold, and the open camp—with nothing but a tent-cloth stretched out as a protection against the rain, but allowing the cold wind to blow through and the mist to enter—really did not offer adequate shelter at a height of 7,545 ft. This gave Camp 40 its nickname of "Frigidaire Camp". A double-walled tent was carried for work higher up in the mountains, and only small groups went off in turn from this point, because of the limited accommodation in this special tent. The first to climb higher were Vervoort and Reynders who set off on the 18th July. They climbed steadily, taking a rest now and then to enable them to get a better view of the surroundings. During this trip Reynders showed to what extent the catching of animals was often a matter of pure chance. On their way, at a height of 8,790 ft., he found himself obliged to turn aside from the path for a moment, and as he

Fig. 13. Bower-bird's "play-nest" or bower, Antares 5,250 ft.

retired into the bushes he almost sat on a brightly-spotted tree-frog, which was promptly added to the collection! They lost a good deal of time trekking around the steep rock cliff at 9,420 ft., which had caused the climbing team so much trouble. Moreover, the forest gave way here and there to a subalpine shrub vegetation. Between the shrubs there were patches of moss forest, even at 9,840 ft. The conifer species *Papuacedrus*, which grows to a height of 45 feet, was very common here; other tree species (broad-leaved trees) did not exceed 20 ft.

Reynders and Vervoort set up the double-walled tent at Camp 41, at a height of 9,775 ft. One bearer stayed behind with them, while the others returned to Camp 40. Next day they left the bearer in the tent and together climbed to the western summit of Antares. Here Reynders took soil samples, from which Vervoort extracted a number of earthworms. Between 200 and 300 ft. from the summit were two little pools, which they examined to see what fauna they contained; Vervoort caught a few *Entomostraca*, tiny crustacea creatures. When the sky cleared for one moment, they saw far away to the west the gleaming white Juliana Summit; it looked as though it had snowed very heavily there, as the white snow-cap stretched much farther than usual. They returned to the tent with a large number of plants, and found that meanwhile Van Zanten and Bril had arrived, bringing an extra tent-cloth with them. Towards evening the sky cleared again for a while and they were able to signal back by lamp to Camp 40 to tell them how they had fared. They then made all the necessary preparations for shifting the camp to a point close to the western summit. On 20th July, just before they were leaving, a runner from Camp 40 reached them with letters from Brongersma, emphasising once again that the time-table had to be strictly observed and that they would therefore not be able to extend their research. This news caused some consternation, and it was not to be wondered at that a few things were forgotten. It was blazing hot, but they reached the summit after two and a half hours. The bearers were absolutely exhausted and saw no likelihood of bringing up the rest of the equipment. They had only brought the inner tent with them, and this was set up, forming Camp 42 at 10,825 ft. Van Zanten's blanket had not arrived, and so they had to divide the blankets they had among four men. In addition, one of the bearers had put the cooking utensils down somewhere on the path and had forgotten to pick them up when he started off again. This was not the worst, because after all they were able to cook the rice in an empty carrying-case. What was less agreeable was that instead of meat, only the liver paste had been brought. Bril had carried his gear (33 lb.) himself to the top, and therefore had all he wanted and did not need to borrow anything from the others. That afternoon it began to rain hard, and it poured all night. Reynders remained awake a good deal of the night and Vervoort was troubled with intestinal disturbances, and they did not find it very disagreeable that the weather was exceptionally bad outside so that they could with a good conscience stay quietly in the tent. There was one man, who whatever the weather, felt in the best of condition; this was Corporal Bril. Early in the morning he would begin to play his mouth-organ, on which he had an extensive repertory, ranging from "Awake, the sun is shining bright!" to "The sun is now about to leave us", to say nothing of a few marines' songs, which were frequently rather melancholy. This music was always much appreciated by the bearers, and after one of Bril's concerts they were readier to begin slogging uphill than without it. During the afternoon the rain stopped, and Reynders set off with Bril in the direction of the eastern summit, but they were not able to reach it because of the thick mist. However Bril did catch at 11,159 ft. a small frog (Cophixalus sp.).

In the vicinity of the camp there were still a few trees scattered here and there between the low shrubs. Most of them did not grow any higher than some 7 to 10 feet; only the Papuacedrus attained a height of some 30 feet, but generally they were twisted, gnarled, miserable specimens. Only a few of the slopes had a covering of low shrubs, and on the steep yet boggy patches they found a few true alpine plants of the buttercup family (Ranunculus), together with eyebright (Euphrasia) and a gentian (Gentiana lorentzii).

The menu consisted solely of rice and onions, which are not particularly nourishing, and they therefore decided to open the emergency rations. These consisted of crisp little cakes, which are best eaten in the hand, but some of the expedition members felt that they had to behave decently to the end, and laboriously ate their emergency rations with knife and fork.

They were relieved on 22nd July. The first group returned to Camp 40, while Kalkman, Van Heijningen, Staats and Brandenburg Van den Gronden set off on their upward journey. Reynders had left the flag standing at Camp 42, to help the new group to find the way easily. Unfortunately things did not turn out this way, as Staats spent one hour turning round and round the camp before he found the tent.

The second group also met with bad weather on the western summit of Antares. Every now and then there was a shower of ice-cold rain, and the sun would only shine for an hour. Van Heijningen used this hour to catch wasps; there were no other insects flying about. The ferns were soaking wet, so the sweeping-net and separator-box yielded no catches. Heijningen therefore tried another method—beating. He held an umbrella, on which a white cloth had been spread out inside the ribs, upside down under the branches of shrubs and bushes, at the same time tapping the branches with a stick. All sorts of little beetles, bugs and cicadas fell out on to the white cloth and were easily caught; in this way he was after all able to obtain a fine collection of specimens. At the summit Staats collected two birds—(*Pachycephala lorentzii*). Satisfied, the group trekked back to Camp 40 with the material they had collected. On the way down one of the bearers managed to tread on a sharp branch, which pierced the thick layer of horny skin on the sole of his foot; he was limping when he entered the camp, where Marine Brandenburg Van den Gronden successfully operated on him with the scalpel lent by Staats.

Meanwhile Camp 40 had had a visit from Mr. De Bijl, the Civil Aviation Dept. Inspector, who had come to start an enquiry into the helicopter accident. He had been brought to Camp 39 by helicopter and had come the remainder of the way on foot. On his return journey Mr. De Bijl learned the treacherous nature of the moss forest, as he broke through the layer of moss and dropped several yards along a tree-trunk, injuring his knee in the fall; as a consequence he had to rest for a couple of weeks in Hollandia.

The work of dismantling Camp 40 was now in full swing. Vervoort had already had as much as possible of the collected specimen material and equipment carried down to Camps 39a and 39. He did have a certain amount of trouble to get the bearers to do a couple of journeys up and down; once they hid in the forest and came out only when they thought that Vervoort and his companions had gone. It was a disappointment for them, as Vervoort had seen their game and waited for them a little farther up, so that they did after all have to take a small load with them. The only people remaining behind in Camp 39a were a few of the survey officials, who were still waiting for one or two fine nights to enable them to make their astronomical fix. They had however discharged their cook, because he ate two and a quarter pounds of rice per meal on his own. The food-transport arrangements were not calculated for big eaters like this.

They had a grand washing day in pouring rain, near Camp 39, in the Ok Bon. After so long a period of real mud baths this was anything but an excessive luxury. The river current and the rain made it an easy matter to rinse the clothes.

The major part of the specimens and equipment had to be carried back to Mabilabol by bearers. It was not possible to do this in one trip, and a shuttle service had therefore to be organised; this operated first of all on the stretch from Camp 39 to Camp 36, then from Camp 36 to Camp 34a on the Ok Tsyop and finally from there to Mabilabol. The bearers grumbled at this trotting to and fro, but finally did their job notwithstanding. Marines and police kept an eye on each group to see that the loads were not thrown away. The helicopter flew in on one occasion only to fetch the very heavy items. It also carried food for the survey group to Nimdol, whence it was brought up by bearers to Camp 39a. They collected very busily on the return trip. Around Nimdol the inhabitants brought in numerous lizards and frogs; they also collected here a honey-eater (*Melidectes torquatus*), a kingfisher (*Halcyon sancta*) and a Queen Carola's Six-wired Bird of Paradise (*Parotia carolae*). Near Camp 34a they caught a white-eye (*Zosterops atrifrons*) and two fly-catchers (*Monachella mülleriana* and *Peltops* sp.).

Vervoort fetched out his plankton nets and fished in the Ok Tsyop. The most difficult stretch on the way to Mabilabol is that from the Ok Tsyop to the crest of the Uteksigin, a climb of about 1,900 feet up a very steep slope. The journey was made by different groups and by 3rd August they were all back again in the base camp. The record for covering the distance from Camp 39 to Mabilabol was held by Sergeant De Wijn with Gevelhof of the Survey Group. They left at half past six in the morning and reached Mabilabol in bright moonlight at half past twelve; in eighteen hours they had covered a distance which normally required three days.

One more member of the expedition visited Antares. This was De Wilde, the anthropologist, who trekked through the valley of the Ok Bon to take anthropometric measurements of Papuans. He ran into certain difficulties in this operation. A few Ok Bonners had visited the base camp and had had to provide drops of blood as specimens for blood-group studies. This frightened them badly and they were scared by the measuring instruments; even a brightly-coloured plastic drinking-straw to wear in the nose was not enough to win their agreement to being examined. None the less De Wilde did find here and there people who were willing, and one day while he was waiting in Camp 39 to see what results would be achieved by the messages sent to villages in the vicinity, he climbed quite a way up the slopes of Antares to take a look at the moss forest.

Pouwer had made an exhaustive study of the social life and culture of the Sibillers. For his next investigation of a population group in the Star Mountains he selected inhabitants of the villages of Oksitbakon, Nimdol and Wagumbon in the valley of the Ok Bon. The social pattern of Papuan life in Oksitbakon and Nimdol appeared to be no different from that in the Sibil Valley and he therefore attempted to visit the village of Yummukur on the upper course of the Ok Arka. The tribe that lived there made it clear that neither Pouwer nor his bearers were welcome. New gardens had been laid out and they were busy renewing the roof of the iwool—activities during which they did not want strangers to be present. They might well suffer from a bad harvest and illness among their numbers if uninitiated men were to visit them. This also made the bearers from Oksitbakon unwilling to take Pouwer to Yummukur; they were afraid that they would fall ill or die if they transgressed the commandments. As a result this investigation was shifted to Wagumbon, whose inhabitants had no objection to receiving a visit. Two tribes had become mixed in this village, each with its own version of the creation story: the Upi-tenna, who like the Sibillers were descended from an earthworm and the Awot-tenna, whose ancestor was a lizard. According to the information Pouwer picked up here, other versions of the story exist in the Kiwirok region and along the Ok Bi. The culture of the tribes was identical and they spoke the same language. Keladi seems to grow less successfully in the Ok Bon and in consequence all sorts of tabu restrictions are far more strictly observed than in the Sibil Valley.

On 5th August Pouwer returned to the Sibil Valley and on 8th August De Wilde walked into the base camp. Camps 39 and 36 had now been dismantled and one of the most important undertakings of the expedition was completed. A great deal of data had been collected in this region and interesting collections of specimens assembled.

33.   After a journey; boots hung up to dry.

9

Interlude

IT WOULD BE A MISTAKE TO THINK THAT SILENCE DESCENDED ON MABILABOL when the various groups had gone off to work in the mountains. True, there were fewer people in the camp and the company at meals was smaller, but the expedition leaders and their staff certainly had no time to be bored. On top of the worries of bringing up supplies and equipment from Tanah Merah and Hollandia, they now also had the anxiety of arranging to transport them farther to the mountains. There was still only one Twin Pioneer available, which also had to perform a number of other tasks, which sometimes went to Biak for several days for the engines to be serviced, which every now and then lost a day by being grounded for some small technical default and which had to fill the gap created by the temporary withdrawal—due to some minor trouble—of any other aircraft. The weather remained changeable and it was never possible to say in advance whether the aeroplane would arrive on the agreed day or not. This left an abiding uncertainty, as one would expect with a system of supply by air. Naturally this caused a good deal of grumbling, but this uncertainty also made the expedition life more exciting and more attractive. The pilots of De Kroonduif, under the energetic leadership of the chief pilot, L. Van Rijswijk, did what they could to help the expedition; they were welcome guests in the Sibil Valley—and not alone for what they brought with them. If the post was inadvertently sent to Tanah Merah, the Dakota flying the scheduled service from the south to Hollandia would try to drop the mail-bag. If bad weather prevented this, we would hear Sentani called up on the radio, and asked to keep the Twin Pioneer which was standing ready for a flight to the Sibil Valley waiting for the mail. This was a service which the expedition members valued highly. The short conversations with the Dakotas flying overhead were always a welcome change.

34. Warman (left) returns to Mabilabol after his accident
on Antares (Brongersma on right).

The departure and return of groups of expedition members also pro-vided some diversion. Anceaux went to Hollandia for a week and planned to return via the south. Doctor Romeijn broke a tooth on a peppermint and seized the opportunity offered by the Twin Pioneer's arrival to visit the dentist in Hollandia. With him there also went his house-boy, who performed various tasks for the occupants of the silver house. This house-boy was a Biakker, who always went around with him, smartly and colourfully dressed, but who preferred life in the town to that among his gourd-clad fellow-countrymen. Govern-ment official Herberts was relieved by Dasselaar. De Wilde left for Katem to carry out research there. The geologists and biologists went off into the mountains and returned with a great deal to tell. In this way the population of the base camp was constantly changing and even the permanent inhabitants of Mabilabol had plenty of variety.

One special event was the visit of the Governor of Netherlands New Guinea, His Excellency Dr. P. J. Platteel, who arrived at Mabilabol on 10th July with Mrs. M. A. Platteel-Laseur, and with Messrs. H. Boender-maker, Th. C. Van den Broek, Denninghof Stelling (ciné-cameraman) and Fruneaux (photographer). This party inspected the entire camp and also watched a dropping flight by the Dakota. That afternoon the slogan used in so many advertisements—"Enjoy a longer holiday by flying"—took on a deeper meaning, as the sky was covered when the plane was ready to leave again and the pilot judged it inadvisable to take off. Instead of returning after a visit of a few hours, the party left four days later.

Fortunately the possibility of a longer stay had to some extent been foreseen; the guests had brought blankets with them, and Mrs. Platteel surprised us by producing all sorts of delicacies to accompany our rice, so that we were able to arrange a feast. The problem of accommoda-tion was also solved. The small room in the silver house, normally occupied by Tissing and Nicolas, was now made ready for the Governor and his wife, i.e. one of the brightly-coloured lengths of cloth we had brought out for bartering was used as a curtain to close off the entrance. The other members of the party and the crew of the Twin Pioneer slept in the research workers' hut. Since there were not enough camp beds for so many visitors, extra ones had to be made up, using two small tree-trunks set longways, across which were stretched jute bags. Each bed required two sacks fastened together with rattan. Vervoort, who had tried out one of these beds the day before, said that the taut strand of rattan cut into the body in such a way that sleep was almost impossible, and he felt that the guests could not be expected to put up with this. Brongersma therefore tried the beds, one after another; apparently he was so heavy that part of the rattan cord snapped, and the bed fell into just the right shape, providing a solution to this difficulty too.

Even the toilet was provided with a roof in honour of the important visitors; a waterproof cape was spread over the top—a luxury much appreciated by the inhabitants of the camp. It was no joke to visit this convenience during a tropical rainstorm. There were therefore loud protests when the roof was taken off again after the guests' departure.

A police guard was set over the silver house, but this caused some difficulty since the constable kept out all the Sibillers, even those who had come to be treated in the polyclinic. The guard was therefore withdrawn. He only took up his post again during the hour of rest, when it became clear that the Sibillers were irresistibly attracted by the fine blue curtain and badly wanted to see what was behind it.

The arrival of Mrs. Platteel caused a sensation in the Sibil Valley. For a long time the inhabitants had been surprised that men who owned steel axes and so many other special things should not possess wives, since it must be a very easy matter to purchase them with so many precious articles. Now they could see that white women also existed, and the appearance of Mrs. Platteel on the scene called forth a long wondering cry of "Ieee". The news naturally spread rapidly to the villages and during the next day or two many more people came to take a look. When Mrs. Platteel was in her room, the Sibillers approached Sneep with the request: "Let us see the woman again," while one of the Sibillers felt moved to offer to exchange his three wives for this one white woman. He was really sorry that the Governor did not take up this offer. In the eyes of the Sibillers it was remarkable that such an important man should have only one wife, and the expedition ethnologist told them that His Excellency had three further similar wives at home—a tale which noticeably raised their respect for the Governor.

It was a pity that the weather was too bad for the Governor to be flown up to one of the camps; instead, they were able to fly a few times through the Sibil Valley. This visit was a relief for Brongersma; in order to pack the butterflies, they had had to make little triangular packets of folded paper, which the entomologists called envelopes, and this gave a great deal of work. One such packet was needed for each butterfly, and there were thousands of them in all. When it started raining in the morning, the visitors took a hand in the work. Venema cut the paper to size, Mrs. Platteel folded the envelopes, Mr. Boendermaker cut off the superfluous corners and Mr. Van den Broek stamped on the packet the name of the place where the butterfly was caught. In one morning this do-it-yourself party made enough packages to last the remaining months that the expedition was to remain in the field. It also meant that the Governor had a quiet day or two. This visit, which had caused the occupants of Mabilabol a certain amount of misgiving, because they feared that it would be a formal and official occasion, was an exceptionally enjoyable interruption in the normal life in the Sibil Valley.

The expedition plans were discussed in detail with the Governor and with Mr. Boendermaker and Mr. Van den Broek. The financial worries were by no means over as yet. After the extra credit of one hundred thousand guilders, they still needed another two hundred thousand to carry out the plans completely. It was very good that the Governor should himself have seen and experienced the difficulties in the Sibil Valley, so that during the visit he made shortly afterwards to the Netherlands, he was able to plead more forcefully the importance of continuing the expedition activities. On Monday 13th July the weather had improved again sufficiently for the party to leave, the send-off being given by all the occupants of the base and by a large number of Sibillers. Two of the inhabitants of Betabib—Bomdogi and Wasilin —received mementoes of the visit: each of them was presented with one of the large, white ear-rings which Mrs. Platteel had worn. Bomdogi put his in the lobe of his right ear (he had a roll of adhesive plaster in the left), while Wasilin fastened his in his beard. They trotted round full of pride at these special marks of distinction.

When the Governor left, everything looked very rosy. The scientific research work was in full swing and the helicopters were making numerous flights to the Antares. Tissing had set off towards the Ok Tsyop to lay out a helicopter route, starting from Camp 34 along this river in the direction of Juliana Summit. Then on 14th July there occurred the helicopter accident, and all the plans were upset; the loss of one helicopter restricted the activities of the other machine, and the project of making a trip to the Juliana Summit had to be revised once again. Tissing and his bearers were recalled. The best thing now seemed to be to trek as far as possible westwards through the Sibil Valley, and then to try to find a path over the Orion Mountains to the valley of the Ok Tsyop. This would then enable the helicopter to stay in the Sibil Valley, so that it would no longer need to fly over mountain ridges, thus substantially reducing the risk. On 15th July Warman returned from Antares with a report on the accident. On 16th July the weather was bad again, but on the 17th he set off with the remaining helicopter to make a reconnaissance flight with Brongersma to the western region of the Sibil Valley, after which he repeated the trip with Escher. From the air it did look as though it would be possible to work along this route. It would only be necessary to make a few clearings for the helicopter, since there was a good deal of open ground where the aircraft could land easily in an emergency.

Marine-Sergeant De Wijn and Marine Scharff left with a guide and twenty-one bearers on 22nd July, to reconnoitre the route to the West Sibil Valley. Wherever necessary along their track they set up platforms for the helicopters to land on, as at all events the government doctor would be travelling to the western region of the Sibil Valley to initiate a study into the incidence of framboesia (yaws). They left in fine weather, and made good progress during the early part of the day. But then the guide took them off on a considerable detour; he obviously wanted to make a loop round the village of Lewengbon, and led them along the lower slopes of the Orion Mountains, so that it was pretty late in the afternoon when they eventually did reach Sagsaga. Efforts to obtain a guide for their journey farther westward were unsuccessful; the western area of the Sibil Valley was alut (taboo) and they were not allowed to go there. Probably the inhabitants of the eastern region of the Sibil Valley did not favour the idea of allowing the white men to go farther west, either because they themselves were not on very good terms with the West Sibillers, or because they could not bear to see the steel axes which they considered so precious being obtained by the inhabitants of other villages. Twenty minutes' walk from Sagsaga they made a clearing, and on 23rd July Sneep landed there with a helicopter to have a look round. A little later Romeijn arrived to examine the local population. The inhabitants of Sagsaga were still unwilling to provide a guide, but eventually one man gave way when offered a large steel axe as a reward for showing them the way to Tabiem. A patrol set off at eleven o'clock. As they reached the boundary between the East Sibil and the West—a boundary formed here by the Ok Sibil itself—there suddenly arose out of the high grass fourteen or fifteen West Sibillers, decked out in their finest feathered head-dresses and with their faces brightly painted with red earth and pigs' fat. They were fully armed and had set arrows to their bows, ready to shoot. The bearers crowded together around the two Europeans, who regarded the spectacle with astonishment. There was only one thing for De Wijn to do, and he did it immediately. Waving a few attractive "presents" and calling out "kaga mok-mok" (which means "good people") he walked towards the frontier guards, who abandoned their suspicious attitude and seemed prepared to lead the patrol to Tabiem. Here the Europeans were received with great interest. All the inhabitants of the village, men, women and children—numbering a good seventy in all—ran out to see these remarkable beings. De Wijn and Scharff now had to put up with being pinched—to see if they were real—while their hair was stroked by grubby hands. To the Papuans smooth hair was always something quite unusual, so different from their own stiff, wavy hair. The Tabiemers eagerly lent a hand in building a camp and making a helicopter platform. But for all the friendliness that they manifested not one of them was ready to show the patrol the track over the Orion Mountains to the valley of the Ok Tsyop. The mountain was alut and there were no paths in the region; if anyone wanted to go to the Ok Tsyop, he had to cross the mountains much farther to the east. De Wijn and Scharff therefore set out on their own. For a whole day they clambered along the slopes, which were covered with large and small blocks of rock, with bushes between. But they found no path. If all else failed, it would be possible to clear a track, but this would need a great deal of work and even so the path would be too steep for the bearers to negotiate. After searching in vain for ten hours they returned to their camp at Tabiem. The inhabitants made them a present of a pig, and in return De Wijn gave them a machete and four lempengs (plugs of finely-cut tobacco, pressed hard). On 25th July the patrol began the return journey, accompanied to the boundary by twenty brightly-decked West Sibillers; some of the men even went with them as far as Mabilabol as they wanted to see whence these white men came. De Wijn and Scharff did not take up the friendly offer of the Tabiemers to give them a couple of children as a present; they were quite satisfied with the pig.

The western region of the Sibil Valley was a very promising area for anthropological and ethnological studies, but it was useless as part of the route to the Juliana Summit. The only solution to this problem was to trek across the Orion Mountains much closer to Mabilabol. Warman made a reconnaissance flight in his helicopter in this direction, and reported that he thought it possible to fly through the valley of the Ok Tsyop as far as Denmatta if a few more landing-places were made along the route.

* * *

Disturbing reports had been received from the Netherlands about the expedition funds. The Council of the Foundation was moreover horrified by the request for a further two hundred thousand guilders. It was too difficult to try to explain the proposals by letter or by telegram; and anyway the situation was changing far too quickly. Brongersma therefore went down to Hollandia again; the telephone was the only solution. He had a stroke of luck in that the Cessna of the Missionary Aviation Fellowship had to come up to fetch Mr. De Bijl. This small single-engined aircraft could carry three passengers as long as they did not have too much baggage. In addition to Brongersma, Cortel was also able to go; he had finished his investigations in the Star Mountains and was therefore free to return to the Netherlands. They climbed in and the pilot taxied round in a circle to enable him to observe the mountains and the clouds from every point of view, but the sky became completely covered and their departure had to be postponed for a day. On Tuesday 28th July they at last succeeded in taking off, and two very busy days followed their arrival in Hollandia. The plans were once again discussed exhaustively with Mr. Th. C. Van den Broek, LL.D., the representative in Hollandia of the Foundation, and with Mr. A. Boendermaker, the Deputy Director of the Internal Affairs Department, who continued to show a great deal of interest in the expedition. They calculated and re-calculated, but every time their figures showed a requirement of two hundred thousand guilders. The telephone conversation took place on Wednesday evening. It turned out to be a short one, as the chairman of the Foundation, Prof. Dr. H. J. Lam, was able to tell them of a hopeful turn in affairs. While the telephone conversation was actually taking place, the vice-chairman, Prof. Dr. Ir. F. A. van Baren and the treasurer, Mr. H. Müller, were following up this possibility. The result of their discussion was revealed on Thursday morning when Brongersma received from the Netherlands the following telegram: "Funds assured this morning. Stop. Fifty thousand guilders transferred today to credit at factory Merauke. Stop.

Carry out expedition entirely according to plan including Juliana Summit and break-through. Stop."

Mr. C. Verolme had personally made himself surety for the deficit. Now all the plans could be carried out. Brongersma drew a deep breath of relief, and in Mabilabol Venema and the other expedition members threw themselves with renewed spirit into the task of preparing for the ascent of the Juliana Summit and for the trek from the Sibil Valley to Hollandia. In Hollandia itself, everyone was so interested in the fate of the expedition that a committee was established to collect funds, in particular for the break-through journey right across the mountains. This committee was set up before the arrival of the news of Mr. Verolme's magnificent gesture, but it was decided to allow this committee to proceed in any event, to demonstrate that Netherlands New Guinea too was capable of giving support to such an important undertaking. It was very encouraging to see the active interest of the Papuan population in this work of assembling funds. The fishermen of the Humboldt Bay caught a large sea-turtle and sold it to raise money for the committee; thus the return from one night's catch was placed at its disposal. The committee operated in a number of different ways; contests were organised not only in Hollandia but in other places as well.

As always, it was not easy to return to Mabilabol. On this occasion the Twin Pioneer was not able to land in the Sibil Valley and flew on with its cargo and passengers to Sentani, the airfield at Hollandia. Then the passengers and the baggage had to be fetched up to the valley. In addition the American journalist John Dominis from Hong Kong came to make a report for Life, ciné-cameraman P. Ter Laag wanted to go with the climbing team to the top of the Juliana Summit and Major of Marines J. Knegtmans had to come to the Sibil Valley to carry out an inspection. It was impossible to transport all these people together by Twin Pioneer and the assistance of the Missionary Aviation Fellowship was once again sought. Major Knegtmans and Brongersma were flown up to the valley by Cessna. Flying in this little aircraft was a real pleasure, although this time the pleasure was somewhat tempered by the smell of the dried salt fish carried as freight. The bearers found this a delicious food; moreover, it was easy to transport. A few of the expedition members also liked this fish; the only curious thing was that when the Muyus prepared the fish, only heads and tails were served up in the silver house!

The enjoyable thing about flying in the Cessna was that the plane flew low and it was therefore possible to see a great deal more of the landscape. Once the plane was flying high enough, the automatic pilot was switched on. Pilot Johannsen was in the habit of taking out his sketch-book and sketching the silhouette of the mountains. In this way he was able to record a great many details which enabled him to recognise the individual peaks rising above the clouds when a large part of the mountainous area was covered. As they flew on the mountains drew nearer and nearer and the peaks and ridges rose high above the aircraft. The two passengers looked surreptitiously at the pilot, feeling that they were flying rather too straight towards a steep rock face. Johannsen went on with his drawing, undisturbed; he had done this journey many times before and knew what he was about. At the very moment when his two passengers were really getting a little scared, he laid his sketch-book on his knees, grasped the joystick again and neatly swung the aircraft through a pass into the next valley. And so they safely reached the Sibil airfield. Next day the Twin Pioneer brought in Dominis, Ter Laag and Marine Koeman, and then flying was finished for the time being. Bad weather, mechanical faults in the Twin Pioneer, a week's stoppage for maintainance of the engines—all these things contributed to making Major Knegtmans, who had intended to spend four days in Mabilabol, in fact stay for a fortnight. This was not really a severe punishment; but it was unfortunate that he did not know in advance when there was an opportunity to get a seat on the plane so that he was unable to make any long trips. The bad weather also restricted the flights made by the helicopter, and thus the only thing that the Major could do was to go out for a day at a time in the immediate vicinity and take photographs. After a certain amount of trouble, he eventually succeeded in chartering a Cessna a fortnight later. Nijenhuis, the blood-group specialist, left at the same time as Major Knegtmans, as he had to be back again in his laboratory in Amsterdam by the end of August. He had determined the blood groups of a large number of Papuans. People who came from other valleys to take a look round the base camp were immediately hauled off by him, and before they knew it, he had pricked their finger and drawn off a couple of drops of blood. True, they were given a small reward, but the Papuans decidedly did not find this pricking business very agreeable.

While Vervoort was busy with his assistants up in the Antares Mountains, at Mabilabol the trade in lizards, frogs, snakes and rats

was continuing. Nijenhuis was responsible for part of this operation: he paid for the animals which were offered and preserved them in
alcohol. But Brongersma too had his share in the business, and it was
generally just when he was peacefully sitting down at his typewriter to
prepare his reports that the "supplies" arrived. Offers of certain species
were so numerous that the price fell. Instead of a button the Sibillers
received only a couple of small beads for a frog or a lizard. Staats had
already introduced the idea of supplying the beads strung on strings,
so that there was nothing for it but for Brongersma to add to his activities that of stringing necklaces. When things were quiet in the "market"
he would work making the necklaces, with due attention to the fact that
red beads were the most attractive and that the white beads were of
considerably lower value. A few children had also earned themselves
a couple of beads and they insisted that their new acquisitions should
be strung too. The marines constantly ensured that the supplies of
coloured cloth in the storehouse were always adequate for the trade in
animals. Here too red was the most highly-prized colour, followed by
dark green, with light blue a poor third. A few Sibil women wrapped
themselves in their cloths, but the men also liked to wear a red cloth
around their heads on festival days.

Every now and then, a festival was held in the valley. On these
occasions we could hear from Kigonmedip singing accompanied by
drums. Sometimes we learned by rumours that the festival was being
prepared, but the people would rarely tell us precisely when it was to
be held. It turned out later that there was good reason for this. A few
Sibillers had learned to value the riches of civilisation so highly that
they had overcome their fear of going out at night to come and steal
from our stores. We first of all unjustly suspected our Muyu bearers,
who had regular access to the godown. Two police-constables hid in
the store-house and, a long while after the lights had gone out, in came
the thieves. Suddenly there was a loud cry; Pattipeilohy rushed down
and switched on the generating set. Everybody jumped out of bed and
hurried to the store-shed. When the lights came on again they revealed Kagawera from Kigonmedip firmly held in a constable's arms; a
second Papuan had managed to escape. The thieves had smeared their
bodies with pigs' fat, and were as slippery as eels, so that the constables had difficulty in getting a hold on them. For one night Kagawera
was kept under arrest. He maintained that he had not come to steal,
but that he had been looking for a quiet spot to sleep. Next morning

he owned up and was taken back to his own village under police guard to show where the loot from his previous thefts had been hidden. As the police were taking him to Kigonmedip, they met just at that moment a Papuan coming along the path from the air-strip towards the camp. Seeing the procession approaching he jumped into the cane thicket to make off. It was natural to assume that he was an accessory, and the police therefore began a wild pursuit. Muyus and even the missionaries who lived a little way away rushed towards the place where all the noise was. When the man had been caught and had told his tale, it became clear that he had simply been frightened by the approach of the arrested man with his captors and that was why he had run away. A few of the Kigonmedip people who had slipped away into their houses were brought out again and Sneep gave them a serious talking-to; if they were to bring the stolen goods back again they would be allowed to go home in peace. Some twenty axes were handed back in this way; a few more had already been traded for something else and could not be recovered. Some tinned food had been taken as well, including tins of spinach. It seemed a pity that these chaps did not know the "Popeye" films, as then they would surely have eaten all the spinach up! But they had actually thrown the contents away, since they dislike spinach as much as we dislike manure. Corned beef was more to their liking and they had eaten it up at one of their festivals. No wonder we were not allowed to know when the feast was being held. Just imagine if they had had to share our corned beef with us, of all people! It was a pity that this should have happened, since honest men were worth a lot. There had not been a great deal of theft previously, not even between the local people, as is the custom in the Baliem Valley. If an isolated case of stealing did arise, it was sufficient for the local government official to give the robbed person a letter containing instructions that the stolen goods had to be given back immediately. The victim would take this letter to the village where the (suspected) thief lived and show it there. Not that the owner nor the thief could read, but it worked notwithstanding. In most instances the stolen articles were returned, either being given back directly or found again in the house by the owner some days later. Things had now changed and here too the influence of civilisation had made itself felt.

The theft and the capture of the thief were a sensation throughout the valley. Bomdogi from Betabib, a village that tended to look down somewhat on Kigonmedip, came and talked it over with great amusement and, since we did not understand him very well, gave us a vivid demonstration. He came creeping into the silver house crouching on half-bent knees, peered to his left and then to his right, and followed this by imitating the action of taking something off the table and popping it into his carrying-net. Then he rose to his full height and said in a tone of deep conviction: "Kigonmedipki kaga torgoi" which conveyed the idea that the people of Kigonmedip were a worthless crew. His contempt for so much wickedness was very clearly expressed. A day later his son came back with a stolen axe which (as often happens in the civilised world too) he had received from someone unknown! It had been an exciting change but twenty-four hours later everything was quiet again. As an atonement Kigonmedip gave the expedition two large pig's feet, and we accepted them with gratitude although we were still short of as many axes as would buy four pigs. All this was an unfortunate disappointment for Dominis, because he wanted a sensation for his newspaper report. On the evening that we caught the thief he expressed the hope that the camp would be attacked, saying, "That would be a story." The peaceful Sibillers, who do not perform wild war-dances and who nearly all work with steel axes, were too tame for him.

Subsequently, there was after all a sensation, as we were given the opportunity of attending part of the festival during which Kigonmedip was to dance for three nights. Hours before the festival was to begin in the evening, men and women from Kukding and other villages started passing our camp. They were walking at a brisk pace to make sure of arriving in good time. For the whole of two nights we could hear the drums and the din made by the singing men. By this time it had become too much for us too and early in the afternoon we set off, not because we were afraid of arriving late, but because it was much more attractive to trek through river and forest in daylight than at night. Moreover we had been told that the dancing would begin early on this, the last night. There was a very large and interested attendance at Kigonmedip. In addition to the inhabitants of the village there were also many guests, but everyone was still waiting for the people from Ebonatera, a village lying farther to the west.

Most of the men were brightly decorated with a mixture of red earth and pigs' fat. Some of them had only painted their faces red, but others had also painted part of their trunks. In some instances they had drawn a red ellipse over the forehead, cheeks and chin, but frequently they had restricted themselves to a vertical stripe on the forehead and horizontal bands of colour running from the corners of the eyes up towards the ears. Inside the red ellipse one man had painted his face ochre colour, so that in the half-light he looked more like a corpse than a living human being. Black stripes were also very much favoured. In addition to the indispensable gourd and a black cord wound many times round their middle, the men wore bunches of cassowary feathers or Bird of Paradise feathers tied vertically on their foreheads. Their toilet was completed by a string of dogs' teeth slung around their hips, armbands and necklaces of pigs' teeth, and a ring made of cassowary quill feathers and a few lories' beaks. The women had also painted themselves, but since they were not allowed to employ pigs' fat, the red colour was duller and darker in their case. They wore the usual rush skirts, with necklaces of mussel shells and yellow bands of the best of certain kinds of orchid, worn around the neck as a decoration.

While we were still looking round the village, we heard loud singing in the distance. The contingent from Ebonatera was drawing near and the crowd of people already present rushed to the edge of the village to watch their arrival. On a hill on the farther side of a ravine we could see the procession approaching. The inhabitants of Ebonatera were walking in a long file, one after another, halting every now and then emitting a loud noise, to which they danced for a short while. Slowly the procession drew nearer through the ravine, and we could hear their loud, rapidly-repeated cry of "Wa, wa, wa . . .", the cry which they always use when they are excited for one reason or another. At the bottom of the slope up to Kigonmedip they stopped again and we could now see more clearly what was happening. At the head of the procession danced four or five women. In addition to the rear apron they wore a bundle of long rushes behind, and as they gently lowered and raised themselves by flexing their knees, this tail whipped up and down, producing a rustling noise. Six men gave the rhythm by slapping their drums with the flat of their fingers. These men too had a "dancing tail"; in their case it consisted of the primary feathers of birds, which rattled as they jumped up and down. The other men crowded together in a small group; one of them acted as a precentor, the rest following him with a long drawn-out cry. Every now and then the men jumped up and down, stretched their bows and imitated the action of shooting arrows, probably to keep ghosts at a distance. As the group came nearer, it was pointed out to us that it would be better if we went to the village to watch the arrival of the procession on the little open

space in the middle of the village. Dominis had been waiting for a
festival like this and he continued to photograph the proceedings for
some time. But one thing annoyed him; one of the leading personali-
ties of Kigonmedip had been given a shirt by one of the expedition
members, and he was proudly trotting around wearing this, thus
threatening to spoil the effect of uncivilised Papuans which Dominis
wanted in his photographs.

The women who were dancing at the head of the procession crossed
the boundary of the open space at one particular point, the men entered
at another; it was not proper for them to use the same entrance. These
women had painted their faces with yellow and black pigments; in
their hands they held a couple of thin pieces of firewood, possibly as a
symbol of the fire which would be lit at the end of the festival to roast
the meat. They took up their positions to the left and right of the
entrance to the iwool and remained there for hours on one spot, gently
bobbing up and down. The men crossed the fence in a long row one
behind another; each held a bow and a couple of arrows in his left
hand, while in his right hand he carried an arrow tipped with several
feathers. They walked forward until they were in front of the iwool,
where they formed up in a small group and delivered their song with
all their might. The group then broke up; forming a long row, they
walked along the edge of the open place until they were exactly opposite
the iwool; here they crowded together again, repeated their song and
then went back again to the spot in front of the iwool, keeping to the
same side of the open space during all this. The men with the drums
walked along next to the file and they were really the only members
of the party who executed anything like dance steps. It is not only the
initiated men and boys who may participate in this "dance"; in the
middle of the file was a father leading by the hand his son, a little boy
of somewhere about three years of age, with a couple of feathers in
his hair as his only clothing.

The women of Kigonmedip, all of them wearing a dancing tail of
rushes, also came out into the open space. They stood in rows next to
each other (Plate 19). The women on the right-hand wing had their
right arms held across their breast and were holding with their right
hands the right arms of their neighbours, supporting the neighbour's
right elbow with their left hand; on the left-hand edge of the group
they did the reverse. The row shuffled a couple of steps forward
until they were right by the group of men in front of the iwool and

then took a couple of steps back again; during this movement the women repeatedly bent their knees to make the bunches of rushes whip up in the air creating a rustling noise. The whole night through these movements were constantly repeated, to and fro. At intervals exhausted dancers, men or women, would fall out of the ranks, but their places were directly taken by others. The fact that the rain of the last few days had turned the open space in the middle of Kigonmedip into a pool of mud did not deter the festive Papuans in the slightest; they calmly shuffled on through the soft mud. Those who were not dancing sat on the fence or on the narrow platforms along the front of houses, looking on.

This was such a monotonous activity that we took our leave after somewhat less than an hour, and, accompanied by a couple of young Sibillers, laboriously walked back to Mabilabol along the slippery track by the light of our electric torches. In the distance we could still hear the noise of the drums and the loud cries; the feast was continuing.

After the third night came the festival meal, for which the pigs had been slaughtered. Both Kigonmedip and their guests contributed towards the meal. Each pig was tied to a small stake by means of a band of rattan and then killed by being shot with one or more arrows. In Kigonmedip there had first of all been a thrilling hunt for a pig which had managed to tear himself loose, and had to be caught again. The pigs were slaughtered and the meat roasted above the fire; everything apart from the bones was eaten up; there is no such thing as the throwing away of offal here. Moreover, Papuans are not easily satiated, but go on eating until there is no more to eat. The meat was accompanied by baked batatas or roasted keladi roots. It was indeed a real banquet. When it was all over the guests from Kukding returned, tired and sleepy, passing our camp on their way home. They were no longer trotting along at a good rate, as they were completely exhausted.

The Sibillers very much enjoy going to the valley of the Ok Bon for a feast of this kind, and there were Kiwirokkers who claimed to have gone to a dance in the Sibil Valley. Pig banquets are quite customary throughout the whole of New Guinea and in densely-populated regions very great festivals are held for which ten or even more pigs are slaughtered.

On various occasions Pouwer had camped in Kigonmedip and Betabib and had visited from these camps the more distant suburbs of these communities and also other villages. He now spoke the local language very fluently and was therefore able to converse with the many friends he had made there. For the very difficult cases he had at his disposal an interpreter by the name of Yawok, a Muyu married to a Sibil woman. The Sibillers are quite willing to have a serious conversation, but they are also very fond of a good joke, and Yawok was always able to provide this. He had for a time been a pupil at the police school, where he had to do a good deal of gymnastic exercises. He was particularly good in free movements and the Sibillers were delighted when he gave a demonstration; arms forward, arms raised, "arms sideways and knees full bend" made a very amusing impression on them. The whole village was obviously interested and at once Pouwer had enough people assembled together to enable him to put questions. If they entered a village or suburb where no one was at home, Yawok would give a loud imitation of a baby crying. This brought an immediate reply from the garden where the people were working and thus the first contact was made. The conversations gave a considerable amount of information about the social life of the Sibillers and as the local inhabitants came to know Pouwer better, they related more and more tales to him about all kinds of events.

In the Sibil Valley they found that there were clans, each of which had its own name. In Kigonmedip there were members of the families Urupkuin, Uropka, Kagyarmabil, Kayakmabil and Kasipka; Betabib possessed members of the families Uropmabil, Kagyarmabil, Deyal, Tapyor, Simpanki, Ningmabin (only one person), Kasipmabil and Kayakmabil. From this it was clear that the members of one clan might be found living in different villages; the family of Uropmabil was met with in the villages of Betabib, Welding, Banumdol, Kolemsanglamabib, Diseleng and Ebonatera. Although the people belonged to the same family, the relationship was often so distant that they hardly knew each other, if at all. Members of one family coming from different villages can marry each other, but if war comes they can also belong to different parties. It may even turn out that in a war two brothers are fighting one on each side. If one of them happens to be severely wounded, however, the others are quite prepared to give his brother the opportunity to go through the lines and care for his wounded relative. Should one of the brothers die, they might on occasion consider that the survivor should receive compensation and this is contributed by both the warring parties. The Sibillers were now free to tell Pouwer about the way in which war is waged, and they very much relished

35. (1) Mabilabol: the tall trees are *Araucarias*.
(2) The visit of the Governor: His Excellency Dr. P. J. Platteel, Venema, Mrs. M. A. Platteel-Laseur (left to right).

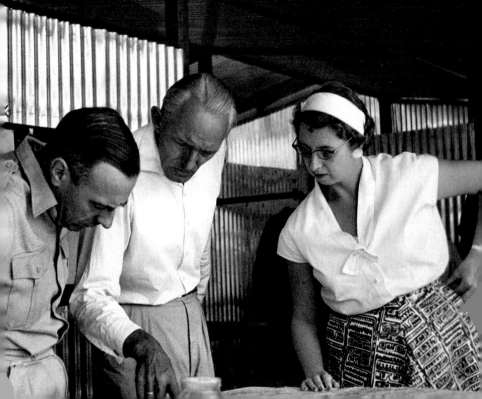

giving him this information. Up to a certain limit war is considered a game of skill and might be compared to medieval jousts, but with a certain serious element. The men try to approach as closely as they can and each discharges an arrow; the opponents have to show their skill by jumping aside as quickly as possible so that the arrow misses its target. A war does not necessarily have to be waged as one continuous operation. If one of the parties considers that they need to work in their gardens for a period, the hostilities are suspended; this is also the case when it rains. The expedition could consider itself fortunate that it was in a region where the population were on the whole peaceful and where fighting was generally of the nature of a sport. Things are often quite different in other parts of New Guinea; the radio gave us the news of an attack near Kepi (in the southern lowlands) in which thirty or more people were killed, and also of a murder party in the Baliem Valley (in the central mountains) where a number of men, women and children were slaughtered. In the Sibil Valley however the members of the expedition were able to move about peaceably and the population too undertook quite long journeys without having any fear that they might walk into an ambush.

The dancing festivals play an important part in social life; it is here that the young men and girls of marriageable age learn to know each other and this acquaintance frequently leads to a wedding. In the choice of their marriage partner the young women and young men enjoy a great degree of liberty. The bridegroom and his family have to pay the bride price and the family of the bride makes a present in return. These gifts reinforce the bond between the two families. The bride price does not necessarily have to be paid all at once; it is possible for a man to buy his wife on the instalment system. Government official A. A. Hermans, who had settled in the Sibil Valley when the airfield was constructed, records certain facts on this point in his report entitled "The Sibil Valley and its population". One man from Kigonmedip married a woman from the Kiwirok Valley, but he was not able to pay the bride price all at once; consequently, the wife's family called on him every now and then to remind him of his debt. Now that the men were able to earn steel axes and many other articles of great value to them which had not been available before—as a result of working for the government post or for the expedition—the constitution of the bride price had altered. Whereas it had earlier been the custom for a number of stone axes to form a part of the bride price,

36. A rest en route; the boy on the left wears the heads of rhinoceros beetles on his nose; the man on the right has lid of a peanut-butter tin as an ear-ring.

steel axes were now required and even here there was a noticeable depreciation in value. The situation was no longer what it was fifty years earlier, when widely-travelled people who had seen in the south country the first steel axes brought back splinters of wood cut with these axes to the Sibil Valley as evidence to support their tales about these exceptionally sharp axes. Everyone had by now come to know steel axes and the aeroplane is called the "Mother of the Axe" because it brought axes to the valley. Hermans gives in his report examples of the way in which the bride price was made up during the period when the steel axe was beginning to become known in the Sibil Valley. Awolki of Kigonmedip had paid for a wife from Betabib thirty cowrie shells, thirty bows, thirty rats, three steel axes and three pigs; the family of the bride had presented four pigs as a counter gift. At this time three steel axes and three machetes were sometimes considered sufficient; if the bridegroom worked for three months and was, in addition, assisted by his brother, the bride price could be paid in cash down. Sabuntok from Tulo had married two wives. For one of them, from the region of the Antares Mountains, he had paid fourteen cowrie shells, two steel axes, two machetes and four bows; the present given in return consisted of the head and trotters of a pig. For his second wife, who came from the western region of the Sibil Valley, he had paid six steel axes, no counter gift being recorded in this instance. In more recent times, a bridegroom had paid ten steel axes, five bows, fourteen carrying-nets, a string of dogs' teeth and a pig; this pig was however short of one foot, which the bridegroom had secretly eaten. Bomdogi, who was in comfortable circumstances, had paid much more for his wife. He gave seven steel axes, five pigs, seven bows, eight head-bands and later an extra six axes and two pigs. As more and more steel axes became available, their value fell, and more had to be paid. It is satisfying to see that here the wife is at least constant in value; this is in contrast to other regions where the bride prices were so high that a bachelor could only marry by running himself into debt for the rest of his life and where, to solve this difficulty, they had allowed the wife to become devalued.

As a general rule the bride price is settled before the marriage is celebrated, but it does also happen that a man runs off with a girl and the bride price, which now has to be paid after the event, is therefore much higher. On one occasion there was an abduction, in which the man carried off the wife of another man; this could lead to war. If a

woman commits adultery, her husband has the right to kill her and
her lover, but under the influence of the local government officials this
custom is in process of being replaced by a payment of compensation.
One such case occurred during the expedition. The second wife of our
interpreter Kotanon, who was a woman from the Sibil Valley, mis-
behaved with another Muyu, but this only came out when the adulterer
was on his way back to the lowlands. Kotanon wanted to set off with
his bow and arrow to kill the man, but we were able to prevent this.
The occurrence was reported by radio to Mindiptana, where the culprit
was expecting to receive payment of his wages, and after some negotia-
tion the affair was settled by levying a compensation payment of 75
guilders.

If a married man dies, one of his brothers takes his widow to wife;
if he himself is already married, she becomes his second or third wife.
When a married man is killed in fighting, the man responsible for his
death generally takes the widow and her children into his house. Thus
Kagawera from Kigonmedip had killed Ganggam during a war in the
Ok Bon region and had taken his widow with her little son back to
Kigonmedip. He had completely adopted the boy and considered him
as his own child; he was named Ganggam after his real father. If a
married woman dies the bride price is raised after the event and the
husband has to make an extra payment to his parents-in-law.

A man can marry more than one wife and he is then duty bound to
treat his wives alike. In many cases this does indeed happen, but if one
of the wives is slighted by her husband, she has little or no redress.
She cannot go back to her family, because the bride price has been
paid. The consequence therefore seems to be that in such circumstances
the woman commits suicide.

However, you should not think that the Sibil women are simpletons;
on the contrary, they are no more stupid than their husbands. This was
clearly demonstrated by a couple who had gone out into their garden.
The wife, hankering for a tasty morsel, was eagerly searching for caterpillars. While she was tucking-in this way, her husband had to carry
the carrying-bag containing the firewood and the baby. This soon
became too heavy for his liking and the delay was longer than he could
tolerate, but all his exhortations to his wife remained without effect;
she simply went on munching her titbits. This made the husband so
angry that, to call her to order, he shot an arrow into her rump. The
wife, considering that she had to make an appropriate reply to show

her husband quite clearly that she was mistress of her own time, gave him a heavy blow on his arm with her jungle-knife; fortunately, she used the blunt edge. None the less, the husband had to have his arm bound up and was for a long while obliged to go around with a bandaged arm, to the great hilarity of his fellow-villagers.

The pigs really form part of the household; they sleep with the family in the house. We were not able to observe whether customs go quite as far here as elsewhere in New Guinea, where the piglets are suckled by the women. At all events, the animals are very well cared for. If a pig falls ill, this is because it has become possessed of a spirit and this spirit must therefore be driven out. The pig is tied to a stake and the owner runs round it in a circle holding in his hand a pig's jawbone which has been held in the fire long enough to make it smoulder and smoke. When the pig inhales this smoke (and the beast can hardly do anything else), this is thought to drive out the spirit and the pig will become well again. If a pig injures itself in the house, this is a reason for the entire family to move house. Only on very special occasions (for example, dance festivals) are pigs killed and eaten. In the normal everyday life this does not happen, as pigs are too scarce and precious for this.

The population of a village, together with its associated suburbs, owns common keladi gardens, since the tubers of this arum-like plant (*Colocasia esculenta*) are eaten only at feasts where the entire population is present. Batatas (*Ipomoea batatas*) are cultivated for daily use and the batata gardens are as near as possible to the houses in each suburb of the village. When the keladi tubers are harvested, the head is lopped off with the leaves. This head, together with the leaf-stems, cleaned of their leaves, is set in the ground again and gives rise to a new plant which forms a new tuber. The keladi plant forms runners which root at some distance from the parent plant, and thus increases the total number of plants growing. Gardening is a simple operation. A hole is made in the ground with a dibble, and the plant placed in the hole. The garden does not receive a great deal of attention. A keladi garden is used for eight months and a batatas garden for only six months, because the ground is exhausted by the end of this time and a new garden has to be made elsewhere. In order to have sufficient supplies of food it is therefore necessary to be constantly occupied with the preparation of new gardens. True, there are muddy puddles in the old gardens where they grow the rushes which the women use to make

37. View of Antares from Camp 36; a screw-palm
(*Pandanus* sp.) in the foreground.

their aprons. The gardens are surrounded by fences to stop the pigs from coming in and eating their fill of the crops. All sorts of rubbish is thrown out of the garden close by the fence, thus creating an ideal hiding-place for many kinds of creatures, such as lizards, etc. In this way good supplies of meat are assured. In the case of the batata gardens which frequently lie on steep slopes, the fence protects the soil from being washed away by heavy showers of rain, even though the Sibillers are not aware of this function of the fence.

According to the shape of the tuber and the patterning on the leaves, the Sibillers distinguish between more than seventy varieties of keladi and twenty to thirty varieties of batatas, each of which has its own name, but they are planted without any distinction.

Food is an important thing. Consequently there are all kinds of regulations to be observed in planting and harvesting, especially in the case of keladi, and which lay down in what circumstances the gardens may be entered or not, a difference being made between the old and new plantations. If there is a threat that the keladi harvest will fail, one plant is pulled up, the tuber is smeared with mouse's blood and secretly eaten somewhere by the men. The head and leaf-stems of this plant are set in the ground again. Perhaps this is also a warning to the mice to leave the garden alone.

Dominis took photos for his article in Life in and around the base camp. He went out after pictures armed with three cameras. He made a whole series of photographs of everything which he considered worth photographing; his series comprised photographs with different exposure times, taken with a larger or smaller aperture, in colour or in black and white. When another aeroplane came up, he despatched packets of exposed film. Ter Laag tried to record as much as possible of the activities of the expedition on 35mm. colour film for public exhibition. There was no mistaking the fact that—with one single exception—the members of the expedition slowly came to have more than enough of being photographed and filmed. First of all they had had to pose for the television film reports of Van Sprang and Ter Laag and for the illustrated article by Klaarenbeek, and now the whole game was beginning all over again. Vervoort had set up in the laboratory building a device for filming with the expedition's film camera the trapping of insects attracted by the light. When Dominis saw this, he considered that the spectacle was well worth a photograph. The laboriously-mounted structure was dismantled and modified and

38. The moss (or mist) forest on the slopes of Antares.

Vervoort transformed from cameraman into model. Patiently he had again and again to stand for two minutes at a time, holding up in the air his hand—in which was clasped a catching-bottle—in front of the screen on which the moths, cicadas and beetles landed. The other members of the expedition, who were not required to appear in this scene, sat on the bench in front of the laboratory building and enjoyed the show. They provided the commentary, and it was a good job that this was delivered in Dutch. Ter Laag was allowed to assist Dominis as a colleague, and had to sit with his arms in the air for half an hour holding a desk lamp in each hand. It must be said that Dominis himself did not have too easy a time, because one of the expedition members wanted to profit by the flash-bulbs which Dominis discharged. He would stand behind him and try to make photographs at the same time. Although Dominis kindly counted up to three before pressing the release, our expedition member did not succeed in taking his photograph at the same time. To provide a suitable finish to his illustrated article, Dominis wanted to photograph a Sibiller who had become the proud possessor of all the "advantages" of civilisation. For this he did not choose Kapkasser, a little boy who worked for the marines and who ran around dressed in two shirts, two pairs of trousers and a pair of shoes far too large for him; he wanted to photograph a finely-decorated Sibiller. With Sneep's help he selected a man who was provided with a magnificent red cloth around his head, a string of beads around his neck and who was given in addition a shirt, a pair of trousers and shoes to put on. The victim was far from being at his ease in this outfit and was probably even less so with the great interest shown in him by the inhabitants of the camp, for as Sneep went to the radio to pass on a weather report, the man threw down all his treasures (for which he would in other circumstances willingly have worked for days on end) and rushed off at great speed. To the accompaniment of tremendous laughter from the expedition members, but to the great dissatisfaction of Dominis who saw himself being robbed of a fine photograph, the man ran down the slope and across the airfield, and did not stop until he had reached the safety of the canefield at the western extremity of the air-strip.

*   *   *

After Marine-Sergeant De Wijn had opened up the route to the western section of the Sibil Valley, government doctor Romeijn went to this part of the valley—as we have already related. His interest during this journey was in the first place directed to the incidence of framboesia. (yaws), a disease caused by a one-celled organism (*Treponema pertenue*) which occurs in many regions in New Guinea. The population of the Sibil Valley was not particularly ready to be examined (neither in the eastern nor in the western sections). Half—and even more than half —of the people did not present themselves, although the doctor remained camping near a village for several days, and also in spite of the fact that the interpreter clearly explained to the people what was his purpose. It must, however, be pointed out that yaws is of rare occurrence here. Of the five hundred and thirty-six people investigated in the Sibil Valley, only three were found to have infectious framboesia. This is not sufficient to give a clear picture of the occurrence of this illness, because the government officials have been giving injections against framboesia for some years and the number of people so treated is not exactly known. The injections had not yet obtained here the popularity which their rapid healing effects had given them in other districts, where the people considered themselves hard done by if they did not receive an injection, although they might be healthy. The three observed cases of framboesia were found in the east of the valley, where the population have more contact with people from other regions, such as the Muyu region, in the western part of the valley no cases of framboesia were met with at all. An investigation into the occurrence of malaria showed that this disease is only exceptionally found here and that it too occurs predominantly in the eastern section of the valley. Of the two hundred and fifty-four people whose blood was examined, twenty were suffering from malaria; thirteen were affected by quartan malaria (third-day fever) and seven by malaria tropica. Of those suffering from malaria tropica, two originated in Lewengbon, a village lying approximately on the boundary between the eastern and western regions of the Sibil Valley but a village which none the less has a certain amount of contact with the government post. Probably this malarial infection was brought here by the Muyu bearers or by trading parties from the lowlands, who imported the parasites into the valley, the local mosquitoes having been responsible for the further spread of the disease. Leprosy and goitre were not found in the valley.

While the Sibillers were not willing to take part in mass medical investigations, they were ready enough to come to the sick-bay to be bandaged for each little scratch. This was certainly largely due to the fact that the bandage around the arm or the leg constituted a fine decoration, and Pouwer observed that they would try to wash the bandages as clean as possible to be able to wear them at a festival as an ornament.

There was not a great deal of work for our doctors during the expedition, as all the members enjoyed good health. The position with the bearers was somewhat less satisfactory: one or two had slipped through the inspection when the selection was made. One Sansapor bearer had to be sent back because he was suffering from chronic malaria and was completely unfit for work. We were really frightened when two Sansapor bearers, who had accompanied Cortel to the Ok Bon, returned to the base camp with chicken-pox. On the way they had slept in Camp 36 together with the Muyu bearers and it was only after they had spent a night in the base camp that it became clear what they had caught. We feared an epidemic among the bearers; it was, however, not possible to have them shipped out, because they were not allowed to travel by the Twin Pioneer. Consequently, we set up a small quarantine camp behind the base camp and the patients were installed there. Fortunately everything turned out well, for the disease did not spread seriously. Only a few bearers and a couple of police-constables caught the chicken-pox and that was the end of the affair.

It was quite pathetic when a Sansapor bearer fell ill and had to remain behind in the base camp when the others went out on a trek. The man could only speak his own language and had hardly any contact even with the Muyus and Sibillers. But on one occasion a very pleasant day was arranged for him. One of the expedition members, who did not feel very well, stayed in bed for a day; he asked to be provided with fruit in syrup which our Muyu servant was instructed to take to the patient. The Muyu only understood half the message and carried a plate of stewed fruit to the sick Sansapor, who could not understand to what he owed this luxury, but who nevertheless enjoyed it considerably. Illness did not arise among the bearers very often, but they did try on occasion to avoid doing their work. They lived in their own camp on the Ok Sibil to the east of the airfield, and early each morning they would come up to the base camp in a long file. While they were still walking across the air-strip, they were all quite fit, but the closer they came to the sick-bay, the more the bearers began to limp; they then arrived on sick parade overflowing with complaints. However, Romeijn

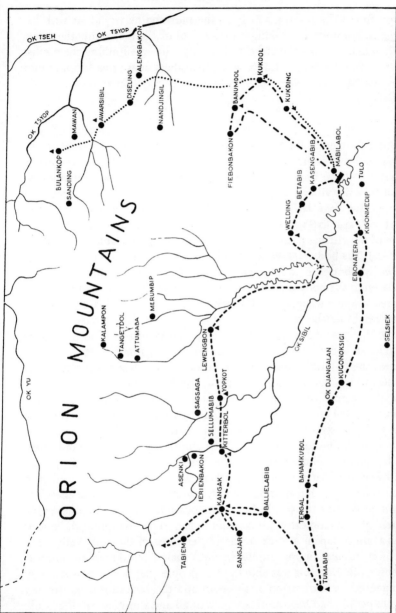

Fig. 14. The Sibil Valley. — · — · — Romeijn and De Wilde's route, 9th–12th July. – – – De Wilde's route 13th–23rd August. · · · · De Wilde's route, 16th–31st August. ▲ Camps.

soon found the solution. Early in the morning he would sit with his prismatic binoculars making his diagnoses of the men while they were still walking across the airfield; anybody who was limping there must be suffering from something, while the others who came limping into the sick-bay were only swinging the lead. This system worked perfectly satisfactorily.

*   *   *

After Romeijn, De Wilde travelled to the western section of the Sibil Valley accompanied by Marine Ruygrok and a police-constable. They set off on foot on 13th August, because it was their intention to visit as many villages as possible and to measure the people they found there. Five days later Pouwer and Dominis travelled with the interpreter Yawok to Tabiem by helicopter where they joined De Wilde. In one of the villages a little girl had died and they were able to attend the funeral. The body was wrapped in leaves and tied upright in a tree. Here it was supported by a number of stakes. The father and his three wives sat around the body on the branches to lament their loss. Dominis took a great many photographs, although Pouwer was afraid that the population might not be very pleased at this. However, the contrary appeared to be the case. If anyone dies suddenly, this is attributed to murder or witchcraft because they do not really believe in natural death. A seer can detect the culprit in this case; he takes a pisang leaf containing some water, which acts as a sort of mirror, and by peering into it is able to see the picture of the person responsible. The Sibillers had got the idea that the Europeans were able to do this with their cameras (because the lens was seen to have reflections). As Dominis was photographing the dead child, they believed that the culprit would soon be indicated. Although this did not turn out to be the case on this occasion the people still believed that we could help them with our cameras. An old man had killed a pig, but next day the pig had disappeared and he therefore came to Pouwer to ask whether it was possible for him to discover the thief "photographically"; this man too had to be disappointed. Pouwer and Dominis spent a week in the western area of the Sibil Valley. For Pouwer this was an opportunity to check again a number of his observations, while Dominis was able to meet people who were not as strongly influenced by civilisation as those around the base camp. Hardly any white people had been in this region at all and the West Sibillers only seldom reach the eastern regions of the Sibil Valley.

Together with his companions, De Wilde trekked farther towards the southern region of the valley, where white people had never penetrated before. This was a genuine karst region where the hard limestone out-cropped everywhere through the thin layer of earth which covered it. The soil is exceptionally infertile and the region is also very dry, because the water runs away through fissures in the rocks after a heavy shower of rain. "Tum kanong" (rock impossible) said the Sibillers when De Wilde suggested that they should go to the south of the valley. But for a box of matches and a razor in addition to the normal wages, they were willing to accompany him as bearers. It was difficult to find a guide, be-cause most of the West Sibillers did not know the way. Finally there did however seem to be a man from Tuyeider who was willing to show them the way to Tumabib (Rock Village) on payment of a knife. This village consisted of three houses, an iwool, a bogaam and a sugaam, and was situated on an almost bare mountain ridge. Huge blocks of rock lay on the ground between the houses. The track that runs from Kangak via Ballielabib was difficult to find and even the guide was not always sure of the route. The inhabitants of Tumabib had little contact with the other villages and the track was not very frequently used. When De Wilde entered the village it looked as though it had almost died out. There was only an old man, the guardian of the iwool, to be seen. The Sibil bearers and the guides repeated many times that the white people were kaga mok-mok (good people) and that they had many knives, matches and much salt. And then it became clear that the village was far from uninhabited, because suddenly inquisitive faces of women and children appeared everywhere. The camp was set up outside the village and the women and children came out to take a look. They did not enter the tent, which they considered as a bogaam, a men's house which was therefore forbidden to women. The men now also showed themselves; they first of all had had to paint themselves for this special occasion, but they did not want to miss anything of what was going on. They calmly came and sat down in the tent, closely following the way in which the food was cooked and how De Wilde made his toilet. Some of the women had fetched a few batatas from the gardens to exchange them for salt. Next day the population of the village stayed at home when they were asked to do so to allow them-selves to be measured. One of the bearers, who had already been through this measuring process several times, demonstrated what was about to take place; as a reward for those who allowed themselves to be measured there would be tobacco, biscuits and buttons. All the men allowed themselves to be measured, and to have their finger-prints taken, and they even agreed to having samples of their hair to be taken. A few women also subjected themselves to examination. Camp was then broken. In ten minutes everything was packed up and a man from Tumabib went farther on the journey as a guide to Banamkulol, a second rock village. Whereas it had been difficult to walk about in Tumabib because of the huge blocks of rock which blocked the path, in Banamkulol it was no easier because there thick greasy tree-trunks made up the track from one house to another. In this village too the population was willing to be subjected to anthropological study. De Wilde gave them a tremendous fright by preparing to shave himself, the first step being of course to lather his face. When his visage was covered by a thick layer of white lather they all decamped rapidly. Pouwer had already discovered that this happened when he was cleaning his teeth; when suddenly white foam came out of his mouth all the spectators suddenly disappeared. They probably thought that Pouwer was taken with a fit of madness.

Passing through Ebonatera and Kigonmedip, De Wilde returned to the base camp on 23rd August, and two days later left by helicopter for Bulankop in the valley of the Ok Tsyop, whence he returned on foot to Mabilabol. Again he travelled from village to village, measuring as he went. The bearers considered that this journey was lasting too long and they therefore tried to persuade the population to hide. The idea was that if there was nobody in the village, there were not so many folk to be measured and they would therefore get to Mabilabol more quickly. But they were not very successful in this venture, because De Wilde was not in a hurry. The last young lady that he met was presented with a brightly-coloured piece of cloth because it was assumed that she was the thousandth Papuan who had been subjected to this particular research; it later became clear that an error had been made and that she was the nine hundred and ninety-ninth. It was a good thing that this only turned out later because when he returned to Mabilabol De Wilde stood treat because he had brought his score up to a full thousand.

Mabilabol also received some foreign visitors. On Tuesday 1st September the Twin Pioneer landed with the French film expedition led by Gaisseau; this team was first of all to work in the southern lowlands and then intended to trek right across the country throughout the mountainous region to the northern coast, like our own expedition.

39.   Frigidaire Camp (Camp 40) on Antares.

The aircraft was packed full of men and equipment; the door had been taken out and a film camera had been lashed in position opposite the open doorway to enable them to film the region over which they were flying at the moment, but which they intended to cross on foot. A second camera had been set up in the gangway to record the first cameraman filming the world outside. Gaisseau stopped for an hour in Mabilabol with his men and we were not able to offer them anything but tea and chocolate milk-shakes, because our supplies of coffee were exhausted. They made the acquaintance of government official Sneep, who had been assigned to accompany them on the trip through the mountainous area and who was to join their party once they had finished their work in the lowlands. The expedition leaders and the members of the party which had gone to the Star Mountains provided the Frenchmen with information about the difficulties of the terrain, as well as a great deal of advice, e.g. on the necessity of taking sufficient bearers, on the need for providing the bearers and themselves with warm clothing, on the best type of shoes to wear and where to get them, etc. Chief-Pilot Van Rijswijk was pressing to be allowed to leave quickly. For a moment it even looked as though the party would have to stay for a while, because the sky was rapidly becoming covered. But the Twin Pioneer started off just in time flying with a following wind towards the west, where the plane disappeared through a small gap in the cloud cover. A little later we heard them above the clouds setting course for the south, bound for Tanah Merah and Merauke.

There were not many expedition members left in the base camp. Two major enterprises were under way. Verstappen and Sergeant De Wijn had set off on 1st August to the valley of the Ok Tsyop to open up the route to the Juliana Summit. On 8th August Tissing set off in this direction, followed on 13th August by Escher and Ter Laag. Dasselaar, who was to accompany Bär on the trek to Hollandia, had left on 3rd August bound for the Ok Bi to make some more preparations there and Bär followed him on 8th August. Vervoort was in Tanah Merah to carry on with his collecting in and along the Digul. While the Dakota was still coming up to drop supplies and the Pioneer was also able to bring in quite a good amount of gear, the outward transport was also under way. Whatever equipment could be spared was being brought down to Tanah Merah to be packed there for shipment to the Netherlands.

In spite of the fact that the number of people was small there was a

40   (1) An old Papuan examines the portrait of H.R.H. Princess Beatrix.
(2) Looking out at the front door.

great deal of activity in the base camp. The marines were very busy packing and despatching the supplies needed by the groups out in the field. Each morning the usual telephone conversations had to be held with Merauke, Hollandia and Tanah Merah, and each conversation meant work for the people in those places. Over and over again extra items of equipment or food were asked for. There were no more hobnails for the shoes, nor did the police in Tanah Merah have any more—could Mr. Van den Broek in Hollandia make sure that 24 lb. were sent down by the first aeroplane? Mr. Van den Broek would set off on this mission; he enquired at the stores, the police and the marines, but without success. Finally he found just over three pounds of nails in a shoemaker's shop in Hollandia-Binnen. Whether the indents were for hobnails, jungle knives for the payment of Sibil bearers, knives for the zoologists to barter for specimens, dried salted fish for the bearers—they all finished up in the hands of Mr. Van den Broek. He telephoned or went with his car to fetch anything and everything the expedition asked him for, and once he had got it there was still the problem of getting it to the Sibil Valley. Each week a meeting was held in Hollandia at which the flying programme for the available Twin Pioneer was laid down for the next week. This was not a simple matter. The Resident wanted to have the aircraft for the supply operation to the Baliem Valley. Mr. Van den Broek required it for the expedition, Sarmi must be given a flight—and there were a great many other requests beside, but Mr. Van den Broek did his best and so the aircraft came again and again with a consignment of goods. While Mr. T. H. C. Van den Broek was busy in Hollandia, Dr. J. W. Schoorl was doing the same sort of thing in Merauke; he too did a lot of buying in and sometimes he had to do some selling. For instance, there was the time when he bought dried fish for the bearers, which had to be sent to Tanah Merah by Dakota; but the airstrip at Tanah Merah had been out of service for two weeks as a result of heavy rainfall and the fish was threatening to go bad, so that the only thing for him to do was to sell the fish at a loss. In this way work was done to help the expedition in a number of places in New Guinea. The communications with Tanah Merah became steadily worse. While we in Mabilabol could clearly understand the transmissions from Tanah Merah, they could not hear what we said. Every word had to be repeated two or three times and then Tanah Merah would put out the request: "Would you mind saying that again, we can't understand you." Sometimes Mindiptana helped and passed our messages on. The conversations were thus frequently confused and one of the expedition members reconstructed in "Het Sibillertje" the telephone conversation that Brongersma had held with Professor Dr. Ir. F. A. Van Baren about the expedition's finances, in this style. According to this reporter the conversation ran as follows:

Prof. V. B. : We are very worried about your telegram asking for 126,000 guilders. Over.

Br. : That's good news—that's very good news. Over.

Van Baren : Why do you call that good news? Over.

Br. : I'll have to ask Venema about that. Over.

Van Baren : The till is completely empty—we've got no more money— have you got that? Over.

Br. : That's good news—that's very good news. Over.

Van Baren : I said no money—no money—we're broke. Over.

Br. : Well, that's something, anyway. Over.

Van Baren : Nothing—absolutely nothing left—the till's empty. Over.

Br. : Then we can carry on again—that's good news.

Although this special conversation was held on a line which did not present any difficulties and although the contents of this report do not agree with the actual conversation, it clearly illustrates the course of many conversations in New Guinea.

*   *   *

There were new occupants coming into the silver house. The remark made by Police-Superintendent Oosterman was very applicable to the Muyus who worked there and who had a very peaceful life: "They're getting too soft, sir, they'll have to go back to the forest." It was indeed time for these men to have a change of occupation and we sent them as bearers with a group that was trekking into the mountains. Other Muyus, who had hitherto been working as bearers, were now able to have a rather quieter life and were able to look after the house. This was not a great success because these men did not really understand a great deal of what we wanted. At eleven o'clock in the morning, when we expected our coffee, our new house-servants first of all set the pepper on the table, then a pot of syrup, next to which they put seven forks. Finally they put out some mugs and a pot of coffee. Then they scrubbed the table with coffee instead of warm water! Of the salt fish which were baked in the galley, and were put in the pan in the form of whole fish, the occupants of the silver house received only the heads and tails when the meal was served up. But this was still nothing to complain of. Various members of the expedition went every now and then to eat with Sneep in the government post, but Van Zanten could never be persuaded to go there and nobody could understand why. Towards the end of the expedition, however, the reason came out: Van Zanten had once gone into Sneep's house at midday and had found the Muyu houseboy, who had calmly sat himself down on a perch to stir soup . . . with his big toe. "I didn't want to tell you that, otherwise you'd probably

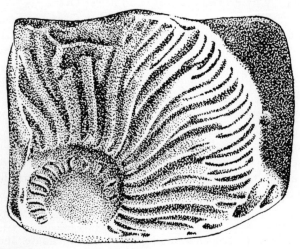

Fig. 15. Fragment of an ammonite impression; 2× (boulder from the Ok Sibil).

've gone without," said Van Zanten as he finished his tale. The doctor tried to teach our house-servants the first principles of hygiene, but this was far from easy. Whenever they went into the galley to help with the cooking we considered that they should be relatively clean. However, they did not think much of our ideas. If you gave one of the boys a clean white shirt, he would keep it with him to take back to his village after the expedition was over; next day he would therefore come to camp again in a grubby, almost black "white" shirt, which consisted largely of holes held together by small strips of cloth.

Another problem was the laundry. Some of the expedition members gave their dirty linen to the Muyus, who—with a few small Sibillers to help them—tried to get the clothes more or less clean. Once the clothes were finished they were laid out in the silver house on a rack

41.   Near the Juliana Camp; a man wearing a bamboo tube in the nasal septum and heads of rhinoceros beetles on his nose.

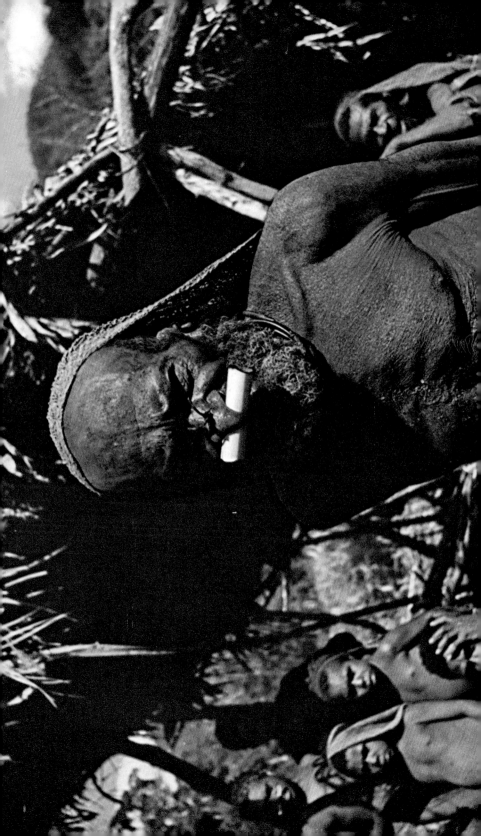

and each person had to look for his own property. Now and then this led to a deal of confusion. Two socks were often put together in a neat roll; it rarely happened that two socks of a pair were put together in this way. Other members of the expedition thought it a better idea to do their laundry themselves; they considered that in this way they would get the clothes cleaner. It must be said that the water obtained from washing clothes which had been worn during the whole of a trip through the rimbu was pretty filthy, but the clothes were never really white again in spite of this. Thus one of the expedition members was looking with satisfaction at a shirt and a pair of trousers whose colour clearly showed that they had seen long service in the bush; in his opinion he had got them really clean, until Menge, the pilot, walked by with the comment: "Now you'd better tar them again, they are beginning to show white spots."

In the middle of the day when the occupants of the camp were resting and there were no radio conversations, Brongersma took a walk through the Ok Sibil. He always wore shoes and a pair of long trousers and this was consequently a pretty wet operation. But then, when you are wading through the river, you are in such a good position to study the vegetation on the banks with the innumerable liverworts, small orchids, ferns and fungi. In addition, the boulders in the bed of the river had a great attraction for him, as they also had for Nicolas. These stones could give very detailed information about the mountainous region farther upstream and about the formation of these deposits. There were boulders with alternate layers of very fine-grained and very coarse-grained material. The fine-grained layers had been laid down in slowly-flowing water, while the coarse-grained strata were deposited in quicker-flowing currents. There were sandstones with alternating bands of grey and green glauconite-containing rock. Special attention was given to the rounded, spherical pieces of shale; these they would break in two with a hammer, because they often contained the remains of fossil cuttlefish (*Belemnites*). Imprints of Belemnites were also found in blocks of sandstone and one small piece of black rock was marked with part of the impression of an *Ammonite* (an involute cuttlefish shell, with clear imprints of the transverse partitions which divided the shell into chambers). The harvest was very large and on one day Brongersma dragged a whole pile of boulders up to the airfield; he asked a police-constable who was coming back from a dip in the river to send a couple of boys down from the camp to fetch the stones. He

42. Papuans crossing the Ok Tsyop.

himself sat down in the sun to dry off a bit. After a very long time, the constable came back with the message that there were no boys there (they were all away busily playing football) and after passing on this information he disappeared again. Consequently, Brongersma himself laboured away at dragging the stones home.

The fact that the soil of New Guinea is not entirely at rest was clearly shown one night when suddenly the aluminium plates of the silver house began to shake, first on one side and then, after a short pause, on the other side; it was a small earthquake, which was however noticed by few people. Most of them slept peacefully through it.

10

The Juliana Summit

"SOME TEN MILES, AS I SHOULD JUDGE IT, INLAND THERE LAY VERY HIGH
mountains which were in many places white with snow; it was surely
somewhat strange so near to the linie aequinoctiailis to find snow
lying upon the mountains," wrote Jan Carstensz—who sailed along
the south coast of New Guinea with the ships *Pera* and *Arnhem*—on
the 16th January 1623 in his journal; on his map he drew "The
Snow Mount", which was named Carstensz Summit in 1908 by
Rouffaer.

This was the first observation to reach Europe about the snow-
covered mountains in the interior of New Guinea. Subsequently
travellers did see snow-capped mountains from out at sea, but such
observations remained rare because the summits were generally hidden
by huge masses of cloud. The observers' opinions were frequently
divided. Modera, in his account of the journey of His Majesty's Corvette
Triton, did not believe that they had seen snow; he and some of his
fellow-voyagers believed that what looked like snow "was nothing else
than patches of cloud which lay upon the mountains". S. Müller, who
accompanied them on this trip, wrote of the snow-topped summits in
these words: "We however were unable to assign the glittering white
layers which covered the crowns and high ridges to any other cause."
Changes in the shape and size of the white patches, observed at different
times, made it practically certain that the observations in fact referred to
snowfields. The confirmation of this was provided by H. A. Lorentz and
J. W. van Nouhuijs, who reached the edge of the snowcap on the
Wilhelmina Summit on 8th November 1909. Only a few years later the
summit itself was reached: on the 21st February 1913, Captain A.
Franssen Herderschee, P. F. Hubrecht and Second-Lieutenant G.
Versteeg of the Netherlands Army Medical Corps stood on the 15,585-

ft. summit. On 4th December 1921 the Wilhelmina Summit was again climbed, this time by Captain J. H. G. Kremer, P. F. Hubrecht and First-Lieutenant K. Drost. Hubrecht was standing on the summit for the second time; the first time he had come from the south, and the second time from the north, so that he was the first European who had crossed the whole of New Guinea to reach this point. The glacier of the Carstensz Summit was reached on the 20th January 1913, by First-Lieutenant van de Water and Dr. A. F. R. Wollaston, but they did not continue as far as the top. This was first climbed on 5th December 1936 by Dr. A. H. Colijn, Dr. J. J. Dozy and Flying-Officer Ir. F. J. Wissel of the Royal Netherlands Navy. To the west of the Carstensz Summit, the Military Exploration Team discovered another mountain with permanent snow—the Idenburg Summit. Another snow-covered mountain was observed in the eastern area of the central mountainous region—first of all on 6th November 1909 from an observation post in the hills near the confluence of the East and West Digul, and again between the 9th and 13th October from the second Swallow Camp (the place where Tanah Merah is now); this mountain was named the Juliana Summit, after the Princess born in that year.*

In drawing up the expedition plans the possibility of climbing the Juliana Summit had not been considered. As the crow flies it lies some 25 miles from Mabilabol, but the journey on foot would be certainly well over 30 miles. The problem of supplies over so great a distance would be very difficult, above all because it would involve the use of a large number of bearers. It had however been decided to investigate the valley of the Ok Tsyop (the upper course of the East Digul); this valley lies one day's march from Mabilabol. In a north-easterly direction this valley runs as far as the Juliana Summit, but it was still problematical how far it was possible to travel upstream through this valley. At the beginning nobody dared to say openly that they did in fact hope to get near to the top of the Juliana Summit. For Verstappen a visit to the vicinity of this peak was very important; he wanted to study the influence of the glaciers on the shape of the mountains and valleys. Earlier the glaciers had been much larger and it would undoubtedly

* On the maps prepared by the Military Exploration Team both the Prince Henry Summit (in the Moon Mountains) and the J. P. Coen-Mountains are shown as snow-covered peaks. But at present they do not have permanent snow cover. Either the snow-line is higher now than it was then, or the observations were made when the summits were temporarily covered by snow.

be possible to find traces of their original extent in the region around the Juliana Summit.

The experience which had meanwhile been gained in the mountainous regions brought everybody slowly to the conviction that it must nevertheless be possible to get near the top of the peak. Once the plans had progressed far enough, it did not take very long before the ascent of the peak was taken for granted. This was bound to be the case with enthusiastic mountaineers like Escher and Verstappen in the group, and when the snow- and ice-covered peak had never been climbed before.

The only thing was that the expedition was actually equipped for the tropics and decidedly not for a mountainous ascent in ice and snow. It was necessary to bring special equipment out from the Netherlands to provide for the ascent of the Juliana Summit and this would be a task for the Expedition Foundation. To the great joy of the climbing team— which was to consist of Escher, Verstappen, Tissing, De Wijn and the cinematographer Ter Laag—the Expedition Foundation gave its approval for the ascent of the peak. On the 1st August Verstappen set out with Sergeant De Wijn and a number of bearers to clear landing-sites for the helicopter in the valley of the Ok Tsyop. Near Kukding there was already a clearing which was used for the air route to the Antares, but from this point onwards a further eight new landing-sites had to be prepared. The route passed near Banumdol and Ebabding, along the headwaters of the Ok Mimka and Bulankop to the Ok Tsyop, and then passed Bomakot and Yumakot, on the Tennomabee (7,216 ft.) to Biluming and Bilumabol. After passing the last village, they crossed the Ok Tsyop; they then continued along the northern bank of Denmatta, which they reached on 5th August and where they prepared the last landing-place. The route was not an easy one to cover on foot, and Verstappen proposed that groups of bearers should be sent off along another route. They could trek over the Atemsigin to the Ok Yu, a distance which they could cover in a day. An intermediate camp would have to be made along the Ok Yu and on the second day the bearers could march from there to Denmatta. While Verstappen and De Wijn were setting up a camp outside the village of Denmatta, they sent a number of bearers back to Mabilabol to bring up fresh supplies. Warman, who had not lost heart after his accident on Antares, made a flight on the 7th August to reconnoitre the route to Denmatta. To the west of the village he detected a suitable place for a landing-site, and Verstappen and De Wijn moved camp to this site. The Juliana

Camp was set up in a loop of the Ok Tsyop, in an abandoned garden on a site named Molbakon by the inhabitants of the neighbouring villages of Monggatil and Esipding, at a height of 5,910 ft. above sea-level. This was a large camp, which was to serve as the end-point of the helicopter route and as the starting-point for the trek on foot to the Juliana Summit. The camp was provided with a permanent team of marines, and fitted out with a radio station and a storage-place for supplies. On 8th August Tissing left with a number of bearers, arriving in the Juliana Camp on 10th August.

In Mabilabol Escher and Ter Laag waited for the equipment which had been ordered from the Netherlands, and which was already under way. On Saturday 8th August Escher reached the conclusion that it was necessary in addition to send for five down sleeping-bags and two small, lightweight tents. But it was no good ordering them unless they could arrive in Mabilabol within fourteen days. This would certainly not be a simple matter, because it often took more than three weeks to get something up from Hollandia or Merauke, and in addition the radio communications were already finished for that morning. But in New Guinea there was always a solution. Some of the Dakota aircraft were still flying on scheduled services, and as long as they were in the air the traffic-control tower on the airfield at Sentani was listening out for reports. Sneep therefore telephoned to Sentani with the request to ask Intel (the radio-telephone service of the Postal Telegraph Department) for a special connection. As always Mr. Valenbreder was ready to help; at half past ten in the morning Hollandia came on the air for us and gave us the connection with the Telegraph Office. Filled with optimism, Brongersma entered the following telegram: "Request despatch KLM this evening five sleeping-bags in down, repeat down, two two-man extra-light mountain tents." The bystanders shrugged at such optimism; how on earth could anybody think that they would get those tents sent off that same evening from the Netherlands? Precisely ninety-six hours later, on Wednesday 12th August, the Dakota came over to drop supplies and among them was the complete set of mountaineering equipment, including the two tents. It was at such moments that one felt that the distance between the Netherlands and New Guinea had become very small indeed as a result of modern methods of communication. For one moment longer we were slightly fearful that we had not received everything, because two sacks had unfortunately fallen outside the cleared area, even beyond the village of Betabib; but it became clear that these were only bags of rice and they were later carried up to the camp by Papuans.

Huge bundles were carried into the silver house. It looked almost like the arrival of Santa Claus as everyone started unpacking: woollen sweaters and training suits for the climbers and bearers, woollen helmets, gloves, snow-glasses, climbing-irons, hooks for rock and ice, anoraks, light rucksacks, ice-picks, sleeping-bags and the two tents. The equipment was there, and now the climbers would have to show that the Juliana Summit could be climbed. On 13th August Escher and Ter Laag left by helicopter to go to the Juliana Camp. Marines Portier and Scharff, who were to man the camp, also set off there.

The inhabitants of the villages near the Juliana Camp were very interested in what was going on there. They had never seen white people before and the whole thing was a sensation for them. They set up a number of sheds with sloping roofs around the camp, and a number of men camped there, to make quite sure that they missed nothing of all this activity. Each new arrival had his arms and legs pinched, not to see if he would make a good meal, but to be quite sure that he was real; trouser-legs were pulled up so that the Papuans could be sure that the wearer was white underneath them and the visitor's hair stroked because it was so soft and smooth. Verstappen and De Wijn had undergone this many times already and they were very pleased that there were now other people who could have the pleasure of having such interest taken in them. No women turned up, but Verstappen and De Wijn were asked whether they were willing to show themselves to the women as well. The arrival of the helicopter caused one particular difficulty. The local people naturally were not familiar with such machines and could therefore not be expected to know that it was dangerous to go near the whirling rotor-blades. It was not too difficult to begin with, because all the Papuans around the landing-place lay flat on the ground when the helicopter landed. But subsequently it became more dangerous as they lost their fear and wanted to show to the newcomers among their fellow-tribesmen how brave they were. When this had happened, it was only with a great deal of shouting and gesticulating that the Papuans could be kept at a safe distance.

Dominis who went to Denmatta with Pouwer, began to take new courage here; at last he had some people who did not know the whites at all, and therefore reacted better than the blasé Sibillers.

*   *   *

On 11th September Verstappen and De Wijn set off with eight Muyus to prepare the route through the valley of the Ok Tsyop. Escher, Tissing, and Ter Laag were to be responsible for the supplies, together with twenty bearers, their task to be taken over by the Marines later. According to the local inhabitants there was no track that went farther along the valley. With the help of aerial photographs and the map prepared from them Verstappen drew in a route along the southern bank of the Ok Tsyop. They crossed the river on a bridge of branches close by the camp. The local population still had gardens on this side of the river and there was a section of path which they cleared here and there, where necessary. The group made good progress on the first day. They covered almost three and a half miles and then made their first camp in the forest at a height of 7,775 ft. above sea-level. And then their difficulties began. They had to labour all day to cover a distance of from 550 to 750 yards. In this way they continued, day in day out; two days were taken up with clearing and then they could shift the camp forward by between 1,000 and 1,600 yards. The path was cleared at some distance to the river to enable them to make a loop round a kloof. There was no water at the first four camps in the forest. At Forest Camp 2 they could fetch water from the Ok Tsyop, but that meant a journey of three hours there and back. Thus after seven days they reached Forest Camp 4 at a height of 8,400 ft.

In the meantime the follow-up group had also set out. From the Juliana Camp the bearers trekked back and forth several times to the first Forest Camp to bring up all the necessary supplies; once everything had been brought up to this point, they "shuttled" in the same way between the first Forest Camp and the fourth. In this way all the supplies were carried up in stages, the follow-up team keeping as close behind the clearing team as possible. Escher, Tissing and Ter Laag appeared suddenly and completely unexpectedly in Forest Camp 4 together with nineteen bearers, somewhat to the dismay of Verstappen and De Wijn, who barely had enough water to boil rice and make coffee for their own team.

It looked as if the follow-up group would have to go without eating or drinking for that day and then return next day to the first Forest Camp without breakfast. That afternoon—fortunately this time—it came on to rain hard and they were able to collect some twelve gallons of water from the tent-cloths so that the situation was saved. The follow-up team then went back again to fetch fresh supplies. Verstappen and De Wijn meanwhile trekked on farther, over a ridge 7,775 feet in height, to the 5th forest camp where they found a piece of level, open ground with brushwood, grass and little patches of marsh. Here they actually had a fair view of a part of the surrounding countryside, and could see as far as the Dirksz Summit. This was certainly a welcome change after clearing a path through the forest for nine days on end, without seeing anything beyond tree-trunks and creepers. They made camp on the bank of a small clear stream, and in this way they were sure of water supplies as well. Eleven days after leaving the Juliana Camp they reached the bank of the Ok Tsyop above the kloof and established Forest Camp 6 here at 7,680 ft. They were now about five and a half miles from the Juliana Camp as the crow flies, and were not yet halfway towards their objective. The whole journey was taking much longer than they had expected. De Wijn, who wanted to reconnoitre the terrain, went straight across the rushing river to the opposite bank, where he was struck dumb with surprise by suddenly coming face to face with two Papuans, who were looking at him with quite as much astonishment.

One of them ran off to fetch his bow and arrow; the other was less frightened and accepted a little tobacco, but in spite of this he followed De Wijn at a distance to see what he was doing. The most important question, however, was where these men came from. Was there after all a local path made by the inhabitants through the Ok Tsyop, a path by which they could have reached Forest Camp 6 in a day instead of sweating for eleven days literally to no purpose? This did indeed seem to be the case. But why should the people have kept this path secret? Perhaps they wanted to hinder the white men, who had so many precious things, from leaving them, or perhaps because the region farther up the valley was alut and they did not therefore want to allow anybody to penetrate so far. It was a shame that they had lost so much time, but now at least the transport of further supplies would be an easier matter. They found a few more short local villagers' tracks in the vicinity of Camp 6, these paths having probably been used by hunters. An attempt to persuade the two Papuans to go farther with them was unsuccessful; they were not ready to budge one step from where they were. On 22nd August the entire climbing team had assembled in Camp 6. Here they stayed for a couple of days to allow the whole team of bearers to bring up the supplies from Camp 4.

Ter Laag then went back for one day to the Juliana Camp to leave his exposed films so that they could be sent off. In this way he brought down the latest news of the group that was slugging on through the valley of the Ok Tsyop and he in turn was given the news from Mabilabol. The aerial transport of supplies had again been delayed by a fault in the Twin Pioneer. The helicopter had to be used very sparingly because there was little petrol available. In the Juliana Camp, Ter Laag met Reynders, who had arrived from Mabilabol to carry out soil studies in the valley of the Ok Tsyop. On 16th August Reynders flew with the helicopter to Bulankop, where an intermediate station had been built on the route to the Juliana Camp. Marines Timmer and Vlaanderen were manning this camp. They were not very hopeful about Reynders' plan to engage a number of bearers in this region. The people in the neighbourhood of this camp were not very keen on working and moreover did not appear to be willing to go to Denmatta. They said that the people down there were "kaga torgoi" (bad people), while the inhabitants of the Sibil Valley were "kaga mok-mok" (good people); they were quite prepared to accompany Reynders to Mabilabol, but there was no question of them going to Denmatta. Fortunately there was in Bulankop a trading party from the Muyu area, who were trying to sell bows for bundles of tobacco. These Muyus offered to act as intermediaries. They held long consultations which Reynders could not follow, but the result was that seven of the men offered to go with him on payment of a knife. One whole day was given over to these negotiations and to the taking of soil samples. From the earth samples Reynders was able to collect earthworms and the local inhabitants lent their aid so enthusiastically that they turned out more of a hindrance than a help. On 18th August he set off with his seven bearers to continue his journey, up hill and down dale. They passed through several small villages where the men stood inquisitively looking out from the "front door" of the huts at the procession, while the women prudently peeped out at the group from behind the houses. Near the confluence of the Ok Yu and the Ok Tsyop there was a moment when things threatened to turn out badly. There suddenly appeared three men carrying bows and arrows, which they held ready to shoot. Only when Reynders had called out repeatedly "kaga mok-mok" were the bows slowly lowered, and the men came nearer to them. They chatted, as far as this was possible, and after Reynders had distributed cigarettes to them, they became friendly. These three men continued part of the way with them and they were also given something to carry. They climbed the Tennomabee (7,216 ft.) by a bad, muddy path, after which their route led them downhill over slippery moss-covered tree-trunks or over stretches of treacherously

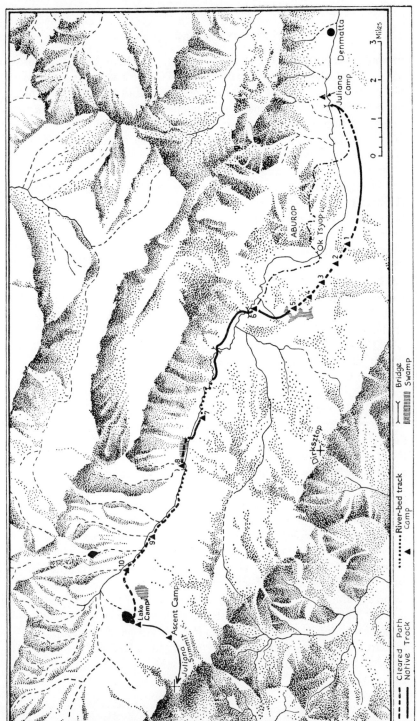

Fig. 16. Route from Juliana Camp to the Juliana Summit.

Cleared Path .... River-bed track | Bridge
Native Track | Camp ▲ | Swamp

smooth limestone. The bearers were beginning to have enough of this and repeated over and over again that it was still a very long way to Molbakon. They said that the village of Minomabol would shortly be reached, where there were many good people and it would be an understanding action on the part of the tuan to spend the night there. This is in fact what they did. Reynders was assigned the bogaam (the men's house, access to which is also allowed to uninitiated men; this is in contrast to the iwool or ritual men's house) as his lodging. They had a good company in the bogaam because some of the men from the village also came to sit round the fire. Reynders gave them tobacco and biscuits and in return the inhabitants of Minomabol presented him with boneng (batatas) roasted in the fire. Fathers came up to show their children proudly and Reynders showed them a photograph of his wife and little daughter, which called forth many cries of wonder. The fire was kept burning all night and the guests slept in the most comfortable manner imaginable. Next morning Reynders set off to continue the trek, with a woman leading the party as their guide; she came from one of the villages near the Juliana Camp and thus knew the best way to take. The route ran for the most part to the south of the Ok Tsyop and west of Denmatta the party crossed the river finding a few tyemaras [trees of the *Casuarina* genus] growing on the loose rubble which formed the banks. Soon after this they reached the Juliana Camp (19th August). From this point Reynders climbed the slopes of the Buming, a mountain lying to the south of the river; gardens were maintained on these slopes up to a height of roughly 6,560 ft. When he asked to whom these gardens belonged the answer given to him was: Sagsaga. It appeared that there was another village with the name Sagsaga here in the valley of the Ok Tsyop on the northern edge of the Orion Mountains, precisely as there was a village of this name to the south of the mountains in the Sibil Valley. It would appear that the Sibil village had been established by people who had migrated from the valley of the Ok Tsyop; there must therefore be a north-south connection over the mountains, something of which the inhabitants had no knowledge when Sergeant De Wijn carried out his reconnaissance to the western section of the Sibil Valley. The Ok Tsyop village of Sagsaga is situated 6,170 ft. above sea-level. To the north of the Ok Tsyop they climbed the slope of the Mol. At a height of 6,300 ft. is the village of Monggatil; the gardens continue to a height of 6,790 ft. Reynders studied ground sections and took samples of the soil on these slopes and took samples of the earth. It was far from an easy matter to get the Papuans from the region around the camp to go with us as bearers for the short journeys up the mountains slopes. As soon as they saw Reynders trying out his shovel, earth-drill and a few bags, most of the men disappeared, but after some tobacco had been distributed to them and the wounds of some of them bandaged, a couple did agree to go.

Time and again they claimed that the party could certainly not go any higher; the top of the mountain was alut (taboo) and they were not at all keen on penetrating into the forbidden region. Moreover, they certainly did not follow a direct route; they repeatedly made large detours and it became clear that they were carefully avoiding the gardens where the women were working.

On 22nd August Marines Brandenburg Van den Gronden and J. W. Hendriks left Mabilabol with a party of bearers bound for the Juliana Camp. Their journey was not an easy one. On the second day their route led them through extensive groups of gardens, where they continually had to climb over slippery tree-trunks which also caused the bearers considerable difficulties. Every now and then their path ran close by the river, passing precipices where tree roots gave them a fairly firm hold. When one of the bearers dropped a pan, the soft impact was enough to bring 700 cubic feet of earth and stones into movement and cause the whole lot to fall into the river. The weather was bad and the group took much longer over the journey than would have been necessary in dry weather. On 24th August they arrived in the Juliana Camp after having walked for twelve hours on the last leg of their journey. The team in the camp now consisted of four marines, who were responsible to see that the team which was trekking along the Ok Tsyop to the Juliana Summit would receive fresh supplies in good time and also for ensuring that they received the precise quantity of rations laid down beforehand. The marines executed this task perfectly and thereby contributed greatly to the success of the whole expedition.

Marine Scharff shot a bird of prey, intending to add it to the zoological collection, but he was given no opportunity to fulfil his purpose. As the bird fell to the ground, the Papuans rushed up to it and before Scharff could intervene all the large feathers had been pulled out; they are used by the Papuans to decorate their carrying-bags. The bird itself served to make a very nice meal. It was held over the fire to burn off the last small feathers; a small incision in the breast was sufficient to enable them to withdraw the intestines, which were thrown into the fire. Two small mats were then woven out of the leaves of a sort of ginger plant. The leaves were laid one on top of another and woven together by means of a few thin and narrow strips of rattan. The mats were laid on top of one another in such a way that the longitudinal axis of the leaves in one of them lay at right angles to that of the other. On top of these mats they laid a leaf of a sort of fern and an umbellifer, on top of this again a red-hot stone taken out of the fire, followed again by a few more fern leaves and finally the bird. The mats were folded over the bird and tied together. This package was then laid in the hot ash and covered with hot stones and glowing wood charcoal. After it had roasted for a while in this way, the mats were taken off and the bird polished off, together with the fern leaves and the flowers.

Fortunately this was not the fate of all birds. Scharff sent back four birds to Mabilabol from the vicinity of the Juliana Camp so that they could be skinned there: two fly-catchers, a flower-pecker and a wood swallow. One of the fly-catchers (Machaerirhynchus nigripectus) had a very broad and flat beak; the back was brownish-black. The wings were of the same colour, but dotted with little white patches and a lengthwise white stripe; the under side is yellow with a black patch on the breast. The other fly-catcher (Peltops montanus) is black with a large white blotch behind the eye and white patches on the neck; the rump and the beginning of the lightly-forked tail are red. The flower-pecker (Dicaeum geelvinkianum) is brownish-black above with a bluish metallic sheen; on the top of the head and on the breast the bird has red patches and the root of the tail is also red; the underside is greenish. The wood-swallow (Artamus maximus) is blackish-brown with a white neck and white underside. They did not collect a large number of birds here; this was not because the district was poor in birds, but because there was no point in shooting them unless they were certain that the helicopter would be arriving shortly. In this climate it is not possible to let the bodies lie for so much as a day because they are completely ruined by the end of 24 hours.

*   *   *

Reynders wanted to go farther up the valley of the Ok Tsyop, to Camp 4 which had been set up by the clearing team. It was difficult to get bearers for such a trip. One morning twelve of the Muyu bearers reported sick; most of them had injuries between the toes, which had been produced during their trek to the camp. Of the local forces one took to his heels when he saw the carrying-cases being prepared.

Another one did accompany them, but five minutes later he returned to the Juliana Camp convincingly "lame". Reynders first of all walked through gardens and on good paths, after which he climbed upwards along the track which Verstappen and De Wijn had cleared. The path deteriorated later, in the moss forest, but after seven and a half hours' walking he had none the less reached Camp 4, where the clearing team had left a tent standing. He had not taken any water with him and it was not raining, so that he had to wring out some of the moss to obtain sufficient water for his rice and coffee. Next day they collected samples in the region around Camp 4 and then began the return journey in mist and rain. It was a difficult journey over a muddy track and there was a lot of scrambling to do as well. On the way they collected a few more samples and Reynders came back to the Juliana Camp just as darkness was falling. On 28th August he returned to Mabilabol by helicopter.

Pouwer bivouacked near the village of Denmatta, where he was able to collect new data about the local population. The inhabitants were not yet affected by European influences. Matches appeared to be a novelty. Many of the people here wore thick armbands of woven rattan, which were not so much intended as a decoration, but which were employed in making a fire. The thin band of rattan is wound around a piece of dry wood which is pressed on to the ground with a foot. The band of rattan is rapidly drawn up and down, the friction producing so much heat that the wood begins to smoulder; generally the wood is split and into the gap are pushed dry leaves and moss which easily burn. As soon as the wood begins to smoulder the fire is encouraged by blowing on it. One of the Papuans who was given a box of matches was so impressed by this modern magic that he threw his rattan armband into the bushes, remarking: "This is now a thing of the past."

In this region the people had the same kind of decorations as in the Sibil Valley, but they were clearly poorer, as very few men were seen wearing necklaces of pigs' incisor teeth. Generally they wear thick pieces of bamboo through the inter-nasal septum and the heads of rhinoceros beetles are also worn on top of the nose (Plate 41).

* * *

On 25th August Verstappen and De Wijn left Camp 6 with their eight Muyu bearers to clear the rest of the route. Initially they were still able to follow a path used by the local population, first of all along the northern bank and then later along the southern bank. At two places the

Papuans had made bridges, i.e. they had felled large trees in such a way that they had fallen across the river. When the track ended, the group walked for some distance along the bed of the river in order to make better progress. Near Camps 7 and 8 there were open spots on the bank and they were able to cross these without a very great deal of clearing work, but then they had to follow the bed of the river again. This did allow them to advance at a fairly good rate, but it was not very pleasant to trudge through water up to your waist at a temperature of 9°C.; the bearers did not like this at all. There was no visibility at all and it was up to Verstappen to show his skill in determining where they had to leave the river to take a rather more westerly course instead of the north-westerly line they had followed. He had aerial photos, a map and a compass, but virtually no fixed points from which he could orientate himself. On 28th August, as they were setting up Camp 10, he decided that this would be the end of the route along the Ok Tsyop. From here on they would move in a westerly direction. It turned out that he had chosen precisely the correct point. They stayed in Camp 10 at a height of 9,575 ft., until 31st August. Along the Ok Tsyop they cleared a path which followed the bank of the river, back to a point beyond Camp 9. This was a safety precaution. If it rained heavily in the mountains, the Ok Tsyop would rise suddenly and be transformed into a wildly-rushing river. If that happened the follow-up groups would no longer be able to reach the climbing team. It might also happen that the climbing group would be forced to make the return journey at a fairly rapid speed and in this event they could not afford to find their passage barred by a swollen river. On the way Verstappen had every now and then looked during the night at the level of the river, and what he had observed had given him some anxiety. They now had to wait for the follow-up groups and this offered a good opportunity of putting the path to rights. When they had left Camp 6 they had taken supplies for five days with them, expecting to receive further supplies on 29th August, but on 31st August there was still no trace of the follow-up group. If they did not come on this day the clearing team would have to return to a camp lower down, but fortunately contact was made with Tissing between Camps 9 and 8, and fresh supplies arrived at Camp 10 in the nick of time.

At Camp 10 Verstappen and De Wijn left the bed of the Ok Tsyop, as we have said already. They cleared a path in a westerly direction in the hope of coming out by an unnamed lake that was known only from

43. (1) Juliana Summit seen from the East.
(2) Ice and snow covering the Juliana Summit.

aerial photographs. Their fixes and the change of course had been successfully made and on the 1st September they saw, at a height of 10,662 ft. above sea-level, in a cwm between dark-green steep mountains, a reed-fringed lake. This was about 800 yards long (Plate 46, Fig. 16). There were coots (*Fulica atra novae-guineae*) swimming on the inky-black water, and in it were small water-beetles; De Wijn was able to collect a few small molluscs. The ring of reeds and the undergrowth surrounding it provided shelter for numbers of frogs. Near this lake we set up the tents of "Lake Camp", where a group of bearers was to stay while the climbing team went higher and made a small food depôt ready for the return journey.

While still at Camp 6 Escher had requested that a permanent team with adequate supplies of food should be assigned to the camp while he continued his journey. First of all Marine Scharff was sent up there with eleven bearers. He followed the newly-discovered track made by the local population. This track did not please him much; there were a number of steep slopes which even the bearers could only negotiate with difficulty, carrying their 40-lb. loads. Scharff left the supplies behind in the camp and returned to the Juliana Camp. On the 1st September Marine H. J. W. Hendriks set off with eighteen bearers to Camp 6, where he stayed with two bearers; the remainder he sent back to base. Three days later Marine Brandenburg Van den Gronden also arrived, and with Hendriks he made up for the time being the permanent team at this camp.

On Sunday 30th August, a day without telephone conversations, Brongersma had a fine opportunity to go up to the Juliana Camp. The weather was fine and clear and he left at a quarter past eight in the helicopter. Warman flew across the Orion Mountains to the valley of the Ok Tsyop; far below them they could see the river flowing in a narrow steep-walled valley. The bed of the river was full of huge blocks of rock, between which the water foamed wildly. A little farther on, in a bend in the river, was a larger camp in front of which flew the Netherlands flag—this was the Juliana Camp. Juliana Camp was situated in particularly beautiful surroundings, almost enclosed by a loop of the Ok Tsyop and with Mount Aburop standing out against a strip of blue sky as a background. Since the day before, the camp had been provided with a receiving/transmitting radio set and Brongersma made contact with Mabilabol every hour to ensure that he was kept up to date with news about the weather. Not that he would not be very pleased to spend a day or two in Juliana Camp, but his presence in the base camp

44. (1) En route for the Juliana Summit; Verstappen leading, followed by Escher, de Wijn and Tissing. (2) 9th Sept. 1959, 11.45 a.m. planting the flag on the Summit (left to right) De Wijn, Escher, Verstappen, Tissing; Ter Laag, the fifth climber, took the photographs.

was essential. The visitors to the camp were received by Marines Portier, Brandenburg Van den Gronden, Scharff and Hendriks with coffee. They were very pleased with conditions here. The only thing they really seemed to need was a few fresh books, some cigarettes and tobacco. The zoological collections were not forgotten, and there was a box containing four birds ready for despatch to Mabilabol; a number of insects had been brought together too. The villagers were still camping around the bivouac and as a newcomer Brongersma had to submit to having his arms and his legs pinched. Brongersma was able to stay for about a couple of hours and he therefore had an opportunity to look round in the immediate vicinity. On wet spots along the river bank there were scores of butterflies, predominantly blues (Lycaenidae). Small light-blue gentians were growing on the rocks and Brongersma took one or two with him for Kalkman. Subsequently it turned out that this was a species which had not previously been described and which also occurred around the Wissel Lakes. Much less prominent were the small, yellow buttercups (Ranunculus mentiens), a species previously known only from Mount Albert Edward at a height of 11,800 ft. and was now therefore found nearly 6,000 ft. lower. The language here was the same as in the Sibil Valley and Brongersma therefore shouted out: "Awotson, kolson burotai" (lizards, frogs bring). And it was not very long before a little boy actually did arrive with a frog. He was visibly delighted that he was given something for this; the people round here were not yet accustomed to the idea of asking for payment for every fly or beetle. Other boys brought handfuls of large bugs (Lyramorpha persimilis subsp.) which, as is usual with these creatures, emitted a penetrating smell. In the area around the Wissel Lakes a similar type of bug (Lyramorpha edulis) is eaten and here too it was clear that these creatures—which have an unpleasant smell to European nostrils—are considered as a tasty morsel. At least when Brongersma pointed to the bugs and asked: "Nam-nam?" (Eat?), the answer was "Nè" (Yes).

*   *   *

Warman had warned him that they must be back in Mabilabol before twelve o'clock whatever happened, because the valley of the Ok Tsyop frequently became covered with cloud at about that time. They therefore decided to leave at half past ten. The helicopter, which had landed right by the camp, took off without any passengers and then came down again on a platform somewhat farther up the hillside. There was not a great deal of room to manoeuvre in the valley near the camp and with a heavy passenger or with cargo on board it was better to take off from the hill, because this gave the opportunity of directly attaining a reasonable height above the forest, so that they could fly off directly in an easterly direction through the valley of the Ok Tsyop. On their return journey they could see Pouwer busy in Denmatta; he was sitting in the middle of a group of Papuans in the tiny village square. The weather was still so fine that they landed for a short while near the camp at Bulankop, occupied by Marines Timmer and Vlaanderen. They too were in the best of spirits, but they would have liked to have a few more cigarettes. These camps had been well supplied; everything that we had available in the way of meat, milk and coffee in Mabilabol had been sent to the camps because the base camp would naturally be able to get fresh supplies. But now the base camp was without meat or coffee, because the Twin Pioneer had not been able to fly. Their stay in Bulankop lasted for ten minutes and they could not have afforded to stay longer, because just as the helicopter was leaving great banks of cloud came driving into the valley of the Ok Tsyop. Brongersma would not have been surprised had he had to camp in Bulankop, but Warman climbed somewhat higher and made a small detour. The helicopter passed between the clouds over the Orion Mountains and then below them the Sibil Valley appeared through a gap in the cloud cover.

To look after the provision of supplies for the climbing team and to deal with the outward transport from the Juliana Camp, Lieutenant Nicolas went to the Juliana Camp on 3rd September. It was a sound idea that there should be somebody in the camp who could take decisions if set-backs should occur. On top of this he was an eager collector. He sent back to Mabilabol large specimens of rock containing fossil shells, a preserving-jar full of tadpoles, frogs and lizards and a number of ethnographical exhibits. The tadpoles were of the same kind as those found in the Ok Sibil and in the Ok Bon; flat tadpoles with a large sucker-mouth by which they fastened themselves firmly to stones in the rapidly-flowing water. Among the ethnographical specimens were a number of rattan armbands and two bags of amulets. One bag contained a dried rat's head and a fossil shark's tooth, the other contained five fossil shark's teeth (among others, teeth of the tiger shark, *Galeocerdo cuvier*), a small shell (*Corbula erythrodon*) and a small pebble. Nicolas also collected and despatched many insects.

In Mabilabol everybody was waiting excitedly for reports of the progress made by the climbing team. They had not taken a wireless transmitter with them and news could therefore not be obtained by radio. The pilots of the Dakota which flew on the scheduled service from Hollandia to Merauke were constantly asked whether they had seen any

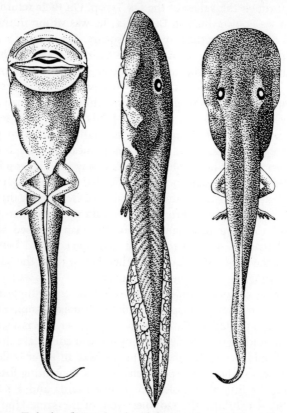

Fig. 17. Tadpoles, flattened and with large sucker-mouths, as found in the fast-flowing rivers. 1½×.

signs of life near the Juliana Summit, but the answer was always in the negative. The only thing that they could tell us was that a great deal of new snow had fallen; many of the peaks which were normally free of snow were now covered by a thick layer. This was not precisely a comforting piece of news, because the conditions on the summit could very well be rendered most disagreeable by this new snowfall and ascent might become much more difficult as a result.

Once more, news had been received from the Netherlands which made it necessary for Brongersma to go again to Hollandia to discuss the problems. He was to stay away for a day, because the Twin Pioneer flew down to Hollandia on 4th September and had to make a flight to the Sibil Valley on 5th September. The trip to Hollandia went off quickly, but when Brongersma saw that the mechanic on the airfield at Sentani was having to ply his spanner very busily, he had a premonition that something was wrong somewhere and indeed this turned out to be true. They had to send for a small spare part to Biak. It so happened that the Governor was flying with the Dakota from Monokwari to Hollandia; since the plane was to touch down in Biak, the new part could be brought up to Sentani by the afternoon. This in fact happened, but when the mechanics tested the machine to see that everything was in order, it was found that the new part was faulty as well. Another telegram was sent to Biak to have the right part sent and fortunately it arrived the following morning with the Dakota. Thus the Twin Pioneer was ready for take-off on 5th September. First of all, a Dakota left with supplies which it was to drop in the Sibil Valley, followed by the Twin Pioneer. The Dakota was flying somewhat more quickly and reached the mountains roughly a quarter of an hour earlier; he passed over the camp and dropped the supplies. When the Twin Pioneer reached the mountains, huge cumulus clouds were piled up against the high ridges. The plane had to play thread-the-needle with huge banks of cloud; into each valley and out again, first to the west and then to the east, but they found no way of getting through. The cockpit door opened, the fliers waved their hands with a gesture of helplessness and the Twin Pioneer returned to Sentani. It was, in fact, quite a normal thing to be three hours and ten minutes in the air without being able to get through. Meanwhile Brongersma had enjoyed his flight. He felt almost like a millionaire, as the only passenger in the Twin Pioneer; this was true, even though the plane was filled with bags of rice and tins of meat. His emotions of pride were reduced quite considerably when he suddenly saw on the consignment note that the cargo was said to be 1,936 pounds of food, in which total weight himself was included; this seemed quite appropriate in a country where there was still numerous cannibals.

For the moment, therefore, he had to remain in Hollandia. Each day he asked Mabilabol to give him news about the ascent of the Juliana Summit, but they could not tell him any more than the fact that on 1st September the clearing team had reached Mountain Lake. It began to

frighten him rather that no further news whatever was received from the
· climbing team and he tried to charter a Cessna to bring him back. But the
Missionary Aviation Fellowship was also very busy and they were therefore unable to make any extra flights, unless obliged to do so by an
emergency. So there was nothing for it but for him to wait until the
Twin Pioneer went up to the Sibil Valley again, and it was only on 10th
September that Brongersma returned to the base camp. But here again
there was no further news. The one thing that was certain was that no
further groups would be able to go to Mountain Lake. It had been
decided in the Netherlands that the expedition must be withdrawn from
Mabilabol by the end of September. This was a great pity, because an
extension of one month would have enabled a great deal of important
zoological and botanical material to be collected in and around the
lake, but there was nothing to be done about it.

Meanwhile, the clearing team and the follow-up team had not been
idle. They had cleared a side track to a marsh which might perhaps be
used for supply dropping. The ground in this region was covered with
clumps of grass which were hard and up to a yard in height; there were
also many tree-ferns with short thick stems. In addition Verstappen and
De Wijn cleared a path in the direction of the Juliana Summit to the
edge of the timber-line which was here about 12,136 ft. On 3rd September Escher and Ter Laag reached Mountain Lake and on 4th September
Tissing arrived with the last bearers. The climbing team was now
assembled and all the equipment had been brought together. Instead of
twelve days, the period originally estimated, they had taken twenty-
five days to reach Mountain Lake from the Juliana Camp.

For two days it poured with rain and everybody therefore remained in
camp. When it did clear up they saw their objective to the south-west—
the Juliana Summit. The gleaming white domed ice- and snow-cap
stood out sharply against the bright blue sky from an apparent chaos of
enormous, grey blocks and cliffs of limestone. The mountains were not
very strongly folded in this region, as is the case in the Alps. At most
there was a slight bending of the limestone strata, which dipped towards the north and there disappeared under the succeeding mountain
ridges. On the southern side of the Juliana Summit the mountainous
region revealed a sharp break, which continued along the whole
southern edge of the central mountainous region. This southern wall
rose practically vertical for 9,840 ft. from the low foothills. Any ascent
from the south was impossible and it was for this reason that the route

through the valley of the Ok Tsyop had been selected. The limestone blocks had been affected by weathering, and there were holes and fissures many feet deep, with numerous small caves in the limestone cliff. The terrain was rough and difficult, the surface of the limestone rock being deeply grooved. It was particularly difficult going for the bearers, who always walked barefoot.

There was no point in holding up a large number of bearers here and the majority therefore were sent back to Camp 6, where they were received by Marines Brandenburg Van den Gronden and Hendriks. On the 7th September the weather improved somewhat and it was decided to trek farther up the mountain. Together with eight bearers the party reached the 13,120-ft. level, where they set up three small tents in a cwm in the mountainside, in a sheltered spot: this was Ascent Camp. It had snowed that night and from the summit down to about 12,790 ft. the mountain was sheeted in fresh snow. The Muyus were very excited about it, as it was the first time that they had seen and tasted snow. Their fun did not last long, however, because the sun soon cleared most of the snow below the snow-line. The bearers went back to Lake Camp, where they were to wait for the climbers; here they lived in double-walled tents which gave them a reasonable protection against the cold, and in addition they wore thick track suits and jerseys. Two of them—Atenem and Wilhelmus—took charge of the camp; they were responsible for seeing that everybody had enough to eat. Escher, Verstappen, Tissing, De Wijn and Ter Laag remained behind in the three small tents at Ascent Camp; here they had to live on biscuits, pea soup and hot-pot from tins, because it was quite impossible to get rice soft at this altitude; the water boiled at a temperature as low as 88°C. So they crept into their sleeping-bags and waited for fine weather. Between the clouds they could see on the opposite side of the Tsyop Valley an unnamed mountain ridge about 13,100 ft. high, where bare limestone rocks alternated with alpine meadows. Shortly after the clouds closed over Ascent Camp, it began to rain and later a good deal of slushy snow fell in large flakes on the tents. That night there was a frost of about 2°C. and they awoke next morning to a white world; the entire surroundings were once again covered with freshly-fallen snow and thick icicles hung on the tent-guys. Once again it began to rain and there was a thick persistent mist. It was no good thinking of climbing that day. The five men lay in their sleeping-bags, peeping out every now and then at the mist around their camp and passing their time by reading Hemingway's *Green Hills of*

Africa. When the owner and first reader had finished reading two pages, he tore the sheet out of the book and gave it to the next reader, each sheet passing in this way from hand to hand. Escher believed that garlic was good for his health, much to the sorrow of his fellow-campers; the tents stood with their doors so close to one another that all three were almost filled with the odour of the garlic. On the third day in Ascent Camp (9th September), the weather was not a great deal better, but the supplies of food they had taken with them were beginning to dwindle noticeably; they therefore decided to attempt the ascent. The route was marked out on the basis of the aerial photographs that they had, together with what they had been able to see on the previous days when the weather cleared enough for them to see the top. There appeared to be several deep fissures on the western edge which would make the climb from that side difficult. Prospects seemed better from the north-east since the slope of the ice-cap was more gradual here. They therefore elected to try the climb along this edge. The mountaineering gear was distributed, while De Wijn also carried part of Ter Laag's photographic equipment. As the weather cleared up they set out. After two hours of climbing they reached an enormous sloping face of limestone which finished on the side nearest to the mountain in a vertical cliff. They crossed the sheet of rock, still looking for a suitable place to climb the cliff which rose before them. Meanwhile a thick mist had come down again and the wind had risen considerably. So as to be sure of being able to find their way back in the mist they set up every couple of hundred yards a cairn or pillar of flat rocks piled one on top of another. Eventually, they reached a kloof in the limestone cliff by which they were able to climb higher. Visibility had become bad; the strong wind, flurries of snow and dense mist made it impossible to see more than about thirty yards. After about half an hour the mist cleared for a moment and between the wisps of cloud they could see directly before them the immeasurably deep precipice forming the southern edge of the mountain. They now changed the direction of their ascent and trekked due west along the eastern ridge. The layer of snow which had fallen on the previous day was several inches thick in some places and more snow was still falling. They could not now be much farther away from the ice, and indeed very soon the edge of the glacier loomed up ahead of them. They crept into a shallow fissure to be somewhat protected from the ice-cold wind and there put on their crampons (climbing-irons). They tied themselves together with a nylon rope 115 ft. long, to make sure that if one of them did slip, he would not fall into the depths below. The mist and falling snow made it impossible to estimate the height of the ice slope which they had to climb. Escher went ahead. With his ice-pick he cut a few steps in the ice and they very quickly reached the more level region of the glacier cap. Here the thick layer of snow gave them a better footing and they were able to make rapid progress. In the mist and without any kind of view, it was not an easy matter to find the point where the ice-cap—325 ft. thick—reached its highest point, but at last Escher, Verstappen, Tissing, De Wijn and Ter Laag stood at the very highest point at 11.45. De Wijn hoisted the Netherlands tricolour. The third of the four New Guinea summits which can boast eternal snow had been conquered and it was once again a Netherlands expedition which could claim this success. The altimeter showed a height of 15,220 ft.; thus the Juliana Summit too was somewhat lower than the altitude indicated on the map (15,454 ft.) although the difference in this case was not so great as in that of Antares. It must be borne in mind that errors of a few score feet are not impossible with a pocket altimeter. The fliers of the De Kroonduif Company who regularly fly past the Juliana Summit said that when they were precisely level with the top of the Summit their altimeters always showed 15,420 ft.

It was a pity for the climbing team that the mist blocked their view; they could not see anything of the peaks in the vicinity nor anything of the hills at the foot of the mountain, and nothing of the lowland plain which extends to the south coast.

They now rapidly returned to Ascent Camp, where every one of them benefited by a plate of pea soup with a sausage in it. They remained for another day in this camp to take certain observations. As they were sitting there in their tent about midday, De Wijn thought that he heard someone calling. When they went to have a look they saw some couple of hundred yards below them a figure in a track suit, wildly waving to them. It was one of the bearers who had come with their mail! Marine H. J. W. Hendriks had come up from Camp 6 with a team of bearers carrying supplies for the return journey to the Juliana Camp and had brought their letters with him. An unfamiliar luxury in New Guinea to have one's mail brought right to the door and that at a height of 13,120 ft. above sea-level; even in Hollandia you would have to fetch your letters from the Post Office yourself.

On the 11th September the climbers dropped down to Lake Camp again and on 13th September they were all back in Camp 6, reaching Juliana Camp next day, the 14th September.

In Mabilabol there was still no information at all. Everybody was busy clearing up and trying to sell the remaining supplies to the Catholic and Protestant Missions. Venema stood in the store extolling to Missionaries Greenfield and Heyblom the tins of curly kale and sauerkraut. Brongersma was an interested spectator—and then suddenly Warman came storming in: "They've got there." Nobody asked who they were or where they were, this could only be news of the climbers. In a moment the godown was empty, and everyone was rushing up the slope to the Marines' shed, where Marine Koster was busy taking down a message. He did not allow all this crowd to confuse him. With his headphones still on, he sat listening, scribbled down a few words and began signalling in reply, but then Venema grabbed the slip of paper. On it he read: "Juliana Summit (15,220 ft.) reached by all five climbers on 090959 at 11.45 hours from Ascent Camp at 13,120 ft. in mist, snow and high wind. Stop." "Congratulations to them," said Brongersma just before the jubilant shouts drowned his voice.

Now they had to pass the news on, but it was already too late to hold an ordinary radio-telephone conversation. Fortunately Koster was equal to the occasion and managed to contact the Marines' communication service in Hollandia. The telegram was sent to the Naval Commandant in Netherlands New Guinea with the request that the glad news should be made known to the Governor and also transmitted to the Netherlands. The Governor happened to be in Biak and the report reached him there; that evening Radio New Guinea interrupted its programme to pass the Governor's congratulations on to the expedition. Next day congratulatory telegrams were received from many sources.

Juliana Camp was evacuated in a very few days. The weather was good. Warman and Menge flew the climbers and Nicolas, Portier and Scharff to Mabilabol in the helicopter, with as much equipment as possible. The five of them arrived at the base camp wearing heavy beards. They were issued with a special rum ration to celebrate their success and then the stories began. Stories about the cold, the rain and the snow and about De Wijn, who had fallen over just before the ascent and injured his knee, but in spite of this had stuck it out and accompanied the party right the way through. Listening to them telling the tale it seemed as though they had done little more than take a Sunday stroll.

Marines Hendriks and Brandenburg Van den Gronden cleared up the last few things left in Juliana Camp and on 18th September they set off with 35 bearers, bound for Mabilabol, which they reached on 20th September. The ascent of the Juliana Summit had taken fifty days—from the moment when Verstappen and De Wijn left Mabilabol to the moment when the last men returned to the base camp.

11

The Break-Through

EVEN AS EARLY AS DURING THE DISCUSSIONS IN HOLLAND, THE BREAK-through—the journey from the south right across the broadest part of Netherlands New Guinea to the northern coast—had been mentioned. Not only would this be the first time that a long journey of this kind been made right across New Guinea, but it was an undertaking which would contribute a great deal to the knowledge of the structure of the mountains. For the time being a great many people considered it only as a pipe-dream, but as the expedition progressed, the people in Mabila-bol began to work on definite plans. Dr. Chr. B. Bär, the geologist, had considerable interest in this undertaking and with his extensive jungle knowledge he was the man to bring such a trip to a satisfactory conclusion. The trip which he had made to the Kiwirok with Dasselaar and also to the valley of the Ok Bi had, after a fashion, been a preliminary reconnaissance. Down at the base camp he calculated what supplies he would need and how many bearers would be required. He also discussed with Venema and Warman the possibility of having helicopter support along the first part of the route; a few helicopter landing-strips had already been prepared for the purpose in the valley of the Ok Bi. But now the loss of one helicopter threatened to render the whole plan impossible; however, anyone who thought that Bär would now cut out his trip had made a mistake. With more energy than ever he threw himself into the work of planning; new calculations were made, the distances to be covered each day were estimated and plotted on the map. It could be done, but supplies would have to be dropped to them roughly half-way along their route; the place where this would have to be done was fixed. Brongersma discussed the plan in Hollandia; the Government showed a great deal of interest in the project. One government official would accompany Bär—it would be Dasselaar;

he was able to get on well with Bär, a matter of the very greatest importance, because they would be together in circumstances which would often be exceedingly difficult. Naturally they would also have to have a police guard since the break-through route led for the most part over "un-governed" territory. Bär was not very keen on being accompanied in this way, since every constable who went with them meant that more food had to be carried, which in turn required more bearers, who of course called for more food, etc.; this is the familiar problem of anyone who is about to undertake a journey into the rimbu. One police official considered that ten constables was a minimum for the team. Bär certainly did not want to take more than two and finally they agreed on a guard of three men. They discussed the possibility of dropping food with the chief pilot of De Kroonduif Company, L. Van Rijswijk, and he considered that the place which had been indicated for the purpose was very suitable. This left only one difficulty: the financial situation of the expedition. The Foundation Council had initially announced that there were no more funds available for this trip, but in Hollandia a committee had been set up under the chairmanship of G. W. Baron Van der Feltz, and they hoped to collect in New Guinea the money required to finance the break-through project. They were highly successful in this because everybody contributed, regardless of nationality. It was most encouraging to see the intimate interest everybody was taking in the expedition. People went round with subscription lists and organised competitions and musical evenings, and in this way the financial difficulties of the expedition contributed to the enjoyment of a great many people. The occupants of the base camp followed with considerable interest the reports given over the radio programmes in Biak regarding the many activities of the local committees. They did not quite understand how it was that Kaimana (a place with 1,065 inhabitants, 169 of which were Europeans) suddenly had an Association for Tourist Traffic, which organised a competition football match in costume in the Stadium (!), as was reported by the radio stations; it was seriously considered that they must first of all have had a jolly good dinner and then have hit on the idea of such an event. From the Netherlands came the news that Mr. C. Verolme had offered to stand guarantee for any deficit that the expedition might have, and this—together with the activities of the committee in Hollandia—settled the question; the break-through could take place.

During the reconnaissance which Bär and Dasselaar had carried out in June and July, they had surmised that the Ok Bi was one of the source rivers of the Sobger, which flows northwards to join the Idenburg River. Their plan was to trek along the Ok Bi towards the Sobger, and travelling north-eastwards from the mouth of the Sobger towards Obrup along a track which had been cleared by a survey group of the Netherlands New Guinea Petroleum Company (Nederlandsch Nieuw-Guinea Petroleum Maatschappij). From Obrup their route would lead via Waris to the Humboldt Bay. If everything went off well, the trip would last thirty-five days; if there should be any hold-up en route it would not last more than forty-five days. Supplies would be dropped alongside the Sobger on the 27th August. Everything was talked over very thoroughly, the route was drawn out on the map and the equipment and supplies were made ready in Mabilabol.

The group which was to make the break-through comprised Dr. Chr. B. Bär,. the geologist, G. H. Dasselaar, the government official, the survey-headman, J. Wattimena, three police-constables (Rumpaidus, Yani and Yorgaimu), the cook Leo Sumanai, with twenty-four Sansapor bearers and nine Muyu bearers. In the beginning they also intended to use some Sibil bearers.

Dasselaar left Mabilabol on 3rd August with two constables, nine Muyus, two Sansapor bearers and twenty Sibil bearers, his purpose being to set up a food depot on the Ok Bi. En route the Sibillers would be able to buy (or obtain) from their friends and acquaintances batatas and keladi, so that they would not completely eat up the food supplies intended for the break-through team. When Bär came through later with the rest of the Sansapor bearers, he could then make up what they had eaten on the journey from the depot which had been set up. The first day was not especially lucky for Dasselaar; after trekking for six hours the bearers' cook came up to say that he had forgotten his pans. Camp was immediately set up, before they reached the Orion Range. It was a long while before all the bearers had something to eat, because they now had to cook the meal one-sixth at a time in a very small pan. Next morning two bearers set off to Mabilabol to fetch the pans and returned before it was dark; as they also brought some mail with them, Dasselaar was not very concerned that the pots and pans had been forgotten. On 5th August he set off again with his group; they trekked along the confluence of the Ok Yu and the Ok Al, over the Tennomabee and over the Ok Tsyop to the village of Ngotding. From here to the

Ok Bi they would not meet any more villagers, and the Sibillers were therefore careful to obtain as much batatas and keladi from the inhabitants of Ngotding as possible. They did not object to eating rice, but they much preferred their familiar boneng (batatas) and om (keladi). Early on the morning of 8th August Dasselaar set off across the Yongsigin, which forms the central watershed at this point, and here he met a group of people from Bi. The Sibillers gave an extensive account of the purpose of their journey. The tuan simitki (the long man, i.e. Dasselaar) was going to walk to Hollandia; half-way along the route a kobaar (aeroplane) was to drop out food; they themselves would not be going farther with him than to the Ok Bi. This description aroused general amazement, because it was a long journey that the tuan wanted to make; how far it really was they had no idea at all, their knowledge of geography being restricted to the immediate vicinity of their home. The Ok Bètèl was reached on 9th August; this is a tributary of the Ok Bi, and Dasselaar set up camp here, where he was to wait for Bär. The Sibillers set off on the return journey with twelve "empty" carrying-cases. These cases were in fact far from empty, because the men had filled them with keladi, batatas and sugar-cane for the return trip. During the time that he had to wait, Dasselaar visited the villages in the district and tried to take a census record of the inhabitants. This did not turn out to be very easy, because the people were afraid to give their names; they clearly feared that the man who could write their name down would have a certain amount of power over them. The supplies of food were further supplemented by a pig which was bought for an axe and a small jungle knife.

In the village of Kutmon there stood a burial platform, a long pole supported by sloping saplings. On top of the pole was a small roof, under which lay the body of a woman, wrapped in the bark of trees and lashed in a standing position. The woman had died ten days before and the smell in the region of the platform was therefore most disagreeable. That afternoon a few men arrived from Lewengbon (a village in the Sibil Valley) to visit the camp. They had heard of the plans for the journey, but wanted to hear for themselves what the intentions were. The Bi people too showed renewed interest, but once it was made clear to them how many days the journey would take they lost all the interest they had had.

Bär left Mabilabol on 8th August. The departure on this occasion differed from those at other times, whenever a group was leaving for a trip in the mountains. This time this team would not return to Mabilabol. The official beginning of the break-through trek introduced the end of the expedition. A large number of people were here beginning their journey home, and with them was leaving one of the scientific research workers who had contributed so much to the success of the expedition. Bär was wearing a brightly-coloured flower-pattern plastic sheet about his middle (his showerproof cape) and carrying a geologist's hammer over his shoulder in the manner that the Sibillers carry their stone axes, and checking if everyone was there.

Patiently he submitted to being photographed and filmed among the bearers, who were squatting on the ground among their loads. Police-Constable Rumpaidus came up to report to Kroon, there were hand-shakes and then Bär said: "Onim-onim" (walk) and the column set off. For the purposes of filming he went ahead of the group, but while the bearers slowly went on their way, he himself came back for a last talk. Then he followed the column away. The break-through had begun. Brongersma looked more or less by accident at his watch; it was one minute past eight. This was the time which he later wrote out and sent in a sealed envelope to Hollandia, where they were offering a prize for the person who could say how long the break-through would take.

The bearers were heavily loaded and were able to progress only slowly. On the first day they camped near Bulankop, where Marines Timmer and Vlaanderen received them cheerfully. On the second day they reached Yumakot, the place where the Ok Yu runs into the Ok Tsyop. On the third day the journey continued along the Ok Tsyop, which here runs through a fairly deep kloof; the track was far from good and the bearers were only able to advance laboriously. Neverthe-less they were able on that day to cross the Ok Tsyop and reached the village of Ngotding. For part of the journey the break-through team had trekked together with Tissing's column, which had started some-what later the same day on its way to the Juliana Camp. Thanks to the outstanding work done by Warman, who had brought a considerable amount of supplies to Denmatta by helicopter, Bär was able to make up his supplies with what Tissing was able to give him. He thus reached Ngotding with full carrying-cases. He gave the first reports on his progress to the Sibil bearers who were coming back from the Ok Bi, and who would see that his letter was delivered in Mabilabol.

Once more Bär sent a letter to Mabilabol. Two little boys from the Sibil Valley arrived with it. They had trekked out with Bär, it had been

45. Good friends: Nicolas with two boys from Betabib
(the left-hand boy is blind).

intended that they should return from the Ok Tsyop, but they wanted to see something of the world too, and they therefore went on to the Ok Bi. They thought that Dasselaar would have bought a lot of pigs there and were very attracted by the idea of a feast. In our view these children were far too young to make the journey over the mountains without anybody to accompany them, but they had different ideas. Fortunately the father of one of the boys was following the group, and there was thus no objection to letting them go on with him. They later delivered Bär's letter, filled with great pride at the journey they had made.

The journey from Ngotding to the camp on the Ok Bètèl went off very well indeed. The weather was good and in two days the group covered the distance that they had expected would take them three days. On 12th August they came into Dasselaar's camp at the end of the afternoon. The two little Sibil boys were given their feast, because Bär's group had only been in for about half an hour when a pig was brought to them, with another one next morning. Dasselaar and his men had lived on the food which the population had been able to give them and had therefore been able to economise in precious food supplies. "The morale of the bearers is outstandingly good," wrote Bär, "and it strikes me we could hardly have set out under better conditions." They had feared that there would be cases of chicken-pox occurring among the bearers, because they had had contact with bearers who had returned from the Antares Mountains with this illness, but fortunately no new cases were detected. Bär ordered one day's rest at the Ok Bètèl; on the 14th August the entire group set off again. The bearers from the Sibil Valley had now turned back, but seventeen Bi bearers went with the party for three days to replace them. The weather was good, the water-level in the river was low and they were thus able to begin their journey through unknown territory in good spirits. On 27th September they were to receive a supply-drop from the air near the Sobger River, and all aircraft following this route were to keep a look out for them.

The 14th August found the group at the northernmost camp that they had reached on their journey to the Kiwirok and the Ok Bi. Next day they passed the mouth of the Ok Sib, made a bridge over the Ok Bi—an undertaking which took some time, but in spite of this they had reached the confluence of the Ok Bi and the Ok Baab by a quarter past nine; the section of river upstream at this point is also called Ok Baab by the local inhabitants.

46. (1) View from Antares: candelabra trees (*Papuacedrus* sp.) in the foreground.
(2) The lake near the Juliana Summit, lying at a height of 10,662 ft; Verstappen in the foreground.

They followed this Ok Baab, travelling upstream. At a height of 2,414 ft. they found a few *Agathis* trees, the species from which dammar resin is obtained. They did not meet anybody of the local population, although they saw several gardens. Shortly after leaving camp on 16th August, they arrived at the mouth of a tributary which flowed from the south-east; this was obviously the Ok Tahin, which Bär and Dasselaar had followed for some distance in June. The Bi bearers called this river the Ok Silka. Beyond the confluence of the Ok Baab and the Ok Silka, the river still goes under the name of the Ok Silka. Once again they passed gardens, but there was no sign of villages, houses or inhabitants.

At a height of 2,330 ft. they found a group of sago palms. The Bi bearers had now reached the end of the trip they were to make, and they therefore returned to their village on 17th August, as had been agreed earlier. The river turned off in a north-westerly direction, a good sign, as it agreed with the course of the Sobger as shown on the map. The terrain was not easy; the river flowed through a kloof and it was necessary to trek sometimes on the right bank of the river, and sometimes on the left. Bär and Dasselaar followed the shortest route, swimming across the river a couple of times; the bearers clambered along the bank higher up until they came to a point where they could wade through the water, and on one or two occasions they felled trees to make a rough bridge over it. However, the group only progressed slowly; after seven hours of heavy going they were only a little more than two miles farther on. On this leg of the journey they met a man who seemed to find the encounter a very frightening affair. His appearance resembled that of the Sibillers, but his language was completely different; conversation did not get very far beyond offering him a cigarette. There clearly were villages to be found in this region, as when the group quitted camp on 18th August they were accompanied by six of the local inhabitants. After rather less than an hour they came to a forest hut full of people. These folk were by no means aggressive, but neither were they in any way frightened; on the contrary, they were very bold, almost rude.

On the subsequent days the terrain was still very difficult. The river wound through a long kloof contained between almost vertical cliffs and there were numerous rapids. It was no longer possible to follow the bed of the river, so the group had to seek its path higher up, farther away from the river bank. Sometimes there were stretches of local

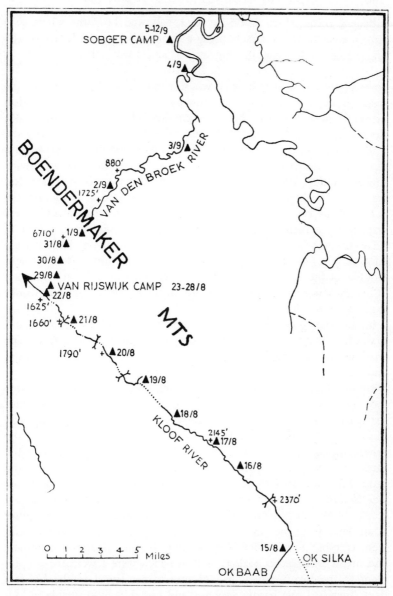

Fig. 18. Route from Ok Baab to the Sobger. (The begining of the break-through route from the Sibil Valley to the Ok Baab is indicated in Figure 9 on page 155).

villagers' paths which could be used, followed by paths where they had to clear their own track, using a compass to get the bearings. The entire journey was nothing but up hill and down dale.

They were rather frightened to find that now the course of the river corresponded very little to what was shown on the map. Judging by the distance they had covered they must by now have reached the section of the Sobger that had been reconnoitred by Second-Lieut. J. W. Langeler between 28th October and 11th December 1914, during the military expedition. Bär remembered having read in the expedition report that the party had travelled on the Sobger in proas in a wide lowland valley. They could hardly assume that the Army exploration party had drawn their maps so badly. Nothing fitted at all, neither the curves of the river nor the heights indicated for the mountains. There was clearly something wrong somewhere. There was no question of their changing their direction and trying to find their way farther along another valley, because the aircraft which was to come to supply them would not find them at the agreed place. Dasselaar jokingly asserted: "Chris, you'll see—we've finished up on the A-River." And that would explain a great deal.

It had been agreed that on 27th August food would be dropped, and it was for them to find a site where they could clear an open space. The work of clearing the dropping zone would certainly take several days, and the clearing must be so situated that the aircraft could reach it without difficulty. On 23rd August they climbed to the top of a 3,000-foot hill, on top of which they cleared a dropping-strip. It was not particularly good terrain, but there was nothing better. Having been busy in one place for a couple of days, they attracted the interest of the inhabitants of the immediate vicinity. Some of them came to visit the camp, but they were exceedingly nervous; they did not enter the camp without more ado. For some time these Papuans would stand outside at some distance, calling and being answered; not that this helped contact very much, because neither of the parties understood the other at all. Finally six men came out of the forest; they were unarmed and were carrying food which they offered: batatas, pisangs, cucumbers and matul (*Abelmoschus manihot*)—all of which were a welcome supplement to the menu, which had become rather frugal in the last few days. They had met hardly anybody and had thus been unable to buy any food supplies. In exchange for what these men brought they were given matches, which were something entirely new to them. Here, as in the vicinity of Juliana Camp, fire was made by means of a thin piece of rattan; (see page 239); thin strips of rattan wound in the form of armbands were worn as part of the normal clothing. The remainder of their dress consisted of a gourd for the men, but of a longer type than that used in the Sibil Valley. The hair extension (kamil) of the men in the Star Mountains is found here in a rather different form; only one small club is worn, and not one large and one small as is the case in the Sibil Valley.

For four days they worked on the dropping-strip. Everybody waited tensely for the Dakota flying to Merauke which was to keep a look-out for the break-through group. On 25th August Bär heard the aircraft flying past them farther to the east, but they were not able to see the plane and on 26th August no aircraft were detected. The weather was not particularly favourable, either; there was a good deal of cloud about and it was quite understandable that the flyers could not see the smoke signals. On 27th August the Dakota came over them again, but it flew straight on and was clearly not looking for them. That afternoon the weather cleared, and the Twin Pioneer left Sentani at noon. Bär and Dasselaar heard the plane and lit a number of big smoke-fires, three of them in a straight line, in accordance with the agreed signal; they had laid out letters made up of bits of wood to tell the airmen that they needed three pairs of shoes, size 46, for Dasselaar and that an extra dropping flight would have to be made on 12th September. The delay had caused them to use up so much of their supplies that one drop would not be enough. The weather was beautifully clear, but the Twin Pioneer was not successful in finding them. They only had enough rice to last them until after breakfast on 29th August, and the situation was therefore becoming rather critical. The morale of the bearers dropped visibly.

Bär, Dasselaar, the police-constables and the bearers were all waiting with great excitement; but they were not the only ones. In Mabilabol the occupants of Sneep's house were sitting round the radio; on Sentani airfield Mr. Van den Broek was waiting for news; and literally the whole of New Guinea was tensely waiting because everyone knew that this was the day when the break-through group was to receive its supplies. We were waiting for the loudspeaker in Sneep's house to give us some encouraging news. Every now and then Sneep tried to make contact with his "Sibil—Papa Yankee" (after the last letters of the Twin Pioneer's registration JZ-DPY) and the fliers replied with a: "No, not a sign." Papa Yankee flew upstream along the Sobger as far as and as long as possible until it reached a point a good deal south of the agreed spot, and then returned downstream in a northerly direction, and then once more repeated the trip up and back. Sneep asked again: "Papa Yankee, how are you getting on?," receiving the disappointing reply: "We're staring till our eyes drop out, but there isn't a sign, not even one smoke signal." The fliers consulted with the ground staff at Sentani; they had been in the air for well over two hours and it was decided that the plane would have to return to the airfield. As a safety measure they were to examine first of all the route from the Sobger, passing by Obrup, Senggi and Waris, as Bär might have progressed much more quickly than expected and have gone farther. But they had no success. The operation was finished for that day, and they would have to try again next day. That evening there was a meeting in Hollandia. The public were given the impression that the weather had been too bad for the drop to take place, because there was no point in stirring up anxiety at this stage.

On 28th August the Twin Pioneer was first of all to fly to the Sibil Valley to bring petrol for the helicopters, and it was then to continue its search on the return journey. In addition, the Cessna aircraft of the Missionary Aviation Fellowship came to the valley to help in the search. Should this search be fruitless, then more aircraft were to be called up. Once again Bär and his men lit three great smoke fires. They saw the Twin Pioneer come out of a cloud bank and continue on its way, but once again they were not seen; fifteen minutes later the Cessna came over very high to the west of their camp. The only thing that Bär could understand was that they were being looked for and that he must therefore have come a good way off his course. Papa Yankee landed in the Sibil Valley, where it was to stay for a short while. Brongersma, Venema and the fliers Van Rijswijk and Van Hulten were bending over the map and discussing what might have happened to Bär. At that moment somebody came running from the hill with the message: "The Cessna has found them." A little bit later the Cessna came taxiing down the landing-strip and Pilot Johannsen came over, map in hand, to say that he had seen three tall columns of smoke in a row along the A-River.

The weather above the valley worsened, and the sky began to be covered. The two aircraft left as soon as possible—first of all the Cessna to show the way, followed by the Twin Pioneer. Bär and Dasselaar were still tensely waiting to see if anyone would find them. And then the tension was broken, as the Cessna returned and circled high above the camp followed by the Twin Pioneer coming in low directly towards them. After having circled a couple of times, Papa Yankee threw out a bamboo tube containing the message "Hurrah, your position is along the A-River. If you continue along this river, light an extra fire. We will return to drop supplies this afternoon or tomorrow. Where do you want an extra drop? (set out in letters). Your message understood. Captains Van Rijswijk and Van Hulten."

Bär and Dasselaar were now reassured, but the bearers did not think much of the situation; an aircraft had come over and there were still no supplies. Bär decided nevertheless to push through to the Sobger; the extra supply drop would therefore have to take place at the original point. His only concern was that an extra flight was costing more money, with which the expedition was not very freely blessed at this time. A message was therefore laid out with pieces of wood: "Extra drop 12/9 on the Sobger."

At a quarter past two that afternoon the Twin Pioneer was back. The supply drop was perfect. Van Rijswijk was able to drop everything precisely on to the small clearing. Bär and Dasselaar had made a platform in a tree at the edge of the dropping-zone and were standing on it, waving. Only one bag of rice broke and a few of the tins were damaged, but all the supplies for which they had asked had now been dropped. As an extra surprise a parachute now came floating down carrying a small box containing a liqueur glass, a bottle of Bokma (finest Dutch gin—Translator's note.) and a few tit-bits for the police and the other members of the party; this was a thoughtful gesture made by the Kroonduif pilots. The group also received a small bag of mail and a map showing their position. Morale in the camp, which was christened "Van Rijswijk Camp" in honour of the Kroonduif Company's chief pilot, was excellent. There was great pleasure at this successful supply drop. A message was laid out on the dropping-strip: "First-class drop. Many thanks."

The A-River is a tributary of the Idenburg River. The military survey team had indicated the point where the A-River flowed into the Iden-burg River, but did not follow the river itself any farther; as usual rivers whose course was not plotted were indicated not with names but with letters. Thus the Sobger was originally known as the B-River. From information provided by the French film expedition, which made a break-through to the north coast at the end of 1959 and the beginning of 1960, it became clear that the river that Bär and Dasselaar followed was not the true "A-River"; this in fact rises farther to the west in the Valentijn Mountains and is broader than the river along which Bär and Dasselaar had trekked. Gaisseau christened the "A-River" Marijke River after Her Royal Highness Princess Marijke. The local name for the river which Bär and Dasselaar had followed is not known. The river which flows from the confluence of the Ok Baab and the Ok Silka is still known as the Ok Silka, but farther downstream, where different languages are spoken, it is probable that the river is given various names along different stretches of its course. Dr. J. Van Baal gave the name Kloof River to a river in this region and this probably refers to this tributary of the Marijke River; consequently we have used (albeit provisionally) this name for the river along which Bär and Dasselaar travelled.

*   *   *

Now that the break-through group was again fully supplied, they were able to continue their journey on 29th August. The route ran in a north-easterly direction over a chain of mountains, which were named the Boendermaker Mountains after Mr. A. Boendermaker, who had done so much for the expedition, first as Resident of Southern New Guinea and later as the Deputy Director of Internal Affairs. Bär, who was initially rather annoyed that he had reached the wrong river, was later very glad that he had done so, because it had enabled him to carry out quite a lot of important geological work in a region of which nothing had been known. The slopes of the Boendermaker Mountains are steep; a path had to be cleared through a very thick forest. On the first day (29th August) the party took a good five hours to cover about one mile, having climbed to a height of 4,070 ft. On 30th August they travelled one and a half miles in four and a half hours, camping at the end of this journey at 5,380 ft. That afternoon they were able to put the bearers, who were not tired, on clearing a stretch of the path to be followed next day. There was no water near the camp; they had to make a two and a half hour journey to fetch it. It is quite understandable that they only fetched the minimum necessary quantity of water for eating and for coffee; there was no washing during this period. Slowly the group climbed to the watershed between the catchment area of the A-River and that of the Sobger. On 31st August they reached a height of 6,560 ft. above sea-level; here they camped by a small spring. The slope was particularly steep and the tent was therefore set at three different levels up the slope. Through a gap in the forest they had a magnificent view of the central mountainous region. The Speelman Mountains could be clearly seen, with the Juliana Summit to the east. Bär and Dasselaar could not help thinking of the other expedition group which was labouring through the mountains and of whose progress they as yet knew nothing. They saw the Twin Pioneer flying low over the Van Rijswijk Camp; on board was the French film team, led by Gaisseau, reconnoitring the area.

The nights were also cold at this height and the tent-cloths did not offer much protection. On 1st September they climbed to 6,673 ft. over the sharp ridge of the watershed, which they followed to the north-west, until their progress was halted by a major peak. From this point they had to descend the very steep slope, but at least the thick vegetation gave some handhold, and they were able to slide downwards here and there, without running the risk of overshooting. The weather was bad; there was much mist and rain, and it was cold. They descended to 3,870 ft. and camped at this height. At the end of the afternoon the weather cleared up and they had a fine view across the Sobger Valley; first of all they saw a few mountains, but behind them was a wide plain dotted with a few hills. The bearers shouted jubilantly when they saw this; they had had more than enough of clambering about on steep mountain slopes. It was clear that there must be people living in the vicinity, even though they could see no villages, as they were able to use on the last leg of their descent a local track, although it was not very easy to negotiate. On 2nd September they descended farther and reached a small stream at a height of 2,784 ft. This was the beginning of a tributary of the Sobger, which was named the Van-den-Broek River in honour of Mr. Th. C. Van den Broek, who had done such an exceptional amount of work for the expedition as the representative of the Foundation in Hollandia.

On their way they saw a pondok (lean-to); this was probably built by people who came here to cut sago. Slowly but surely the going became easier. After days during which the distance covered varied from roughly a mile to a mile and a half, they travelled nearly three miles on 2nd September and even as much as almost seven miles on the 3rd September, By this time they had dropped to 660 ft. above sea-level and were now able to use very good local tracks. The existence of such good paths clearly showed that the local population was in the habit of moving about and had a good deal of contact with their neighbours.

Strangely enough, they did not see houses, people or villages on their route. This continued until suddenly, on the afternoon of 3rd September, four men armed with bows and arrows and a boy came to visit the camp. Their clothing consisted of the familiar gourds, but of a different shape from those common in the mountains; some of the gourds were egg-shaped. Three of the five visitors were suffering from cascado. Apart from this, civilisation seemed to have penetrated to this point, since one of the men was carrying a small machete, and another had a well-worn potato knife. They had been out catching fish; the fish they had caught were bought from them for a couple of boxes of matches, and for the first time in months Bär and his companions enjoyed freshly-cooked fish with their rice. Along the sides of the valley were clearly-developed terraces formed where the river wound through the valley in wide loops. On 4th September they trekked on to the Sobger; the five Papuans who had come into the camp went with them. Here they found a large number of well-maintained gardens, where, in addition to batatas, there were also crops of cassava, maize, katyang pandyang (small beans apparently introduced from the northern coast), pisang (bananas), tobacco and even papaya (paw-paws). Bär and Dasselaar were now finally where they should have been on the 27th August; the journey over the Boendermaker Mountains had not been too arduous, they had only taken seven days to cover this distance instead of the fourteen which had been allowed for it. They now trekked along the Sobger to the north to find a suitable place for a dropping-strip. Just as they had found it on 5th September and were busy setting up their tent at the side of an abandoned garden in a loop of the river, they heard an aircraft. It was the Twin Pioneer in which Brongersma was vainly trying to reach the Sibil Valley. When he did not succeed in this, the plane flew back to Sentani, choosing the route over the Sobger to see if they could see anything of Bär and, as it turned out, they saw a distinct column of smoke; "Shall we pop over and have a look?" asked Captain Van Hulten. Brongersma was decidedly in favour, as it would be a considerable relief to him to see with his own eyes whether Bär and Dasselaar were really on the right road now. Papa Yankee banked a couple of times to lose height and flew low over the forest. "There they are," shouted the second pilot Quené, above the roar of the engines. Yes, there they were; on a sandbank in the middle of the river stood Bär and Dasselaar waving an orange-red flare, the agreed signal that everything was in order. A little farther away stood the policeman and bearers waving. The whole group was very happy that they had been located, and they now made all the preparations for the supply drop which had been asked for on 12th September. It was a great pity that they had to wait a further week, because this was really losing time. They began on the work of clearing in very good heart; in comparison with what they had had to do at the Van Rijswijk Camp the work here was child's play, because the vegetation was very light indeed, consisting only of sparse, secondary forest. They made such good progress that they laid out a signal with pieces of wood reading: "From 9/9 drop four pairs of shoes size 40, rice, fish-hooks, soap." They were hoping that perhaps another aircraft would come and see the message, and then they could have their supplies dropped to them three days earlier. In the meantime they felled large trees to make proas, with which they could travel farther down river. Dasselaar reconnoitred the surrounding area, looking for a piece of ground where a small air-strip could be laid out; one stretch running parallel to the Sobger and a little over 1,500 feet long would have been suitable but for the fact that it was too short. The Sobger has many small tributaries, which made it difficult to lay out an air-strip of adequate length parallel to the river; they thought that perhaps they would be able to make some use of a piece of ground between these two small streams. During his exploratory trips Dasselaar passed a few large houses and gardens but did not meet any people. The houses were built up on stakes, with the floor some six to seven feet above the ground; they had a good roof but no side walls.

There was a great quantity of fish in the Sobger, and the inhabitants were in the habit of keeping the skeletons of the fish which they had eaten, and hanging them up on the inside of the roofs of their houses; they also kept the skulls of rats and mammals in the same way. There was no means of finding out whether this was only intended as a decoration, or whether the bones were preserved as amulets.

They were not without difficulties at this camp. One of the Muyu bearers, by name Athanasius, fell ill; he developed a stubborn fever and stomach troubles as well. In P.O.W. camps in the Indies Bär had had experience of people suffering from similar troubles, and he had, as always, brought a small supply of medicines with him. First of all, he put the man on a course of sulphonamides, but this did not seem to do much good, so that he changed over to globinicol, and prescribed a strict diet. This brought about a gradual improvement. However,

Athanasius was now no longer able to act as a bearer, since he was too weak to be able to carry a load of 45 lb. Another of the bearers developed chicken-pox, but fortunately this was only a slight case, and the man quickly recovered far enough to be able to travel the rest of the way without trouble.

At last an aircraft did come on 9th September, but this was not a reconnaissance trip, it was in fact the Dakota coming to make a supply drop. Now that it was known in Hollandia that Bär and Dasselaar had reached the Sobger it was thought a sensible idea to supply them as quickly as possible. Brongersma was still in Hollandia and Van Rijswijk invited him to accompany him on this dropping flight. The bags were spread across the floor of the Dakota, tied down with a net. The door had been taken out of the plane. The overall-clad dropping team consisted of three men—Mr. Gout, Mr. Rijnenberg and a Papuan—and were provided with a safety-harness round the shoulders and waist, attached to a long cord which was in turn fastened to a rope stretched along the interior wall of the aircraft. This enabled them to move about in the aircraft without running any risk of falling out. The Dakota took off and flew southwards over extensive forests (which were known to the airmen as kale) and winding silvery-white rivers. The level of the Sobger had risen considerably; there was no trace of the sandbank on which Bär and Dasselaar had stood on 5th September. A fine stretch of ground had been cleared, but it was still not an easy job for the pilot. He could fly in towards the dropping-strip over the river, but once the supplies had been thrown out his view was impeded by the forest and it was difficult to see where the packages had fallen. The weather was not very helpful either, since just as they reached the camp a storm started, bringing squalls of rain. There were also a few air-pockets; the Dakota suddenly dropped quite a distance and then bounced up again; in other words, the aircraft danced in quite a lively fashion towards its objective. This was too much for the Papuan helper who was supposed to drag the packages to the door; he tied himself firmly in a seat and grabbed one of the large paper bags provided by the Kroonduif Company for the relief of air-sick passengers. The mechanics took over his job. The pile of sacks were dragged up to the open door and thrown out at a signal from Van Rijswijk. This was not a simple operation; the fact that the Dakota was jumping up and down also caused the bags to bounce up and down. To make sure that they did not drop too early they had to be pressed down to the floor and a few seconds later the entire pile of bags had to be released in a fraction of a second. The Dakota made one run after another. Bär and Dasselaar had again taken up their position on a platform in a tree to keep an eye on the drop. It became clear that they considered that they were getting too much; they stood there waving wildly that enough had been dropped. The crew of the Dakota did not take much notice of this; one can never tell how many sacks are likely to break up and it is better to have a little too much than too little. After one more run everything had been dropped. Unfortunately they could not meet the request laid out in large letters on the open patch of ground. Shoes size 40, fish-hooks and soap were not available on the Dakota. What was more, Brongersma was asking himself why the men wanted to have soap; they were all of them as dirty as one another with mud, and in addition there was nobody to take offence at it. The Dakota returned to Hollandia where, in the meanwhile, an important football match had been held to raise funds for the break-through. The departmental heads and heads of government services, together with other high officials, had played a game against an eleven to form which the Catholic and Protestant Missions had joined together for the occasion. Everybody in Hollandia was there to watch the spectacle and it was considered rather a pity that the weather was so fine; it isn't every day that you get a chance to see your departmental head rolling in the mud. A second disappointment was that the players took the game seriously, because that had not been expected. The two missions beat the government officials 2—0. Van Rijswijk had the fine idea of encouraging the festival spirit by dropping a report of the successful supply drop on a parachute in a bamboo tube over the football field. He then flew on to Yautefa Bay, swung round in a bank and came in low over the football field. This gave him a chance to bring the score up to one-nil for the dropping team, since the tube finished up slap in the goal. He now returned to the Sentani airfield across the Sentani Lake, where the crew left the aircraft thoroughly satisfied with their success. This time the job had not been an easy one. Gout called it a "blood drop".

Despite the fact that the supply operation had succeeded, the 9th September was a black day for the break-through team because one of the Sansapor bearers was drowned in the Sobger. Some way upstream were five Sansapor men, one of whom was Petrus Yondyau, who suddenly had the idea to cross the river to buy some batatas in a garden there. Two of his friends tried to dissuade him, because the level of the river was high and the current was flowing rapidly, but to no avail. Somewhat farther upstream, almost half an hour's walk from the camp, he entered the river, and suddenly disappeared in midstream.

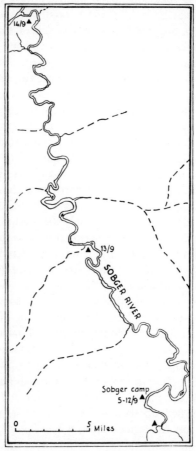

Fig. 19. The Sobger as far as the mouth of the Idenburg River (near the camp of September 14th).

Two bearers stayed on the river bank to see whether he would come to the surface, while the other two went down to the camp to warn the occupants. Bär, Rumpaidus and a number of bearers searched the bank of the river, but without finding any trace of the victim. Who could say whether he had been dragged down by a whirlpool or had been caught and held under water by a tree-trunk, or even caught by a crocodile? Everybody was very shocked. It was a saddening incident, and so much the more that it was unnecessary; there was ample food in the camp.

It took six days to make the proas. It is not such a difficult matter to find suitable trees along the river's edge and to fell them, but it was a very heavy task to hollow them out properly. Finally they were finished, and the flotilla was able to leave on 13th September. On the day before it had clearly rained very heavily higher up in the mountains, because the river rose very rapidly and then dropped again quite as rapidly. This was annoying because it was now impossible to negotiate one particular stretch of the river. They had to pass a great many rapids. Every now and then all the passengers had to jump out of their proa in order to drag it over a sandbank. In the rapids water entered the canoe so that they had to bale almost continuously to keep it afloat. Bär and Dasselaar, together with Rumpaidus and a couple of bearers, went on ahead to reconnoitre the river. Behind them came the baggage canoes, consisting of two and, in one case, three proas tied to each other, rowed and steered by constables and bearers. After they had travelled for almost four hours, Bär saw a floating body. The bearers were landed and the baggage canoes brought to the bank; only Bär and Dasselaar went on with Rumpaidus to bring the corpse to land. It was soon clear that it was the badly mutilated body of Petrus Yondyau; the mutilation of the body showed that it was probably a crocodile which had caused his death. They buried him by a small inlet of the river; a cross was set by his grave and Bär held a short service with the bearers. They stood there between the trees and bushes, dirty and mud-stained, dressed in worn and damaged clothes, to pay their last respects to the first casualty of the expedition. It was a subdued group which embarked again and travelled farther down the river looking for a camping site, which they found by a small side-stream late in the afternoon. The proas were drawn high up on the bank, a precaution which was found to be wise. During the night there was a heavy storm and the rain fell in sheets, so that the river quickly rose a yard and became a roaring, rushing stream, They supplemented their food supplies by shooting a couple of birds; after eating so much fish it was a real treat to have a fresh drum-stick to chew. After another day's sailing they reached the point where the Sobger flows into the Idenburg River.

Here the proas were dragged up on to the bank. Perhaps somebody would come by that way who could make use of the canoes; for the break-through team, they were at all events no longer required. Dasselaar and Bär now had to trek along on foot with their group. After a little searching around they found the track which had been cleared by an exploration group of the Netherlands New Guinea Petroleum Company eight months previously. This was the path they were to follow to Obrup. They left two carrying-cases behind—one filled with rice and the other filled with katyang idyu; one was the case which had belonged to Petrus Yondyau and the other that of Athanasius, who was still too weak to carry it.

After the penetrating cold of the mountainous region they now plunged as it were again into the steamy atmosphere of the tropical jungle with its mosquitoes and leeches. The track was a good one, so that they were able to advance at a good rate. Unfortunately they were only able to enjoy this for one day; they then lost the path because the surveyors of the petroleum group had trekked through the river at one point; they could no longer find the traces of a cleared path. They therefore continued, finding their way and orientating themselves by compass readings. They reached the "civilised world" on 17th September; this was represented by a large house whose inhabitants spoke a few words of Malay. The population of this region had all kinds of Western articles: steel axes, knives and clothing. One of the occupants of the place was willing to take them to Obrup, a mission station with a small airfield and a radio transmitter. Meanwhile in Mabilabol we were waiting tensely for news of the break-through group. It was already known that Bär had left the camp on the Sobger, from the report given by the Kroonduif pilot Arens who on 15th September had seen that the camp was abandoned; all that was left was a message laid out in pieces of wood expressing thanks for the supply drop. No one knew when Bär had left the camp, but it was calculated that he would probably reach Obrup somewhere around the 15th September. Every morning we listened to the telephone conversations between Obrup and the mission in Hollandia, and every afternoon we were able, with the permission of the Postal and Telegraph Service, to have a direct contact between Mabilabol and Obrup, but each time the message was: "No sign of Bär."

Completely unaware of the uneasiness in Mabilabol, where there was a suggestion that Hollandia should be asked to send out a search party

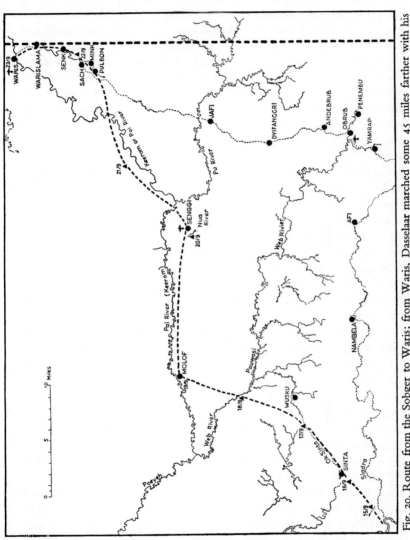

Fig. 20. Route from the Sobger to Waris; from Waris, Dasselaar marched some 45 miles farther with his group, to reach the coast.

to meet them, Bär and Dasselaar trekked on through the rimbu. En route they met a company of people going to a dance festival. Among them was an important man from the village of Molof; he was walking with them, neatly dressed in—of all things —a convict suit, that he had been allowed to take with him after serving his sentence. One advantage of his period of imprisonment was that he had learned to speak Malay really well and was thus able to give them clear indications as to their route. These folk had indeed heard that the "Marskappij" (as they called the Nederlandsch Nieuw-Guinea Petroleum Maatschappij) had "at random" cleared a path to Obrup, but they did not know where it was. According to them Obrup could only be reached by travelling through Senggi. They were three days' journey from Senggi, and they could reach Obrup in another two days; however, from Senggi they could also reach Waris in two days, Waris being nearer their goal. There was no point in making a big detour, and Bär therefore decided to trek to Senggi. Whilst on his way, he sent from Molof a messenger who reached Obrup on 20th September with the reassuring news that Bär was making good progress. Wherever they met people in the forest, or where they passed through villages, the population was exceptionally friendly. Every now and then they had to wade through rivers and in one place they were delayed for three and a half hours while a bridge was thrown across. It was noticeable that they were travelling in govern-ment-controlled territory, because both in the large and well-kept kampong of Molof where they were received by the guru, and also one day later in Torowassi, the Netherlands tricolour was hoisted as they entered the settlement. Under the flag in Torowassi stood a friendly old gentleman who enthusiastically told them that he knew Sorong. "Me serve sentence in prison. Those two men also," he said proudly. Bär supposed that they belonged to the small group of men which had murdered several policemen some time before and had given a bad name to the district to the west of Waris. These men were now the personification of affability.

Bär and Dasselaar were now making good progress; they even marched 12 miles or so in a day. From Senggi there were two routes that they could follow to Waris. One track led through Yafi—a journey of three days—but in this case they would not need to cross a river; if they followed the other path, a forest track, they would have to cross the Pai River (or Keerom River) twice. After two days and nights without rain, they felt they could face the risk of taking the shortest route; the river was not likely to be very high. They were right in this, but the water was still above waist-high level as they waded across the river. Moreover, they only just got across in time; a little later, while they were making camp, a heavy storm broke.

Athanasius, the man who had fallen seriously ill in the Sobger camp, had now recovered and Bär thought himself lucky that this was so, as he had not expected the bearer to survive the journey. But now other men fell sick; one went down with malaria, and two with dysentery. Bär had to keep the dysentery cases on a strict diet, a procedure which they did not like at all. At least, Bär caught them secretly eating baked fish with under-done rice and katyang idyu mashed. It was quite understandable that he should give them a piece of his mind. But it was a good thing that the end of the trip was in sight and that they were soon to reach Waris. From this point they would be able to fly the sick men to Hollandia. Bär little imagined that this would be his lot too. For the last week he had not felt very fit and now he began to get serious attacks of fever. Dasselaar had an improvised stretcher made to carry him, but this was not to the patient's liking. He would not let himself be carried, as that would delay the party, and since it was a case of the earlier they were in Waris the better, this "sticker" continued to trek on laboriously.

Waris was reached on 23rd September, and here Bär was hospitably received by government official Aarts and his wife. It was a tremendous pleasure for him, after 46 days ploughing through the rimbu and sleeping in primitive camps, to sleep in a real bed and be well cared for. The government post at Waris had a wireless station and next day Bär was able to bring Mr. Van den Broek in Hollandia up to date with the situation. When Mabilabol subsequently made direct contact with Waris, Bär crawled out of bed again to give the expedition leaders his short report on their trip. They decided that he should be flown down to Hollandia in a Cessna, together with two bearers. Dasselaar was to finish the journey with the remainder of the party. But first of all, he had to attend to the mail; they had carried with them special "break-through covers" from Mabilabol. These bore the Sibil cancellation stamp as well as the postage stamp; these were followed by the cancellation stamp of the Waris district office and the final cancellation was made in Hollandia.

Passing through Arso, Dasselaar trekked to Holtekang on the Humboldt Bay, taking five days to do the trip. Whilst on this journey he received letters giving a certain amount of information about the way in which he would be received in Hollandia. Two boats would meet the entire group and lead them into Hollandia where there was to be a great reception.

Everybody's clothes in the group showed clear signs of a long trip through the rimbu, as they stood there face to face with a company neatly dressed in white. Speeches were made by the Governor, by the Resident of Hollandia, by the chairman of the New Guinea Committee for the Expedition to the Star Mountains, (which had raised the funds for the break-through) and the chairman of the Oranje Committee. The whole of Hollandia was there; the reception was followed by a ride through the town, and in the evening they were invited to a rijsttafel.* Unfortunately Bär was not there, still being ill in bed with dysentery.

The journey had lasted 53 days, 9 hours and 23 minutes from the time Bär left Mabilabol to the time when Dasselaar arrived in Hollandia, and they had covered almost 250 miles. Dasselaar himself, who had left the Sibil Valley a week earlier than Bär had actually been on the move for 61 days. It had been a long and heavy trek, but it had been successful and had finished well. Not only was it a remarkable physical achievement, but Bär had collected a large quantity of geological data on the structure of the mountains and Dasselaar had assembled many details about the local population.

---

* Translator's note. The rijsttafel (lit. "rice table") is a well-known Indonesian dish consisting of large quantities of boiled rice, with meat and vegetables and many kinds of spices.

12

Departure

THE BASE CAMP WAS TO BE EVACUATED BY THE END OF SEPTEMBER, AS had been decided by the Foundation Council in Holland. In order to implement this decision, a beginning had been made before with the outward transport of equipment to be shipped back to the Netherlands. There were still two groups out in the field and they were to carry out the trips which had been planned for them (the ascent of the Juliana Summit and the break-through) but no further large-scale trips were to be undertaken.

Kloof Camp along the Digul route was dismantled. Marines Binkhuijsen and Boon decided to travel down the Digul to Kawakit with Van der Weiden in a proa. This was a pretty perilous undertaking, because the stretch of river from Kloof Camp to Kawakit could hardly be called navigable. Twice their proa overturned with them and, although they lost some of their supplies in the process, they reached Kawakit quite safely. A Mappi boat brought them farther down river to Tanah Merah.

In the first few days of September eight members of the expedition quitted Mabilabol (Anceaux, Van Heijningen, Kalkman, Reynders, Romeijn, Staats, De Wilde and Van Zanten); shortly after Pouwer left with bearers from the Survey Department, heading for Mindiptana. Vervoort, who had been collecting for several weeks in and near Tanah Merah, was the only one to come back to Mabilabol and to go on from there to Hollandia. In the storage shed, cases and packages stood ready for despatch to Tanah Merah; each of them was marked with its weight, so as to enable the consignments for the aircraft to be assembled rapidly. The research workers' hut was empty; the biologists' laboratory had been evacuated too. It was very obvious that the expedition was approaching its end. But not everything would be dismantled and sent back. The silver house was to be left standing, for use as a Government post; the research workers' hut was to serve as accommodation for the police teams. While the expedition was preparing to leave, another new inhabitant of Mabilabol arrived, Father J. Van den Pavert. For a year two missionaries (J. Greenfield and M. Heyblom of the Unevangelised Field Mission) had lived in the Sibil Valley to learn the language before beginning their actual work; and now a Roman Catholic Missionary was about to settle in the area. A large part of the supplies and also some of the equipment were sold on the spot, thus saving the expedition the expense of transport and also saving the buyers the cost of the inward freight. The Government, the Protestant Mission and the Catholic Mission were very interested in the goods for sale; on the inspection days Venema could be seen crying his wares with considerable zeal.

Everybody was now waiting for the party which had climbed the Juliana Summit; once they had returned and their equipment had been made ready for sending off, the last consignments could be sent off. On 19th September the last bearers were back in Mabilabol, and on 21st September all the bearers were to trek southward with Corporal Bril, via Katem as far as Woropko. Before they left, their wages were paid. The Muyus were paid in money and the income tax due therefore had to be paid. It is a very strange thing to have to fill in tax forms in the rimbu, with the appropriate columns for gross earnings, tax deducted and net earnings. Fortunately it did not extend to holding back one or two matches per box when we paid the Sibil bearers. Kroon filled in the tax forms. Brongersma counted out in advance the various amounts and made up the wages bags; two members of the expedition then counted everything over again, after which the actual operation of paying could commence. Kroon declared that 25 guilders would have to be held back from each bearer; he would be paid this amount in Woropko when he delivered his load there. Without this precaution, there would have been a considerable risk that the bearers would have dropped their loads somewhere along the path in order to be able to get home more quickly. Each name was called out in turn, and Kroon counted the wages out for each man as he appeared at the table. The few who could write laboriously signed their names with great pot-hooks on the wage lists; for most of them we had to take a print of the right thumb. Naturally one man was found to have answered to the wrong name and to have taken another man's wages, but that was soon put right. Here and there the Muyus were sitting down to count their wages over again and one of them came back to say that he had not been paid correctly. Brongersma and Kroon counted the money over with him, but it was clear that the man had received precisely what was due to him. He then wanted to count it over for himself once more; he set down one guilder after another and all the bystanders counted with him. It was an easy matter to keep up with him as he wasn't a quick chap and it must have been a good eight minutes before his 96 guilders were made up in a heap again, and he had come to the conclusion that he had after all been treated honestly.

Wenger and Becker left with the helicopter to go to Tanah Merah. Mr. Lesilolo in Tanah Merah was to come on the air with his transmitter at twelve noon for this special occasion, to say whether the helicopter had arrived. It became clear that it had not touched down at Tanah Merah, having landed in Katem because of low cloud covering the hills between Katem and Kawakit. This gave them time to drink a quiet cup of coffee in Katem, and once the weather cleared up a little they flew down to Kawakit, where they paid another visit. At two o'clock Tanah Merah was able to announce the glad news that they had arrived safely.

*　　*　　*

The expedition had spent almost six months in the Star Mountains and there was one subject which had occupied the members daily: the state of the weather. This was not simply because it was rather more agreeable to go on a march in dry weather than when it was raining, but also because air transport of supplies was to a considerable extent dependent on the weather. Each day the government official put out his weather observations; the amount of precipitation and the air temperature were recorded at six-thirty in the morning, at half past twelve noon and at half past six in the evening, and the relative humidity of the atmosphere was measured. In addition observations were taken of the length of the sunny periods, the amount of cloud cover, the wind direction and wind velocity. Some of the data so obtained were recorded by us in Mabilabol and others were later passed on to us by the Meteorological Bureau in Hollandia.

When anybody thinks of a stay in the Tropics, he imagines a country with a great deal of sunshine, oppressive heat and much rain. There was no doubt that the expedition had had no great trouble with excessive sunshine and oppressive heat, but there was plenty of rain to get on with.

In the period from April to September inclusive (a total of 183 days) the sun shone for a total of 616 hours 30 minutes, that is a daily average of not more than 3 hours 22 minutes. May was the finest month with an average of 5 hours 39 minutes per day; on the other hand, August had a daily average of only 1 hour 51 minutes of sunshine. On 13 days the sun did not break through at all, and on 13 other days it shone for less than a quarter of an hour. The finest day of all was the 2nd September with 10 hours 12 minutes of sunshine.

The highest temperature (in the shade) was 28·5°C. during May; in July and August there were days when the temperature did not rise

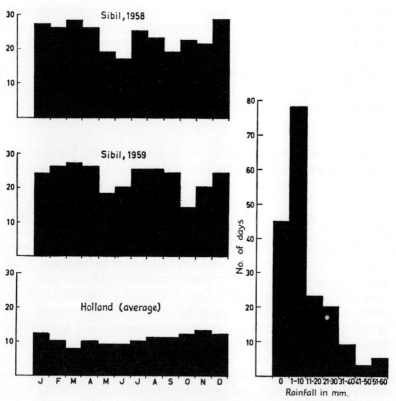

Fig. 21. Rainfall charts.
Left: no. of rainy days per month. Right: daily rainfall, April–September 1959.

above 18·4°C. There were also nights when the thermometer did not drop below 17·5°C. (in May) but there were also nights when it cooled down to 9°C. (in September) and such low temperatures made many people shiver under two thick blankets. It often rained in Mabilabol, although the daily quantity of rain was generally not very great. In the period from April to September inclusive there were only thirty days which were completely dry; on fifteen days the rainfall was not more than 0·02 in., but on 138 days it was 0·024 in. of rain or more. The maximum in one 24-hour period during the whole expedition was 2·32 in.; before this there had been one 24-hour period with 4 inches of rain. A shower of rain totalling 15·1 in., such as that which fell on 13th March in Hollandia, and caused a great deal of damage there (the Water-Level Service almost became the "what-had-been-levelled service," because there was a great stream of mud running through the main office) did not occur in Mabilabol.

On the days when it was observed in the morning that the rainfall during the previous twenty-four hours had been more than ·78 in., the airfield was automatically put out of service. This happened on thirty-five days during our stay. After an even higher rainfall (e.g. 1·96 inches) or after two succeeding days with more than ·78 in. rainfall, the airfield did not dry out completely in one day and was therefore out of service for a longer period.

In 1959 the total rainfall in Mabilabol was 124·13 in., distributed over 273 rainy days; of this total 74·68 in. fell in 138 days during the months of April to September inclusive. The most rain fell during the night, and records for the period from May up to the end of September are available. The total rainfall during these five months amounted to 58·03 inches, of which only 3·86 inches fell between half past six in the morning and half past twelve in the afternoon; between half past past twelve and half past six in the evening there fell 9·29 in. and between half past six in the evening and half past six the next morning 44·88 in. Very frequently it began to pour with rain soon after darkness had fallen, and that is quite an experience if you happen to be living in a house roofed with aluminium sheets; the row was so terrific that we had to turn off the wireless, because the clatter of the rain on the roof drowned the music. With regard to total rainfall Mabilabol is not unfavourably placed in comparison to other places, e.g. Ninati at the foot of the mountains on the southern side, where the average rainfall per year is 245·5 in. However, one bad thing was the higher number of rainy days in Mabilabol—277 days (averaged over 2 years), against only 222 rainy days in Ninati.

During our stay, the month with the least sunshine (August—with a total of 57 hours 30 minutes) was also the month with the lowest rainfall, 6·34 in.; the valley was frequently covered by low cloud and mist. Strangely enough no storms occurred in the valley; we frequently saw storms around us and flashes of lightning on the other side of the mountains, and heard the thunder rumbling in the distance, but these storms never entered the valley. Neither did we encounter very strong winds; it did strike us that it blew very hard when the wind was coming from the west and penetrated into the silver house, which was open to the west. This happened predominantly at night and it did face

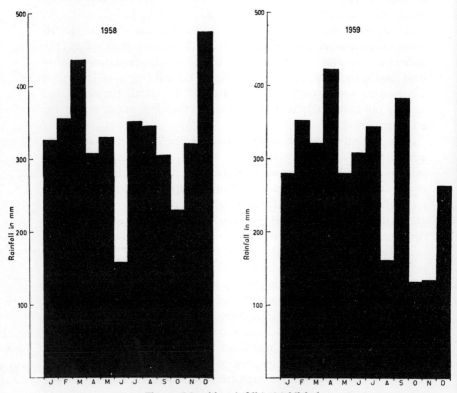

Fig. 22. Monthly rainfall in Mabilabol.

Brongersma with a problem of conscience, as to whether he was obliged to rescue the papers which fluttered off the shelf in his room or whether he could with decency remain under the warm blankets and so let himself be deprived of his records.

We did frequently grumble about the weather, above all that it was frequently fine on the days when no aircraft was available (or when the plane was unserviceable, as during May) and that the weather turned bad on the days when the Twin Pioneer should have arrived. But all in all we had to admit that it was a fine climate in which to work. We could only regret that we did not stay until October and November which were the driest months of the year—with 5·20 in. and 5.15 in. respectively, in 14 and 20 rainy days.

It may be a source of comfort that observations over only two years (and of only one year from the beginning of the expedition) do not allow anyone to conclude what may be considered as normal in the Sibil Valley. As compared with 6·25 in. in June 1958 we find 12·1 in. in 1959; during 1958 the month of November showed a rainfall of 12·67 in. while in 1959 the figure was only 5·15 in.

We still got a bit stirred up about the weather for a few days when it was found that on 22nd September we had had 2·12 in. of rain. The pessimists foretold from this that the weather would turn bad again for a fortnight or that the Twin Pioneer would develop some fault. On this occasion things turned out better than we had expected, and the Twin Pioneer arrived on time. Brongersma, Venema, Tissing, Nicolas and his marines, Kroon and some of the police-constables were flown down to Tanah Merah. Escher, Ter Laag, Verstappen and Vervoort went to Hollandia; at the very moment when they landed on the field at Sentani, the Cessna plane arrived from Waris carrying Bär as a passenger.

It was a melancholy moment for us when we left the Sibil Valley; most of us had no hope of ever coming back. For months we had lived there among the friendly population. How many times Bomdogi had dropped in for a chat, although we never precisely understood what he was talking about, and he understood our replies even less. We would never see them again: the little boy Deiranipki from Tulo, who had been able to say so delightfully "Good day, your Excellency," but who was missing when the Governor visited us; Kapkasser, who had worked with the marines and was the best-dressed Sibiller—having two shirts and two pairs of trousers, one on top of the other, and a pair of shoes far too large for him, in which he stumbled about the place; "Krengetje", a scraggy scarecrow who turned up at our house every day sighing until someone took notice of him and gave him a couple of biscuits, but who consistently refused to say or do anything to earn them; Mina, who came to eat up the scraps at Sneep's house, but fell into temporary disgrace when she took some katyang from the Mission garden. What precisely they thought of us we shall probably never learn. For them it was a golden period, for they certainly had never been able to obtain so many different kinds of precious things so easily—such as brightly-coloured buttons, pieces of cloth and knives—which they had earned in trading in frogs, lizards and rats. How will they get on now that this source of riches has disappeared? How much we should like to have the opportunity to take a look later on, and to "converse" once again with our friends of the Sibil Valley. They also felt that the time to say good-bye had come; in the last few days many Sibillers came to the base camp and when we left, there was tremendous interest in what was going on on the airfield. A last wave of the arms as a farewell; the door of the Twin Pioneer was shut to; then we started taxying and were able to get a last glimpse from the air down at the airfield, at Mabilabol, Betabib, Kigonmedip, at the region where we had had to face some failures, but where we had also worked with so much pleasure and with so much success.

*   *   *

Brongersma and Venema were very hospitably received in Tanah Merah by the Head of the Local Government Service—Mr. Fanoy. There was still a great deal to be settled at Tanah Merah in connection with the outward transport. There were stocks of supplies and equipment which could be sold to the Government, or to the Protestant or Catholic Missions; everybody came along to our storage depot to see if there was anything which attracted his interest. Corporal Goedhart and the marines took care of everything that was to be sent back to the Netherlands, stowing it away in the packing-cases. New cases were made of the wood from old cases which were not to be used again; the remainder were sold to those who wanted them, as there were willing buyers who required the cases to pack their furniture for the numerous moves from one place to another to which officials are subject in this country. The helicopter was standing on the airfield; every now and then it was taken up for a short flight, because this was better for the machine than to stand for weeks without being used. Dismantling would have to wait until the coaster *Cycloop* had arrived. It depended on the level of water in the river where the ship would be able to tie up and the intention was to dismantle the helicopter as close to the ship as possible.

Nicolas and Tissing went with the Mappi boat to Mindiptana; from here they were to go by jeep to Woropko, where they would meet Bril and his bearers, to pay the remainder of the wages due to the latter.

* * *

The canteen in the police barracks at Tanah Merah had been fitted up as accommodation for the marines during the expedition. Vervoort had also stayed here for several weeks. He had made trips up the Digul to Kouh and Kawakit in the north and to Pulu Ikan to the south of Tanah Merah in the Mappi boat. Marines J. G. C. Hendriks and Boon assisted him in collecting specimens. A large collection of insects, freshwater crayfish, fishes, amphibia, reptiles and birds had been assembled here. The police-constables lived in the barracks with their families and the place was swarming with children. As Vervoort crossed the parade ground at lunch time the children would come running up to him with the cry; "Tuan, kasih kuki" (Mister, give us a cake). This was a recognised ritual. The children would give over grasshoppers, frogs and lizards, receiving biscuits as a reward, or if they had brought something really special, a fine piece of coloured cloth; if they were too small to do any collecting, they were even so given a biscuit for nothing.

During the whole expedition period Tanah Merah was the important point from which equipment and supplies were sent up by Twin Pioneer to the Sibil Valley. It was here too that the helicopters were stationed at the beginning, and here that Dr. Bijkerk, the government doctor, had observed that all three pilots had contracted jaundice. Several members of the expedition had visited Tanah Merah on their way somewhere else during the expedition. First of all, De Wilde came by helicopter from the Sibil Valley to see where his case of instruments had got to. From Tanah Merah he went on to Mindiptana with Marines Scharff and Vlaanderen, continuing by jeep to Woropko and then trekking via Katem to Mabilabol after making a visit to Ninati. On the way he was able to study Auyus, Mandobos, Muyus and Ninggrumers, so collecting a very valuable series of data on the body structure, colour of skin, hair and eyes, finger-prints and palm-prints of these Papuan tribes. Reynders paid one visit to Tanah Merah on his way to Mindip-tana, where he was intending to engage bearers for the expedition. He too went back to the Sibil Valley on foot, studying the ground sections en route and taking soil samples. This was a very good complement to his work in the mountains where the lowland deposits had originated. In the gardens maintained by the local inhabitants he studied the various plants which they cultivated. His route carried him through the northern Muyu region, where the houses are built on piles some six or seven feet tall; the entrance to these houses is in the floor and it is therefore easier to shut it against any enemies who may seek entry: the walls are provided with only small openings, which serve as loop-holes through which to shoot arrows at the attackers. Nijenhuis, who had to wait for transport to the Sibil Valley on his journey to Tanah Merah had begun his investigations of blood groups here with Mando-bos, Auyus and Dyairs. Finally, Anceaux passed through as well, on his way back to the Sibil Valley via Merauke, Tanah Merah, and Mindiptana, after a week's stay in Hollandia. Mr. Fanoy and Dr. and Mrs. Bijkerk gave a great deal of help and ready hospitality to all these short-term visitors to Tanah Merah.

These travellers also gave Mindiptana on the Kaoh River an oppor-tunity to play its part in the expedition. It was here that the Head of the Local Government Service and Mrs. Kessler and the administrative official P. Van Diest gave help and hospitality to members of the ex-pedition. When Tanah Merah was not receiving our messages, Mindip-tana stepped into the breach and passed the communications on.

During his stay at Tanah Merah, Vervoort had been unlucky in his fishing in the Digul because the water was too high. Brongersma and Boeseman had had the same ill-fortune when they had stayed for ten days at Tanah Merah in 1955. Now that Brongersma had returned to Tanah Merah in September, the river was exceptionally low: it was a wonderful chance to get some more specimens for the collection. The operation was carried out by means of a large drag-net handled by a number of prisoners. The plan was for them to go out with the net at six o'clock in the morning in a Mappi boat. When Brongersma woke it was pouring with rain and, convinced that the fishing expedition would not take place, he snugly turned over again. But the rain did not seem to constitute any hindrance and he was knocked up a few minutes later. In the chill morning gloom everybody was climbing into the Mappi boat; Mensingh and Pattipeilohy (the uncle of J. Pattipeilohy of Mabilabol)

of the prison staff, Kroon, Brongersma, the steersman and the motor
operator of the boat, with nineteen murderers who were serving their
sentence at Tanah Merah. It was very difficult to realise that these cheerful
Papuans with friendly faces were murderers, at first sight they looked
much more like boys on their way to a fishing outing. Two proas were
towed behind the Mappi boat. They proceeded at a good rate downstream to an almost completely cut-off loop in the Digul. The Mappi
boat could just get through the shallow entry, but after that everybody
had to get out; the fishing team got into the two proas, while the
onlookers had to walk along the bank. The water was low and the bank
consisted of a thick layer of soft, greasy mud, with the result that every
now and then they sank into it up to the knees. This was a source of
great distress to Brongersma, who had put his Sibil suits into the wash,
and was now floundering around wearing the trousers from his best
suit. The rain had now stopped and this at least made life slightly
easier. A pair of strapans (prisoners) remained on the bank holding one
end of the net, the rest of which lay in the bottom of the canoe which
moved in a wide loop away from the bank, returning towards it after
curving round, while the net was slowly slid overboard. Once the bank
had been reached again the net was drawn to land. Meanwhile all the
prisoners had entered the water and were pulling the net towards the
bank with a great deal of noise; the last part of the operation was the
most difficult, because they had to take care that the upper edge of the
net remained somewhat above the water to prevent the fish from
jumping out of it, while the under edge had to remain on the bottom
of the river so that the fish could not escape there. The strapans were
enjoying themselves very much, because they were allowed to make a
lot of noise when hauling the net in—a thing which is normally forbidden them.

The first few casts were only moderately successful. After one or two
casts fishing operations were moved to the opposite side of the river,
where a mud bank closed off a branch of the river. The canoes were
dragged over the mud and everbody trudged laboriously through the
thick mud. Here the catch was a great deal better. In one cast they caught
six small sawfish (Pristis sp.) roughly 20 inches long, various kinds of
cat-fish, garfish, and a male Kurtus gulliveri. When the female of this
species has laid her strings of eggs, they are attached to a forward-
inclined hook on the head of the male and so carried about. In the
catches of fish made in 1955 none of the males caught had a well-

developed hook on the head, but now in September there were several. The eggs had gone and had no doubt been trampled into the mud. Two of the strapans carried a milk churn full of alcohol with them to preserve the important specimens. To the tremendous amusement of all the onlookers (including the strapans) the proa capsized; Mr. Pattipeilohy and several of the prisoners received a thorough ducking. In this way he was not bothered when it began to rain again, first of all a light drizzle but turning later to heavy drops. This was less agreeable for the spectators walking along the bank, because they were also getting cold.

But their zeal was rewarded. A half-grown freshwater turtle (*Caretto-chelys insculpta*) was caught; the back of this turtle is not covered with horny shields, but with a leathery skin; its feet are paddle-shaped, and its nose ends in a short trunk. The catch also included a fine specimen of *Scleropages leichardti*. After a couple of casts in this branch of the river, everybody boarded the Mappi boat again and crossed to the other side of the Digul, to fish in another arm of the river which had been cut off. The layer of mud was so thick here that the men sank in it up to their waists. When Brongersma saw this he decided to stay on board. Really the only way of crossing this mud bank was to lie down flat on it, and "swim" across. In the distance Brongersma heard a great deal of loud shouting; a crocodile (*Crocodylus novae-guineae*) about five feet long had come up in between the fishermen. The noise was followed by two revolver-shots; the crocodile was now no longer in a position to cause any trouble and was shortly afterwards added to the zoological collection. Finally, the collection was enriched by a young river turtle, then a very small crocodile, a second *Scleropages*, a pair of small soles (flat-fish) and a water snake (*Acrochordus granulatus*). In addition to Brongersma's acquisitions (a milk churn full of fish, the crocodiles, the turtles and a snake) this fishing expedition had provided 1,045 lb. of fish for eating. The strapans were given a good helping of fish with their rice and vegetables.

At 3 p.m. the return journey began; progress upstream was slow. The Government ship *Tasman* also came up-river but did not overtake us. As it became dark, the *Tasman* anchored, while the Mappi boat continued its journey and tied up at seven o'clock. Brongersma washed the mud off, set his trousers to soak in a fine bowl of soapsuds, put on dry clothes and went off to eat a sandwich with the Bijkerk family. After this he had a good game of skittles, because Tanah Merah is the only place

47. (1) Bridge of branches over the Ok Tsyop.
(2) Verstappen on a suspension bridge near Katem; a number of cords have given way.

in New Guinea which can boast a skittle alley. Without a great deal of effort he succeeded in finishing last; he had had enough success already that day.

* * *

Things had now been finished in Tanah Merah. Corporal Goedhart, with a few marines, was to see to the loading of the packing-cases on board *Cycloop*. In the pasanggrahan (rest-house) the expedition held a farewell reception for the inhabitants of Tanah Merah who had taken so much trouble with the expedition. On 30th September there arrived in Tanah Merah the Dakota with which Brongersma, Venema, Kroon and a large part of the detachment of marines were to leave for Merauke. Once again there was a Dakota-load of expedition members. While the aircraft set course for Merauke, Brongersma could see around him the cheerful faces of the marines, who could think of nothing else but the fact that they were going home. They had all done their work well. Almost all of them had voluntarily extended their stay in New Guinea and worked for a full six months under especially difficult conditions. Brongersma looked around once more at the well-known faces around him and was glad that he had asked to have a detachment of marines assigned to the expedition. For communications, for overseeing the camps, for looking after stores and for so many other tasks, the marines had proved indispensable. He also took another look at the police-constables who had accompanied various groups of research workers on different trips—men for whom such an expedition was far from being part of their daily round; they too had done their job outstandingly well. There was no doubt that the expedition had been very fortunate in the choice of the marine detachment under the command of Marine-Lieutenant Nicolas and the police detachment under the command of Sergeant Kroon. Both detachments had, in their own way contributed greatly to the success of the expedition.

After spending an afternoon and an evening in Merauke to clear up various matters and to take leave of the Resident, of the remaining government officials and of so many others that Brongersma and Venema had come to know from previous stays in New Guinea—people who had watched over the interests of the expedition here in Merauke—they continued in the Dakota to Hollandia, where there were still many things to be settled with Mr. Th. C. Van den Broek in connection with the expedition.

There was a farewell audience with the Governor, farewell visits to

48. (1) View of the Juliana Summit.
(2) The descent: left, Escher: right, Tissing.

the Naval Commandant in Netherlands New Guinea, the Director of
Internal Affairs and other authorities, and then the only thing left was
to say good-bye to all their acquaintances in Biak. Bär had recovered
sufficiently to be able to travel to Holland by now. The other expedition members, with the exception of those who were staying in
New Guinea because they had found a post there, had already left for
Holland.

On 11th October, Brongersma, Venema and Bär reached the Netherlands and for them too the expedition was at an end.

A wealth of scientific data had been assembled, and large collections
sent back to the Netherlands. Now there was still the study and evalua-
tion of all this material to be done—certainly not the least of the various
operations connected with the expedition. For the specialists in certain
branches it would take years before all the data had been collated and
published, while for others the most important findings could be
published quite quickly.

The research carried out by De Wilde, the physical anthropologist, and
that of Nijenhuis, the blood-group specialist, will give us an idea of the
relationship between the various Papuan tribes investigated. The studies
made by Pouwer, the cultural anthropologist, of the society, customs
and habits of the population of the Sibil Valley and of the valleys of the
Ok Bon and the Ok Tsyop will make it easier to bring those regions
under government control. There will be considerable changes in the
habits of these people, and it is a good thing that the present state should
have been recorded while there is still little influence from civilisation.
Anceaux will not only have made it possible by his linguistic studies to
make contact with the Sibillers more easily, but will also provide
information as to the relationship of these people with other tribes and
with regard to the contacts which they have in the mountainous areas.
The geological investigations of Bär, Cortel and Escher will contribute
greatly to the knowledge of the structure of the mountain ranges and
of the great movements which have occurred in the ground in this
region. From the economic point of view it is disappointing that no
important sources of ores have been found, but it is also useful information to know what is not to be found in this region.

Verstappen had collected information about the earlier glaciation of
the mountain region and on the effects that this has had on the shape
of the mountains and valleys; he also studied the river terraces and will
be able to draw conclusions from his studies as to the ground move-

ments which occurred in the most recent periods of geological history. Reynders had investigated the composition and structure of the soil cover produced by weathering; apart from the fundamental scientific importance of this information, his studies—which also deal with the harvest from the native gardens and the types of plants cultivated—will have a practical application to horticulture in these areas. The botanical investigations of Kalkman and Van Zanten, and the zoological research of Vervoort and Brongersma—with the help of Van Heijningen and Staats, their assistants—will, for the time being, be solely of scientific interest. None the less, data with regard to the composition of the forest can be of practical utility. The study of the fauna will contribute to our obtaining a clear picture of the distribution of various species of animals in New Guinea. In bringing this region under cultivation it is possible that difficulties may be caused by species which cause damage to the forests and to the undergrowth and in that event it is useful to know what species live hereabouts. As civilisation penetrates and large areas are opened up, changes (generally improverishment) of the flora and fauna occur. As time goes on, Nature conservation will also have to be applied in New Guinea, and with this in mind, it is useful to have as soon as possible an inventory of the flora and fauna, and a detailed study of the distribution of the species. Romeijn's medical investigations have made it clear that framboesia is rare here and that there is little point in carrying out a very expensive and large-scale campaign against this disease in the Star Mountains. Malaria is virtually unknown, and tuberculosis has not yet reached this region.

* * *

In recording the course of events in the expedition we have repeatedly named the Survey Group, which was working in the Star Mountains at the same time as the expedition under the leadership of F. L. T. Van der Weiden, and from which the expedition received a great deal of co-operation. In order to be able to map the area properly with the aid of aerial photography, it is necessary for the precise position of a number of points to be determined. This had already been done by means of astronomical fixes at Mabilabol, Antares and Katem. Parts of the region investigated by the expedition have been mapped by the survey staff. The boundary between New Guinea and the Australian portion of the Island (territory of New Guinea in the north; territory of Papua in the south) runs from the northern coast along the 141st meridian East of Greenwich towards the south, to the point where this meridian reaches the Fly River; from this point the boundary follows the western bank of the river as far as 141° 1′ 48″ E. Longitude, and runs from here directly towards the south as far as the mouth of the Bensbach River on the southern coast. A line like this looks very well on a map, but it cannot be found in the field. It has consequently been agreed that the boundary should be fixed as precisely as possible by means of astonomic fixes in the region in question. The honour of carrying out these fixes in the mountainous region, so difficult of access, fell to the Survey Department of Netherlands New Guinea. The Survey Group made use of the presence of the expedition, which enabled them to enjoy a certain amount of helicopter support, to work in the Star Mountains. Every single one of the men who carried out this work under the leadership of Van der Weiden was a good jungle man. They would trek up into the forest and into the mountains in small groups accompanied by a number of bearers; they would camp under the most primitive conditions in the surroundings and wait until a few clear nights gave them the opportunity to make their observations. This might on occasion last for months as for instance occurred in the Antares Mountains, where the necessary data were only obtained after a wait of three months. The group charged with this work ran into supply difficulties towards the end of their stay on Antares, but they did not abandon their task; the result was that the men returned to Mabilabol much thinner than they set out, but they had their data. The observations were made every hour, and their alarm clock advanced by this much each time, so that they could see whether the sky was clear the next time the alarm went off. Little is heard of the service rendered by the Survey Department; their work is not carried out in the public eye. Far from it—they have to labour where there is no one to see them and their journeys certainly belong to the most difficult which have been carried out in New Guinea. It is not to be wondered at that the expedition members were filled with amazement at the achievements of Van der Weiden's "boys". In addition to all their own worries, they were always willing to help the members of the expedition.

13

The Animal World
of New Guinea

SPANIARDS RETURNING FROM A JOURNEY ROUND THE WORLD IN 1523 brought back to Europe skins of Birds of Paradise, which they had obtained from the Prince of Batchian in the Moluccas. Thus, before Europeans had ever set foot in New Guinea, something was known of the fauna of the island. Although many voyages along the coasts of New Guinea were made during the sixteenth, seventeenth, and eighteenth centuries, they contributed but little to the knowledge of the island's animal life. What is more, the farthest thing from the purpose of these voyages was the investigation of the animal world; such studies began in the nineteenth century. In 1828 His Netherlands Majesty's Corvette *Triton* made a voyage along the south coast; on board was Salomon Müller, who—as a member of the Commission for Natural History set up by King William I (of the Low Countries)—was collecting zoological specimens. Very considerable advances were made in the knowledge of the fauna of New Guinea in the nineteenth and twentieth centuries, when expeditions or individual travellers began to land on the coasts and later to penetrate into the interior.

S. Müller and A. R. Wallace, both of whom travelled in the Malay Archipelago, were struck by the changes in the animal world which take place as one moves from west to east, and by the great differences observed between the fauna of Asia on the one hand and that of Australia and New Guinea on the other. Animals which are characteristic of South-East Asia and the adjacent large islands (Sumatra, Borneo and Java) are not met with in New Guinea; thus among mammals, the beasts of prey, the insectivores, monkeys and lemurs, elephants, rhinoceroses, tapirs, the *Bovidae*, deer,* pigs,† squirrels, porcupines and pangolins are all absent; among birds there is no trace of the woodpeckers; among the reptiles, there are no representatives of the land tortoises of the family *Testudinidae*, of the swamp turtles of the family *Emydidae*, or of the adders of the families *Viperidae* and *Crotalidae*; among amphibia, the caecilians, toads (*Bufonidae*)‡ and the tree-frogs of the family *Rhacophoridae* are lacking; of the fishes, there are no members of the carp family (*Cyprinidae*).

As against this, New Guinea possesses animals which are not represented in South-East Asia; among mammals, the spiny ant-eaters (egglaying mammals) and marsupials; among birds, there are the Birds of Paradise, honey-eaters, flower-peckers and the cassowary; among reptiles, tortoises of the genera *Emydura* and *Chelodina*, and the freshwater turtle (*Carettochelys insculpta*), the lizards of the genera *Tribolonotus* and *Lialis*, the frilled lizard (*Chlamydosaurus kingi*), a number of species of venomous snakes (*Acanthophis, Micropechis, Pseudechis, Oxyuranus* etc.); frogs of the families *Hylidae* and *Leptodactylidae*; fishes of the family *Melanotaeniidae*; freshwater crayfish of the family *Parastacidae*.

These examples, to which many others could be added, clearly show the great difference which exists between South-East Asia and New Guinea. Between these two regions stretches the chain of islands forming the Malay Archipelago. As we travel from west to east, the fauna changes in jumps which are more or less marked. Some species have penetrated from the mainland of Asia to Java, but have not spread beyond this (e.g. the rhinoceroses and the panther); the tiger has spread as far as Bali, but is not found farther east. The proportion of groups of Asiatic origin in the fauna dwindles progressively as we move eastwards; on the other hand, the proportion of groups which have originated in Australian New Guinea grows. Wallace considered that it was possible to draw a clearly-defined line of demarcation between an Asiatic fauna and an Australian fauna; he drew this boundary—which is called after him, and is therefore known as the Wallace Line—between Borneo and Celebes in the north and between Bali and Lombok in the south. Doubt-

---

* Recently a species of deer has been introduced in various places in Netherlands New Guinea.

† The "wild" pig is actually a species of pig brought into New Guinea by man and which has gone feral.

‡ In Australian New Guinea, near Lae, a species of Toad (*Bufo marinus*) has been introduced.

less there are many groups of animals (whether families, genera or species) whose area of distribution finishes at this line, but there are others which are not limited by it. It is much rather the case that— between Asia (together with Borneo, Sumatra and Java) on the one hand, and Australia and New Guinea on the other—there exists an area of transition in which the two characteristic fauna are mixed. It has become clear in recent years from investigations made by Dr. D. A. Hooijer that there was once a species of elephant, now extinct, in Celebes and Flores, that is, to the east of the Wallace Line.

In seeking for an explanation of the great differences between the fauna of Asia and that of New Guinea, we have to take into account the genesis of these regions. If we look at a map of the Archipelago running between Asia and Australia, on which the depths at various points in the sea have been marked, we can see that the sea which separates Sumatra, Java and Borneo from each other and from the Asian mainland is very shallow, being nowhere deeper than 100 fathoms and much less in most places; the mainland has a submarine extension known as the Sunda Shelf, and the three large islands we have just named are situated on it. Again the sea which separates New Guinea from Australia and the Aru Islands is very shallow, here again there is a submarine extension of the mainland, this time of Australia, known as the Sahul Shelf. (Fig. 23.)

In the Ice Age, enormous quantities of water were locked up in the form of thick ice-caps covering the continents in the Northern Hemisphere. This withheld so much water from the oceans that the sea-level was considerably lower. At the western end of the Archipelago the Sunda Shelf joining Asia, Borneo, Sumatra and Java was dry, and at the eastern end the same thing happened to the Sahul Shelf, which links Australia, New Guinea and the Aru Islands. The Asiatic animals (either land or freshwater creatures) were therefore able to spread across the Sunda Shelf and thus occupy Borneo, Sumatra and Java; the Sahul Shelf would have enabled the Australian fauna to move into New Guinea and the Aru Islands.

There are deep-sea areas between the Sunda Shelf and the Sahul Shelf, areas which did not dry up in the Ice Age and which formed a barrier to the dispersal of all kinds of land and freshwater animals. In this region we find Celebes and the Moluccas in the north and the Lesser Sunda Islands in the south. In addition to changes in the sea-level resulting from the successive ice ages, other changes were caused by movements in the earth's crust, which is far from stable in this region.

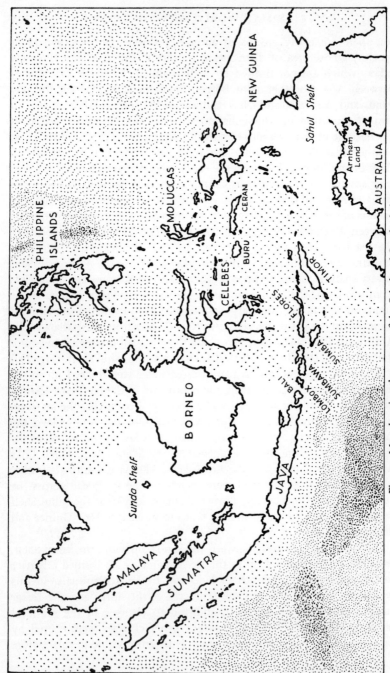

Fig. 23. Map showing the extent of the Sahul and Sunda shelves.

Some parts of the sea bottom were raised, islands thrust up above sea-level and narrow sea channels drained dry; in this way closely adjacent islands became connected, offering the opportunity for different species of animals to move from one island to another. These links were only transitory, and at no time did they affect all the islands in the Archipelago simultaneously. In addition to this, we must not forget that each species has particular requirements which must be fulfilled if it is to move into or stay in a given region. Even where two islands had been connected, the link might be usable to one species and not to another. Supposing such a connection to be poor in supplies of fresh water, this would constitute a barrier for freshwater animals and frogs which lay their eggs in the water. Thus, the climate, the vegetation and the presence or absence of fresh water on these past land connections—which were formed here and there and at irregular intervals—will have enabled some animals to extend their distribution, while other species would have been unable to use these links, because their habitat requirements were not fulfilled. This explains why it was not possible for the entire fauna of South-East Asia to spread farther east.

There is no such thing as one-way traffic in animal distribution. A link which would enable animals living in the west to move eastwards, would also provide the means for other animals to spread from the east in a westerly direction. Thus animals from Australia and New Guinea have also pushed westward. Among mammals the cuscuses (Phalanger sp.) have moved westward, in the north as far as Celebes and the Sanghir Islands, and in the south as far as Timor. One species of Bird of Paradise has reached the Moluccas; the cassowary is found on Ceram; the death adder (Acanthophis antarcticus) occurs in the Moluccas on the islands of Ceram, Haruku and Obi, and has spread in the south-west to the Kai and Tarimbar Islands; the Island of Rotti, near Timor, possesses a species of tortoise belonging to the genus Chelodina.

Probably islands in the western and central sections of the Archipelago had better connections with each other, and thus with Asia, than with New Guinea; this would explain why the Asiatic fauna has penetrated farther east than the Australian fauna has been able to spread to the west. In addition, the far greater number of species in the Asiatic fauna will have played a part in this process.

In many aspects the fauna of New Guinea resembles that of Australia and especially that of North-East Australia. Many families, genera and even species occur in both regions; thus we find Tachyglossus aculeatus, the short-beaked spiny ant-eater, both in Australia and in New Guinea; North-East Australia also has Birds of Paradise. The frilled lizard, tortoises of the genera Chelodina and Emydura, frogs of the families Hylidae and Leptodactylidae, fish of the family Melanotaeniidae, the freshwater fish Scleropages leichardti and freshwater crayfish of the Parastacidae inhabit both regions. There is no doubt that the fauna of New Guinea is closely related with that of Australia, but there are also differences. Thus both the Australian duck-billed platypus (Ornithorhynchus paradoxus) and the Australian wingfish (Neoceratodus forsteri) are missing in New Guinea. Conversely, the freshwater turtle (Carettochelys insculpta) occurs only in New Guinea and not in Australia.

The freshwater fish of New Guinea are remarkable. Anyone who goes fishing in rivers like the Digul will sometimes imagine himself to be fishing in the sea, when he sees his catch. Many groups of fish found in fresh water in New Guinea are descended from sea fish, such as sawfish, anchovy-like fish, garfish etc. Even sharks occur in the Yamur Lake. This does not only apply to fishes; sea-snakes (Enhydrina schistosa) are found in the Digul near Tanah Merah. Although the island is rich in rivers and lakes, freshwater fish are rare. In actual fact, Scleropages leichardti is the only true freshwater fish. In the Eocene period (75,000,000 years ago) this species of fish lived in fresh water, and fossil remains have been found in freshwater sediments in Australia. All the other fish are related to sea fish. Some, such as fish of the family Melanotaeniidae, have become entirely adapted to freshwater life and their distribution is restricted to such conditions; their nearest relatives are the sea-dwelling Sand Smelt. Other species belong to genera which are also found in the sea, and there are even species which live both in salt and fresh water.

It would be a mistake to think that all species of animals are uniformly distributed over New Guinea. In fact the fauna varies from place to place; the animals in the lowlands differ from those in the mountains. In the Merauke region, where the average annual rainfall is 60 inches and where a decidedly wet season alternates with a dry one, the fauna is not the same as that of regions with an annual rainfall of between 120 and 160 inches, where there is little or no distinction between the seasons. Moreover, there is a distinction between the fauna of the Vogelkop Peninsula and the remainder of New Guinea, and again between that of the regions to the north and to the south of the central mountain ranges. Thus the freshwater turtle (Carettochelys insculpta) and the freshwater crayfish (*Parastacidae*) are found only in rivers and lakes flowing towards the south.

Poisonous snakes of the genera *Pseudechis* and *Oxyuranus* and turtles of the genus *Chelodina* are not found anywhere except to the south of the central mountain range.

The Greater Bird of Paradise (*Paradisaea apoda*) occurs to the south of the mountains (and on the Aru Islands) while the Lesser Bird of Paradise (*Paradisaea minor*) lives to the north of the mountains.

Many specimens have been collected in New Guinea and our knowledge of its animals has grown to an exceptional extent during this century, but there is still a great deal to be done before it can be said that the fauna is anything like completely known. Now that the distribution of the species in New Guinea has been mapped in outline, a great deal of detail work remains to be done. The habitat requirements of the different species will need to be studied more closely—i.e. why does one species occur in one place and not in another? This will not always be a simple question to answer. Similar problems already exist with respect to other regions, e.g. why does the tiger occur in Sumatra and Java, but not in Borneo, where there would nevertheless be ample supplies of prey? A great deal of research will have to be carried out on the creatures which threaten human health, such as the malaria-bearing mosquitoes and the mites which carry scrub typhus. As cultivation of the land is extended, it cannot be doubted that pests will be met with which can seriously damage the crops. Thus there is still a great deal of investigation to be done in this island, with its wonderful fauna.

BIBLIOGRAPHY

L. D. Brongersma, *Zoologisch onderzoek in Nieuw-Guinea*. (Zoological research in New Guinea.) (Dutch text.) Leiden, E. J. Brill. 52 pp., 1954.

L. D. Brongersma, *Nederlands Nieuw-Guinea. De dierenwereld*. (Netherlands New Guinea; The Fauna.) (Dutch text.) Schakels NNG 24, 48 pp., 22 fig., 1 map, 1956 (published by Ministry for Overseas Affairs).

L. D. Brongersma, *The Animal World of Netherlands New Guinea*. (English text.) Groningen. J. B. Wolters. 71 pp., 34 fig., 1 map, 1958.

List of Expedition Members

Dr. L. D. BRONGERSMA   General and scientific leader
Cdr. (Air) G. F. VENEMA   Technical leader

SCIENTIFIC STAFF AND ASSISTANTS

Dr. A. G. DE WILDE	Physical anthropology
L. E. NIJENHUIS	Blood groups
Dr. J. POUWER	Cultural anthropology
Dr. J. C. ANCEAUX	Linguistics
C. KALKMAN	Botany
Dr. B. O. VAN ZANTEN	Botany
Dr. CHR. B. BÄR	Geology
Ir. H. J. CORTEL	Ore Geology
Ing. A. E. ESCHER	Ore Geology
Ir. J. J. REYNDERS	Agrogeology
Dr. H. TH. VERSTAPPEN	Geomorphology
Dr. W. VERVOORT	Zoology
C. VAN HEIJNINGEN	Zoology, Senior technical assistant.
J. J. STAATS	Zoology, technical assistant
F. L. T. VAN DER WEIDEN	Cartography

GENERAL SERVICES

F. M. A. OOSTERMAN   Superintendent of Police

MEDICAL SERVICE

T. ROMEIJN   Government Doctor
Surgeon-Lieut. M. O. TISSING

one sick-bay attendant   (Marine Detachment)
one mantri   (Government Health Service)

MARINE DETACHMENT

First Lieutenant   C. B. NICOLAS, commandant
Sergeant   J. A. DE WIJN
Corporal   A. L. M. BRIL
Corporal   A. GOEDHART
Corporal   A. VAN INGEN
Marines   W. BINKHUIJSEN
                     H. BOON
                     F. BRANDENBURG VAN DEN
                         GRONDEN
                     J. G. C. HENDRIKS
                     H. J. W. HENDRIKS
                     J. A. C. HIRTUM
                     J. J. KOEMAN, sick-bay attendant
                     O. KOSTER, communications
                     R. E. PORTIER, communications
                     E. W. ROEM
                     J. RUIJGROK
                     F. SCHARFF
                     A. C. STRAATHOF
                     J. TIMMER
                     R. J. VLAANDEREN

MOBILE POLICE DETACHMENT

Police-Sergeant R. KROON (commandant) and D. RUMPAIDUS,
F. SWABRA, E. KORANO, G. MANSNANDIFU, J. MAMAYAO, N.
TAUDUFU, R. SOUMILENA, T. MERAWEYAO, A. YANI, M. BALAGESE,
K. KAISE alias KASUARI, J. SALOHE, L. G. BASIK-BASIK, A. B. GEBSE,
L. TONGKAP, A. WEFMAYAGAI, B. KAMAGAIMU, A. KAMAGAIMU-
WAGAO, A. KABAKAIMUEPE, R. YURKAIMUGOMUKU.

LOCAL GOVERNMENT

J. SNEEP   District Officer
W. HERBERTS   District Officer
                        (to 19 May, 1959)
G. H. DASSELAAR   District Officer
                        (From 19 May, 1959)

HELICOPTERS

D. ZIJLSTRA   Chief Pilot (to 26 May, 1959)
W. WARMAN   Chief Pilot (from 2 June, 1959)
I. H. J. VAN DEN BOS   Pilot
J. MENGE   Pilot
M. NIERAETH   Chief Mechanic
A. BEKKER   Mechanic
H. G. HOLLANDER   Mechanic

GENERATING SET AND LIGHTING

J. PATTIPEILOHY

SURVEY-HEADMAN OF GEOLOGICAL GROUP

J. WATTIMENA

SURVEY FIXES

Sibil	140°	37′	49″	Long. E.
	4°	54′	43″	Lat. S.
Antares, camp 39A	140°	48′	43″	Long. E.
	4°	54′	32″	Lat. S.
Katem	140°	43′	08″	Long. E.
	5°	08′	26″	Lat. S.

Glossary of Malay and local words and phrases used in this book

Malay words are shown in capital letters, Sibil words in small letters.

abib kopma	= "house or village, where?", i.e. where do you come from?
adò (dò)	= no.
ALANG-ALANG	= alang-alang grass; thatch grass.
alut	= taboo.
awot	= "snakes-and-lizards".
awot mapom	= *Boiga irregularis.*
awot semitki	= "long lizard", i.e. a snake.
awot tenna	= "lizard children"; cf "upi tenna".
BANDYIR	= flood, spate.
BARANG	= goods, gear, baggage.
bilminong	= waist cord, girdle.
bogaam	= men's house, open to uninitiates.
boneng	= batatas, i.e. sweet potato (*Ipomaea batatas*).
bong	= penis gourd.
burotai	= bring!
BURUNG KUNDE	= crowned pigeon, (*Goura scheepmakeri*).
buayah	= crocodile.
dalogi	= big, large.
doyo, dò	= no.
(see also adò).	
GUDANG	= godown.
GURU	= religious teacher, holy man.
imyayma	= male.
iwool	= ritual men's house.
kaga	= man.
kaga mok-mok	= good men, good people.
kaga torgoi	= bad men, bad people.
kaga wok	= white man.
kamil	= club-shaped hair extension.
KAMPONG	= village, settlement.

KATYANG IDYU	=	green peas.
KATYANG PANDYANG	=	beans.
KATYANG TANAH	=	peanuts.
KELADI	=	*Colocasia esculenta.*
KLAMBU	=	mosquito-net.
kobaar	=	aeroplane.
kol	=	frog.
kolson	=	frogs.
kol wopwor	=	brown tree-frog.
korayma	=	female.
KOTA	=	town, walled town.
KUTU MALEO	=	mites carrying scrub itch.
LAU-LAU	=	tree-kangaroo (*Dendrolagus* sp.).
Lempeng	=	cake or plug of finely-cut tobacco, pressed flat.
magison	=	more.
MANDI	=	bath.
MANDUR	=	overseer.
MANTRI	=	official of lower grade.
matul	=	*Abelmoschus manihot.*
mem	=	carrying-net.
mok-mok	=	good.
nam-nam	=	eat (and hence, food).
nè	=	yes.
ok	=	water (and hence, river).
"ok siep"	=	water creatures (in general).
okatu	=	mirror (pocket mirror or any object reflecting light like a mirror; e.g. a camera lens).
om	=	KELADI q.v.
onim-onim	=	trek!, march!
PAPAYA	=	paw-paw.
PARA-PARA	=	raised lattice or cane platform for sleeping.
PASANGGRAHAN	=	Government rest-house.
PISANG	=	banana.
PONDOK	=	hut, lean-to, temporary dwelling, bungalow.
PROA	=	canoe.
RIMBU	=	jungle, forest, wilderness.
RUMAH TINGGI	=	"high house", i.e. tree-house.

SAPI	=	cow, domestic ox.
SAYUR	=	vegetables.
sigip	=	enough.
sirong	=	ear (as a numeral—12).
sugaam	=	women's house.
STRAPAN	=	convict, prisoner (probably corrupted from some Dutch word).
tabar	=	right-hand.
tong (a Katem word)	=	matches.
TUAN	=	master, mister.
tum	=	rock, stone.
"tum tenna"	=	"rock children", white men; cf. "upi tenna".
"tum kanong"	=	"rock impossible".
TYEMARA	=	species of tree belonging to the genus *Casuarina*.
upi	=	worm.
"upi tenna"	=	"worm children" == local men; cf. "tum tenna".
wunom	=	small apron of rushes.
wot	=	drum.
yambulgi (yamburgi)	=	small.

Index

(Latin names of genera or species are given in italics. Native terms are placed between inverted commas; see also separate glossary.)